CBCS
English Honours Compendium
of
British Literature: 18th Century
(CC-8)

[According to the syllabus of Kalyani University]

Semester-IV

BIPLAB BANERJEE

INDIAN BOOKS VIEW

First Published 2020

INDIAN BOOKS VIEW
110/A, M. G. Road
Kolkata-700 007
M : 9051980904

Marketed by
THE BOOK WORLD
90/6A, M. G. Road. (YMCA Building)
Kolkata-700 007
Phone : (033)2257-0007

Typeset in India, by G. D. R. Computer Centre, Kolkata

Printed in India, by Bharat Printing & Binding Co.

ISBN : 978-81-88453-48-1

DEDICATION

To my parents-

Late Sri Sukumar Banerjee

and

Mrs. Kalpana Banerjee

A Few Words from the Author

I feel a sense of pleasure to compile such a Compendium of CC-8 (18th British Literatre) suitable for the English Honours students of 4th Semester of Kalyani University.

I express my special gratitude to Sk. Noor Ahammad of "Indian Books View", who has entrusted me with the noble responsibility of writing such a book. My gratitude to **Prof. Sukanta Datta of Shivanath Shastri College,** cannot be expressed in words. It is he who has always encouraged me to be innovative in my writing. Sir, I thank you from the bottom of my heart for everything with which you have blessed me.

The purpose of this "Compendium" is to motivate and encourage the students to have a sound knowledge of the prescribed texts as well as to answer the questions from those topics. I wish their success from the core of my heart.

–Biplab Banerjee
WhatsApp-9903463479

Syllabus

B.A. ENGLISH (Honours)
SEMESTER-IV

Course Code	Course Title	Course Type	Credit	Full Marks
ENGH-H-CC-T-8	British Literature: 18th Century	Core	6	60+15=75

Group	Text	Marks of Questions to be set	Numberof Questions to be set
A	Samuel Johnson. "London".	2,5	16 X2; 9X5
	Thomas Gray. "Elegy Written in a Country Churchyard".	2,5	
	Eliza Heywood. Fantomina.	2,5	
B	William Congreve. The Way of the World.	10	4X10
	Jonathan Swift. Gulliver's Travels (Books I & II)	10	

Content

Poetry	# London A Poem in Imitation of the Third Satire of Juvenal -Samuel Johnson

❖ An Introduction to Samuel Johnson :

Samuel Johnson, one of the most prolific and esteemed essayists, critics, and lexicographers in English history, was born to a bookseller and his wife in Lichfield, Staffordshire, England in 1709. Johnson was a brilliant child but suffered from the enmity between his parents and poverty. His time at Oxford University was truncated when money could not be procured to finish his degree. An attempt to found a teaching academy also failed, and Johnson moved to London in 1737 to try his hand at professional writing.

He wrote for and eventually edited the Gentleman's Magazine; he contributed poetry, notices, biographies, political articles, and more. His existence in London was also characterized by indebtedness, and some critics trace his radical political stance to his quality of life. He was very critical of the Whig government, and excoriated their corruption, censorship, and lapses in justice.

In 1746 Johnson turned to a project that would help alleviate the malaise brought about by journalistic writing – compiling a dictionary. The resulting Dictionary of the English Language, completed in 1755, features over 40,000 entries accompanied by 116,000 quotes. It secured Johnson's fame and was the most notable reference work until the Oxford English Dictionary many years later.

While working on the dictionary, Johnson published two notable works: Irene (1749) and The Vanity of Human Wishes (1749). The former, now less popular, is a heroic tragedy, and the latter, still read frequently today, is a drama and satire. T.S. Eliot considered Vanity Johnson's ticket to the pantheon of great poets.

In 1750 Johnson began writing essays for The Rambler. Two years later he ceased, having written 208 essays. The essays are noted for their refinement of the English language. He comprised a novel, The History of Rasselas, Prince of Abissinia, in 1759, and received critical and popular approbation.

He continued writing essays into the early 1760s, and received a government pension in 1763 which alleviated his financial duress. He stopped writing as frequently, but founded the Literary Club. The Club was attended by illustrious personages like Adam Smith, Oliver Goldsmith, and Edmund Burke.

Johnson was also the subject of one of the most famous biographies of all time – James Boswell's The Life of Samuel Johnson (1791), which gives scholars insights into the last period of his life. He wrote many political pamphlets and published a piece of travel writing on visiting Scotland. His last major work was his Lives of the Poets; the longest entries were on Dryden, Milton, Swift, and Pope. The volume is lauded for its grasp of literary history, style, keenness of critical opinion, and intuition.

In his last years, Johnson suffered from a stroke and other illnesses. He died on September 13th, 1784. He is buried at Westminster Abbey. Boswell wrote, "His death has made a chasm, which not only nothing can fill up, but which nothing has a tendency to fill up. Johnson is dead. Let us go to the next best—there is nobody; no man can be said to put you in mind of Johnson."

❖ An Introduction to *London* :

London, published in 1738, represents Johnson's attempt to satirize the grubby world of London and also to rise above it. The poem is an "imitation" of the third Satire of the Roman poet Juvenal, which probably dates to the first century. In this poem, Juvenal imagines a friend of the poet, named Umbricius, who is sick and tired of the city of Rome and is leaving for the countryside for good. In doing what was called an "imitation" of his classical source, Johnson is not simply translating Juvenal's poem, but updating it, finding modern correlations to the Latin original. Here, London stands in for Rome, "Thales" stands in for Juvenal's friend Umbricius, and the Tuscan countryside to which Umbricius was headed becomes Wales. Exhausted by the filth, crowds, noise of London, and the difficulty of making a living as a writer, Thales (believed by some scholars to refer to Richard Savage, another hack writer who had become a friend of Johnson's) in some ways expresses Johnson's own frustrations. But London itself, published in a handsome folio edition, written in the heroic couplet form that to readers of the 1730s identified the high style of serious poetry, using the form of the imitation to signify its neoclassical aspirations, and hyped in the pages of the Gentleman's Magazine (which published ads for the poem, and also excerpted it), is clearly an attempt to Johnson to get out of hackdom as soon as possible, to become a poet like Alexander Pope, making a good living independent of the whims and tight fists of the booksellers and magazine editors.

❖ Historical Context of *London* :

The poem, *London* also positioned itself as part of the growing opposition to the government of Sir Robert Walpole, who had dominated British politics since taking over as the de facto Prime Minister (there was no such official position yet) in 1721.

Walpole successfully suppressed dissent through a mixture of brutality, bribery, and control of the print media. By the late 1730s, however, attacks on his regime were becoming more open and frequent, prompting new attempts on the part of his government to suppress dissenting voices. In particular, the Stage Licensing Act of 1737 called for theater managers to submit all plays for government approval in advance of performance. Prompted in part by satires against the regime like John Gay's The Beggars Opera (1728) and the satirical afterpieces by Henry Fielding that had been very popular in the mid-1730s, the Stage Licensing Act had a chilling effect on the theater. In particular, the passage of the Act thwarted Johnson's attempt to become a playwright himself. Johnson had arrived in London just that year with a half-finished tragedy in his luggage, a play called Irene that he probably imagined as a vehicle by which he could make a lot of money and gain status as an author. But in the aftermath of the Stage Licensing Act, theater managers became extremely cautious about new plays in general, and Irene was not staged until 1749. By using Juvenal's Third Satire as a point of departure, London manages to critique the Walpole regime indirectly and through coded references, but contemporary readers, particularly those in sympathy with the opposition, were readily able to see how the poem mocked Walpole's reign as corrupt.

Probably because of its political stance, *London* seems to have sold reasonably well, and Alexander Pope, the most famous poet of the period (and a sympathizer with opposition politics), praised it. But as a vehicle for establishing Johnson's reputation as a significant poet who could make a living off his art it was a dead end. Johnson had to continue to grind out work for hire for another decade and a half. It was not until he achieved fame in the 1750s, first as the author of a Spectator-like series of journalistic essays called The Rambler and then as the editor of the Dictionary of the English Language, which made him a kind of national treasure, since he had single-handedly accomplished for English what it had taken large teams of scholars to do for other European languages. Here, let's read Johnson as eighteenth-century Grub Street's finest product–and its most perceptive critic.

❖ A Summary of *London* :

The reader is immediately introduced to the trope of country and city in the first 10 lines. The poet "regret[s]" his friend Thales (who by many a critic is considered to be based on the impoverished poet, Richard Savage, but Johnson denied such claims) leaving "vice and London" to live in the calm and idyllic "Cambria" (Wales) "to breathe in distant Fields a purer Air". The city of London was marked in this period by abject poverty, in spite of Industrial Revolution, and widespread corruption. London was slowly degenerating into a shell of the city it once was. It was also haggled by the constant presence of the French in the English courts and Spanish in the English seas. Thales is also described as "one true Briton" as he was disgusted by the decline of British liberty and the cultural influence of France in London. For Thales the corrupt capital has become an alien land, and when he resolves to leave, to flee it, he is prompted not by a desire of rural retirement, but a willingness to associate himself with the spirit of his country's ancient inhabitants." However, even though "Malice, Rapine, Accident" are common occurrences of the city, the narrator through the character of Thales has not deluded himself into believing in the bucolic atmosphere of the countryside. Exaggeration was a common satirical device, and the poet suggests that the vices of the city make it far more intolerable than the difficulties faced in countryside.

As Thales waits for the "wherry" that would transport him to Wales, he "dreams" of the "blissful age" and the "calm" which "such happy scenes bestow". These "happy scenes" of "Britannia's glories" temporarily "soothe" both Thales and the narrator. Even though "hope" assuages their anxiety, it does not completely dissolve them and results only to "double" his "distress". He remembers the "guard of commerce" and that "dread of Spain". In this period, the popular opinion was extremely hostile to Spain because of their continued commercial rivalry in the Caribbean. Attacks on British shipping by Spanish coast guards was particularly resented, and Prime Minister Robert Walpole's policy of not going to war was one of the main grievances, not only of his political opponents but also of the nation. According to one critic, "Walpole's alleged failure to protect British merchant ships from depredation by Spanish coast guards" was seen as seen as "cowardly" and "English honour" was "jest[ed]".

Thales was so disappointed by the "degenerate days" of the "neighb'ring town" (London), which was devoted only to "vice and gain" and not "science" which "toil[ed] in vain". He wishes heaven would find him a "happier place" where "honesty and sense" would not be "disgraced" with green willow trees ("verdant osiers") and "nature's paintings gay". Even though Thales wants to retire from the city to settle in the countryside, he seems to have forgotten what the countryside actually stood for- hard agricultural labour, poverty and hunger. Here, he envisages the countryside only as a picturesque place where a city bred man came to enjoy the "paintings" of nature. There is a hint in the poem that Thales' dream would not find fulfilment in the countryside either.

Thales also refers to himself as having a "rustic tongue". According to Johnson's dictionary, the word rustic means "untaught, inelegant, artless". Even though Thales had been living in the city, he still called himself "rustic", as he is unlike those "heroes" whose greed and pride knew no restraint and had gained control over their countrymen's lives, properties and liberty. He also describes London as being the "common shore" that is the drain of the refuse of other corrupt states like France and Rome. He does not want the "dregs" of these corrupted states to come to the "Land of Heroes" (London) and does not want it to become a "French metropolis." Such is Thales feeling of frustration that he bids a "fasting monsieur"- who has later been described as a "parasite"- to "go to Hell, to Hell he goes."

He is thoroughly dissatisfied with the life in London as no criminal feels "shame" or fears "censure" as the "number" of the crimes has increased exponentially. The only crime which remains is that of poverty. He asks heaven whether isn't any place "reserved" "in pity for the poor" albeit it be a "pathless waste" or "undiscovered shores" but safe from the Spanish. He ends his soliloquy with a repartee to the narrator of the poem, who would "fly for refuge" to the "wilds of Kent" that is areas which are far from human habitation, when they are tired of the "follies and crimes" in the city. He urges his friend, the narrator and in turn the readers to "exert their rage" and write incisive satire against the administrators of the city and "animate thy page". Thus, even if Thales' friend moves to the countryside, this musnt act as a deterrent and should not forget their responsibility. They can become writers, warning "succeeding times" against vice and folly.

❖ Word Notes and Annotations :

- **The Title:** ***London: A Poem in Imitation of the Third Satire of Juvenal*** – Eighteenth-century literary criticism recognized three types of translation from other languages, principally from Greek and Latin: "metaphrase" (word-for-word translation; what we would call a crib or trot); "paraphrase" (a version that reads well in English, a literary translation), and "imitation." An imitation follows the structure and patterns of thought of the original, but updates the content to the time of the imitation; if the original author were to write his poem here and now, this is what he would write. Thus Johnson substitutes London for Juvenal's Rome, and Frenchmen for Juvenal's contemptible but culturally dominant Greeks. In the 1730s, the leading exponent of imitation was Alexander Pope, whose "Imitations of Horace" used the Latin poet's satires to attack the administration of Sir Robert Walpole, the same target that Johnson scarifies less subtly in this poem. Johnson's 263-line poem is considerably shorter than Juvenal's 322-line original. Some of what Juvenal describes is not applicable to modern London; Johnson selects what suits his purpose and ignores the rest.
- **Epigraph:** ***—Quis ineptæ / Tam patiens Urbis, tam ferreus ut teneat se?*** – "Who can endure this monstrous city? Who is so iron-willed he can bear it?" (Juvenal)
- **Lines 1-20 :**

Though grief and fondness in my breast rebel,– Juvenal 1-2: "Grieved though I am to see the man depart,/ Who long has shared, and still must share my heart, " ***When injur'd Thales bids the town farewell,***– There is a persistent tradition that Thales represents Johnson's friend the poet Richard Savage, who was compelled by adverse circumstances to leave London and reside in Wales, but Johnson himself insisted that he did not know Savage at the time he wrote the poem, and that the resemblance was coincidental. In Juvenal, the departing friend is called Umbricius; Johnson enhances the authority of his speaker by giving him the name of the great astronomer and sage of ancient Greece. ***Who now resolves, from vice and London far,***–A rference to Juvenal 5-9. "I prefer even the barren island Prochyta to the Subura; for what do we see so wretched, so solitary, that you would not believe that the fires, the constant collapse of tenement roofs, and the thousand dangers of the savage city, not to mention the poets reciting in the heat of August, would frighten you worse?" ***And, fix'd on Cambria's solitary shore,***–Cambria is Wales, of which St. David is the patron saint. In Juvenal, the poet's friend departs for Cumae, near Naples in southern Italy, the home of the Cumaean sibyl (prophetess). ***For who would leave, unbrib'd, Hibernia's land,***– A reference to Juvenal 5-9; *Hibernia*: Ireland. The periphrasis carries the idea of 'wintry' (Lat. hibernus), which balances 'the rocks of Scotland'. ***Or change the rocks of Scotland for the Strand?***–the Strand: a busy street in London, not far from Johnson's house. ***There none are swept by sudden fate away,***–In the contemporary scinario of London, no one is fortunate enough to be favoured by the instant success. ***There none are swept by sudden fate away,***–In the contemporary scinario of London none are fortunate enough to be favoured by instant success, rather they fall prey to hunger. ***But all whom hunger spares, with age decay:***– But all who do not die of hunger, they are destined to dwindle with age. ***Here malice...relentless ruffians lay,* (*ll.* 13-15):** A completely chaotic and lawless situation is described here. ***And here the fell attorney prowls for prey***– The greedy and opportunist attorney's are criticized here. They try to make maximum profit from their clients, treating them as their prey. *fell*–Cruel. *prowls*–move about restlessly and stealthily, especially in search of prey. ***Here falling houses thunder on your head,***– In Juvenal 3: 6-9, it is described as "Houses, with ceaseless ruin, thundering down,". ***And here a female atheist talks you dead.***–A reference is made to the ceaseless beabtes of the town where atheisism became a new fashion of the edicated people-both male and female. ***While Thales waits the wherry that contains/ Of dissipated wealth the small remains,***–In Juvenal 3: 10-11, it is described as "Now had my friend, impatient to depart,/ Consign'd his little all to one poor cart:"The wherry Thales is waiting for is a rowing boat that will ferry him to a sea-going vessel.

- **Lines 21-50 :**

On Thames's banks....gave Eliza birth* (*ll.* 21-23)**– As Johnson notes in 1738 and 1755, Queen Elizabeth I was born at Greenwich, on the south bank of the Thames just below the city of London. Her name recalls the defeat of the Spanish Armada in 1588. *N.B.* Johnson was lodging at Greenwich when he wrote the poem. ***We kneel, ...And call Britannia's glories back to view* (*ll.* 24-26)**– The poet and his friend, before parting, perhaps froever, kiss the shore of Wales, in a mood to remember the glorious past of Britain. ***Behold her cross triumphant on the main,– The poet is refering to England's flag, the large red cross of the White Ensign, flown by the Royal Navy, the red cross of St. George. ***The guard of commerce, and the dread of Spain,***– In the 1730s, popular opinion in England was extremely hostile to Spain, because of commercial rivalry in the Caribbean. Attacks on British shipping by Spanish coast guards were particularly resented, and Walpole's unwillingness to avenge them by going to war was a principal grievance of his political opponents. In 1739 he was compelled to declare war against Spain. ***Ere masquerades debauch'd, excise oppress'd,***– Before the immoral entertainment of masked balls are excessively indulged and high rate of taxes and duties drained the coomon men. *masquerades* refers to masked balls which were popular in fashionable society, but widely condemned as incitements to immorality; *Ere*- before, *excise* – Walpole's efforts to reform the system of duties on various goods were depicted as oppressive by his political opponents. ***English honour grew a standing jest***– "An allusion to the peaceful policies of the Prime Minister, Sir Robert Walpole. His opponents [in the "patriot" opposition (line 52)] called them cowardly";

Walpole's "alleged failure to protect British merchant ships from depredations by Spanish coast guards" was a standard topic of Opposition rhetoric. ***A transient calm.... lull the sense of woe***– the peaceful condition of Britain appears in the minds of the poet and his companion. In past Britain was a place where there were plenty of happy scenes to bestow the mind with bliss and all the woes of mind and body could be laid aside amid those pleasurable sights. ***At length awaking.... the neighb'ring town***– It is as if, Thales was lost in a dream of the past glory. Awakening from his dream with scornful disapproval, aggreived Thales looks around to the town he is going to leave behind forever. ***"Since worth,....reward of empty praise;" (ll. 35-36)***– in Juvenal 3: 21-26, it is said that,

"In mighty councils with his nymph retir'd:
Though now the sacred shades and founts are hir'd
By banish'd Jews, who their whole wealth can lay
In a small basket, on a wisp of hay;
Yet such our avarice is, that every tree
Pays for his head; not sleep itself is free:" (translated by John Dryden)

N.B. from line 35, the rest of the poem is a speech by Thales. Here Thales begins his speech complaining that in these corrupted days, even an empty praise is unavailable for any worthy job.

In those curs'd walls, devote to vice and gain, (l. 37)– Thales calls the establishment of the Parliament of Britain as cursed place that is devoted to vice and cheap and selfish gain. ***Since unrewarded science toils in vain;*** – Since the efforts of learning remain unpraised and a vain affair. ***Since hope...my little less;*** – Thales tells that his hope for a glorious resurrection of the past pushes him to deeper despair and every passing moment leaves lesser blood of enthusiasm in him. ***While yet my steady steps no staff sustains,*** – No event or person can strengthen the hope of Thales now. In Juvenal 3: 27-28 it is described as,

Nor place, nor persons now are sacred held,
From their own grove the Muses are expell'd.

While yet ...indulgent give.(ll. 41-49) – Thales says that though he is passing through an extremely hopeless and degenerated time, still, in his vein runs the the healthy and energetic wave of hope. He begs the almighty to grant him to find out some happier place where the qualities like honesty and sense are not regarded as disgrace; he begs for some pleasing bank where green osiers (willows) dance in wave; he begs for some peaceful valley as picturesque as a painting,where any other careworn Briton (a native or inhabitant of Great Britain) found solace and in spite of his poverty disregard his foes. Thales craves for some secret and liberal corner on the earth for himself. ***Where once the harass'd Briton found repose (l. 47)***: "The ancient Britons retreated to Wales when the Saxons and other Germanic tribes invaded England". ***Let -------- live here, for -------- has learn'd to live. (l. 50)***: The blanks may be filled with the name of anyone who has learned, as Thales proudly has not, to live in the depraved London that symbolizes national vice and shame. ***N.B.*** Fred Springer-

Miller has pointed out that this line is a close paraphrase of Boileau: 'Que George vive ici, puisque George y sait vivre' (Satire, I.34), meaning, 'That George live here, since George knows how to live' and suggested that 'George,' i.e. George II, be supplied for the blanks.

- **Lines 51-74 :**

***Here let those reign,....a courtier white;* (*ll.* 51-52)**– Walpole was accused, not without reason, of having corrupted public life by putting Members of Parliament on the government payroll through appointments to sinecures or the award of pensions. "Patriots" were opponents of Walpole, "courtiers" were those who voted for Walpole, the King's chief minister. Johnson notes that Spanish attacks on British interests were defended in the houses of Parliament. *Pensions*: Johnson was indignant at the allowances dispensed by Walpole, but many years later (1762) he accepted a pension himself. *Patriot:* at this time the name belonged to a heterogeneous group of Whigs and Tories, led by Pulteney and Bolingbroke. These men, who included some very able writers, attacked Walpole in plays, pamphlets, ballads, and especially in *The Craftsman*. They found an ally in the Prince of Wales, who was on bad terms with the king and had set up a separate court at Leicester House in 1736. ***Explain their country's dear-bought rights away,* (*l.* 53)**– Probably Johnson means commercial rights. Since 1713 England was entitled to supply Spanish colonies with negro slaves and to send one ship a year to trade at Cartagena or Vera Cruz. When these rights were illegally extended by British merchants the Spaniards retaliated by conducting searches in mid ocean, often with considerable violence. This and other causes led to a crisis. Walpole, who was anxious to settle the differences by negotiation, was vilified as an appeaser. J. himself notes sarcastically 'The invasions of the Spaniards were defended in the houses of Parliament'. Newcastle, Pitt, and the rest of the opposition were bent on war, which finally came in 1739 (the War of Jenkins' Ear). ***And plead for pirates in the face of day;* (*l.* 54)**– "The invasions of the Spaniards were defended in the houses of Parliament" [Johnson's note, printed in 1787]. "The Parliamentary Opposition denounced Walpole's policy of allowing the Spanish to stop and search all ships trading with their American colonies". The unacknowledged hypocrisy of Johnson's "patriotic" rhetoric here is that English ships were the pirates and smugglers, not the Spanish. Spain had at this time the legal right to regulate the traffic with her American possessions, and the activity with which she enforced the search of English merchant vessels created a popular indignation which was steadily augmented after the affair of 'Jenkins's ear' in 1731 till in 1739 Walpole wâs forced against his will into a naval war with Spain. ***With slavish tenets taint our poison'd youth,* (*l.* 55)**– 'It is impossible to taint a body already poisoned.' This objection was made by William Mudford in 1802 and by William Shaw before him. In fact Johnson has used a Latin construction whereby the adjective 'poison'd' is proleptic-i.e. taken before its time. The sense is 'taint our youth so that it becomes poisoned'. ***"Let such raise palaces, and manors buy,* (*l.* 57)**– Here 'such' means 'such evilness'. What

Johnson wants to mean here, is that only evil men prospered (raise palace, buy manors) in this period. In Juvenal 3: 31-32 and 36 we find a similar decription:

> The marble caves, and aqueducts we view;
> But how adult'rate now, and different from the true! (31-32)
> ....
> Contented with an urn of native stone! (36)

Collect a tax, or farm a lottery, (l. 58)– Tax collecting and 'farming' a lottery (paying a fixed amount to the government to conduct a lottery and keeping the proceeds) were often highly profitable activities. *N.B.* 'Even the Government exploited the universal craze for gambling by raising state lotteries, which were patronized by all classes in society'. ***With warbling eunuchs fill a licens'd stage, (l. 59)***–The "warbling eunuchs" are the Italian *castrati* singers of the opera house, an entertainment greatly patronized by George II, and excepted in 1737 from the restrictions of the Licensing Act, which reduced the number of London theatres to two and required all plays to be approved by the Lord Chamberlain's office, thus eliminating theatrical satire on Walpole's government. The 1737 text reads "our silenc'd stage." *warbling eunuchs*: i.e., the castrati (male sopranos) who sang in Italian opera, then fashionable in London. "The 'warbling eunuchs' of the popular Italian opera had been the object of attack since Addison, partly because the opera was Italian, partly because it was opera, and partly because it was patronized by the court". ***And lull to servitude a thoughtless age. (l. 60)***– Here thoughtless refers to 'too stupid to care.' ***"Heroes, proceed! What bounds your pride shall hold? (l. 61)***–Here pride refers to 'objective case.' ***"Heroes, proceed!***–Johnson calls those hypocrites 'Heroes' in a sarcastic tone. It is supported by the following line (line. 62), where he makes a rhetorical question meaning 'nothing can restrain their greed of power and weath (gold)'. ***Behold rebellious virtue....our lives your own. (ll. 63-64)***–Johnson's sharp criticism pierces those hypocrites here. He sarcastically tells them to observe that all the rebellious qualities are uprooted from citizens and he proposes them to regard the lives of common men as their personal property (our lives your own). ***To such, a groaning nation's spoils are giv'n, (l.65)***– spoils taken from a groaning nation. The 1st ed., and that of 1787, had 'the plunder of a land is given' -a lighter and less tightly packed expression. The phrase means that the property of the common men (groaning nation) is robbed in form of excessive taxes and commercial duties. Here the term 'groaning nation' refers to the distressed condition of the common men burdened with high rate of taxes. ***When public crimes inflame the wrath of Heav'n: (l.66)***– Here 'public crimes' refers to crimes against the people. ***But what, my friend.....and blush at perjury (ll.67-68)***– Here, Thales regrets that nothing is left for him in London now, because he can neither favour these stately sponsored thievery nor eulogize the ruler standing in the court like many other opportunist poets, nor can he overlook such activities of others. ***Who scarce forbear.....poet's borrow'd wing; (ll.69-70)***– 'I can hardly refrain from showing up a poet as second-rate and derivative, even though he has a title and writes in praise of the court.' In Horace, Epist. 1.3.18-

20 Celsus is advised to rely more on his own resources - otherwise the birds may come to reclaim their plumage and the poor crow will become an object of ridicule. This is an adaptation of the Aesopic fable found in Babrius 72 and Phaedrus 1.3. Johnson may well be referring to Cibber, who became poet laureate in. 1730; cf. the ironical passage in Johnson's *Compleat Vindication of the Licensers of the Stage* (1739), where the writer imagines 'those Halcyon-days in which no politicks shall be read but those of the Gazetteer [cf. v.72] nor any poetry but that of the Laureat'. This, however, does not prove the equation Thales =Savage, even though the latter resented Cibber's appointment and set himself up as 'Volunteer Laureate'. All it means is that Thales shares Savage's (and others') dislike of Cibber and is sorely tempted to expose his inadequacies. ***And dare to slumber o'er the Gazetteer;* (l.72)**– Here 'Gazetteer' refers to *The Daily Gazetteer,* founded in 1735, the official newspaper of Walpole's government. "the paper which at that time contained apologies for the Court" (Johnson's note). ***Despise a fool in half his pension dress'd,* (l. 73)**– The phrase refers to one who spends half his allowance on clothes. ***And strive in vain to laugh at H----y's jest.* (l. 74)**– traditionally identified as John, Lord Hervey (1696-1743), Walpole's supporter and confidant of the queen, known to Pope's readers as 'Sporus' and 'Lord Fanny'. But Greene (307-8) argues strongly for John, 'Orator' Henley (1692-1756). Preacher, exhibitionist and wit, Henley was employed by Walpole in 1730 to ridicule The Craftsman in a periodical called *The Hyp Doctor*. 'Clodio's' was substituted in the 1787 edition, by which time Hervey and Henley were both long dead. As 'Clodio' was derived from the Lat. claudus (lame) it suited a feeble wit, and it was in line with other 'significant' names like 'Orgilio' and 'Balbo'. It is not clear, however, that Hawkins had J.'s authority for the change.

- **Lines 75-120 :**

***Others with softer smiles, and subtler art,* (l. 75)**– Here, Thales refers to the cunning arts of the statesmen in Walpole's ministry. ***Others with softer smiles, ...Or bribe a virgin's innocence away.* (ll. 75-78)**– Here, Thales describes the corrupted ministry of Wlapole. They, with their artful and pretentious words and smile try to satisfy their mean desires, erode and weaken the age-old principles, or taint the heart; their praises supersede a lover's addressing to his beloved or their words seem more luscious than that to corrupt a virgin's innocence. ***Well may they rise, while I, whose rustic tongue.* (l.79)**– Here the word 'rustic' is used, not without irony, to suggest the simple, wholesome country as opposed to the false, over-sophisticated city. as in. Boileau: *Je suis rustique et fier, et j'ai l'ame grossiere* (Sat. 1.50), meaning 'I am rustic and proud, and I have the coarse soul'. ***Well may they rise,...unlamented die.* (ll. 79-82)** – Here, Thales clearly draws a contrast between the crafty and cunning men of the city and the innocent rustic men. He calls himself a rustic (*while I, whose rustic tongue*), and tells that he can, in his speech, neither mystify truth nor gloss over a fact that is wrong. So he has to be rejected as a beggar and apprehended and doubted as a spy. He has to live without respect and would have to die unlamented. *Spy* : Savage was accused of spying for Pope (*Lives of the Poets* ii, 362, ed. Hill); but where there are factions there are always informers (cf. 252 below), and so here, too, it is best to see Thales as a figure who shares certain views and experiences with Savage. ***"For what but social guilt ....his fortune shares.* (*ll. 82-83*)** – Friendship of this kind is based on complicity and the mutual fear of exposure. 'Social', from Lat. *socialis,* means 'pertaining to companionship', hence 'shared'; but the phrase 'social guilt' looks like an original stroke of wit. *Orgilio:* from the French *orgueil,* pride; an imaginary character exemplifying any successful racketeer. ***All Marlb'rough hoarded, or all Villiers spent,* (*l.86*)**– John Churchill, first Duke of Marlborough (1650-1722) had a reputation for avarice; George Villiers, second Duke of Buckingham (1628-87), squandered a vast fortune. ***Turn from the glitt'ring bribe .... and conscience ever gay.*(*ll.87-90*)**– Here Thales's appeal becomes universal. He pleads the crafty men of all ages to leave their path of dishonesty and not to indulge in material comfort and wealth (*Nor sell for gold*) as this 'gold' cannot purchase the real gold, i.e., a peaceful sleep and solace of mind (*The peaceful slumber, self-approving day,*). Material wealth cannot buy spotless fame and an ever happy conscience. *Self-approving*: having a good conscience. ***"The cheated nation's happy fav'rites, see!*(*l. 91*)**– The favourites who prosper, thanks to the nation which they cheat. Partly Italians, but mainly French. ***Mark whom the great caress, who frown on me!*(*l. 92*)**– The antecedent of'who' is 'the great'. ***London! the needy villain's gen'ral home,* (*l.93*)**–The shaft is targeted to Walpole by the phrase 'needy villain'. ***The common shore of Paris and of Rome;* (*l.94*)**–*common shore*: the shared sewer in which the corrupt cities of continental Europe dispose of their refuse. John Oldham's imitation of Juvenal (1682) has:

the Common-shore
Where France does all her Filth and Ordure pour.

It seems that Johnson came to regard 'sewer' as the more correct form; in any case 'sewer' was substituted in editions after 1758. The later reading also avoided the ambiguity of 'shore'.

I cannot bear a French metropolis.* (*l.98*)**– As in more recent times, French elegance was regarded with a mixture of admiration and suspicion. In this respect the French provided a suitable counterpart to Juvenal's Greeks. Greece, however, did not present any military threat to Rome, whereas French power under Cardinal Fleury had been allowed to develop as a result of Walpole's foreign policy. Anti-French feeling was widespread. 'The London populace still continued its traditional hostility to foreigners, who were generally classed indiscriminately as French'. Yet the fascination remained. *French metropolis:* i.e., "a London whose customs imitate French ones" ***"Illustrious Edward! from the realms of day,* (*l.99*)**– Edward III (1327-77), initiator of the Hundred Years War against France, and highly successful commander in this enterprise; the victories of Crécy (1346) and Poitiers (1356) were particularly important. *Realms of day* : heaven, earth being a dark vale of sin and woe. ***"Illustrious Edward! ...delineaments to trace,* (*ll.99-101*)**– Thales addresses Edward III (1327-77), for whom he has high regard, and tells his to survey the present condition of Britain where he should not expect to find those heroes and saints, nor he should hope to find any characteristic feature (*delineaments*) of Britain by which it was distinguished. ***The rustic grandeur, or the surly grace, (l.102)– Nor should Edward II, try to find those pastoral grandeur or untaught grace of the villagers. *Surly grace:* here, as in 'surly virtue' , 'surly' is best understood as 'rough'. ***But lost in thoughtless ease, and empty show, (l.103)***– the warriors have lost their character in stupid carelessness and futile showiness. ***Behold the warrior dwindled to a beau (l.104)***– The warrior has dwindled to a beau, who (sense, freedom, and piety having been refined away) is the mimic of France etc. 'Refined away' is ironical, since the expression is normally used of impurities. Dryden had

Your herdsman primitive, your homely clown
Is turn'd a beau in a loose tawdry gown. (119-20)

beau: Dandy, fop.

Of France the mimic, and of Spain the prey. (l.106)– The Britons (the warriors) have lost their identity and have become mimics of French dandyism and victims of Spanish naval attacks. ***"All that at home no more can beg or steal, (l.107)***– Here 'at home' means 'in France'. But the literary implication can be derived as those who have adopted the French dandyism, now can not be demote to begging or stealing. ***Or like a gibbet better than a wheel; (l.108)***– nor they can be punished on gibbet or wheels. *Gibbet:* gallows. *Wheel:* a method of execution used in France before the revolution, when it was replaced by the guillotine. The victim was spreadeagled, and then as the wheel revolved his bones were broken with an iron bar. Sometimes the executioner was ordered to finish the prisoner off; the blows were then called *coups de grace* (thanksgiving). ***Hiss'd from the stage, ... their industry can 'scape, (ll.109-113)***– with their French identity or characteristics, they shout in shrill voices either on the stage (buffonery acting) or in the court (conceited politicians); all of their gestures, attires and political agenda seem borrowed, servile, pretentious, loquacious and light-hearted. ***They sing, they dance, çlean shoes, or cure a clap; (l.114)***– By this line an immoral and corrupted life-style is hinted at. *Clean shoes:* Oldham had :

Foot-boys at first, till they, from wiping Shooes,
Grow by degrees the Masters of the House.

Clap : gonorrhoea, 'the French disease'. ***N.B.*** the descending order of accomplishments.

All sciences a fasting monsieur knows, (l.115)– Oldham (186) had 'A needy Monsieur'. Here the term *monsieur,* a French word for 'Mr.' or 'Sir', directly satirizes those Britons, mimics of French life-style. Here 'fasting' denotes 'hungry' or 'craving'. The line sarcastically expresses that these buffons know every art of pretentiousness. ***And bid him go to hell, to hell he goes. (l.116)*** – *Go to hell:* 'by putting in caelum' (Latin, meaning, the sky, heaven.) 'he will mount to the skies', Juvenal had in mind simply a physical absurdity. Dryden (*l.*141) wrote 'And bid him go to heav'n, to heav'n he goes', which implied instead a religious injunction. Johnson saw that this could be improved, for no Englishman ever told anyone to 'go to heaven'. ***"Ah! what avails it... in English air;* (ll.117-118)** – Thales says that nothing is left in the air of Britain, where he first breathed after his birth. Dryden said:

Then, pray, what mighty Privilege is there
For me, that at my Birth drew English Air?

***Was early taught a Briton's right to prize,* (l.119)** – Britons have forfeited their birthright (i.e. liberty) by surrendering to the flattery of the French. ***And lisp the tale of Henry's victories;* (l.120)** – Henry V (1413-22), won several victories in his campaigns in France, most notably at Agincourt (1415). *lisp:* here, to speak like a young child; *N.B.* Johnson may have in mind the patriotic recollection of St. Crispin's day as foreseen by the king in Shakespeare's *Henry V* : 'This story shall the good man teach his son.'

- **Lines 121-169 :**

***If the gull'd conqueror receives the chain,* (l. 121)** – A satirical version of Horace's famous words *Graecia capta ferum victorem cepit* (Epist. 2.1.156), meaning Greece captured the savage victor. ***And flattery subdues when arms are vain?* (l. 122)** – Early editions read And what their armies lost, their cringes gain? This was a little untidy in that one had to apply 'their' to the French after understanding 'conqueror' of the English. Hence, presumably, the alteration. Later, in 1787, Hawkins (on whose authority?) read 'prevails' instead of 'subdues', perhaps because it gave a more exact balance to 'are vain'. ***The supple Gaul was born a parasite:* (l. 124)** – *Supple* : easily assuming any posture, especially one of deference. *Parasite:* 'one that frequents rich tables, and earns his welcome by flattery', Diet. ***Still to his int'rest true .... lavish tongue bestows;* : (l. 125-126)** – 'True' agrees with 'tongue'. Some editions, on the false but excusable assumption that it agreed with 'Gaul', put a full stop after 'goes'. ***In ev'ry face .... harmony divine :* (l. 126-128)** – Johnson exploits the ambiguity of 'bestow', which can mean 'attribute' or, literally, 'confer'. In 127f. he assumes the second sense, as if people's looks and speech had actually been transformed. ***These arts in vain .... awkward flattery:* (l. 129-131)** – The only triplet in Johnson's mature verse. Unlike Juvenal's Umbricius, Thales does not include himself among the hypocrites. *With diffidence:* without confidence. *Gain:* Hawkins changed this to 'get', perhaps on account of the sequence 'vain', 'strain', 'gain'. Yet the internal rhymes are defensible in a triplet. ***Well may they venture on the mimic's art,* (l. 134)** – [Juvenal 100-01]. The principal London theatres regularly featured French dancers as members of their companies, and a French dramatic company played in a smaller London theatre throughout the 1734-35 season, attracting some patronage from the Royal Family, but French performers did not dominate the London theatre as this passage implies. Juvenal's complaint at this point is that Greek performers are the leading players in the Roman theatre. This is one point where tension arises between following Juvenal and accurately describing the London scene. ***To shake with laughter ere the jest they hear,* (l. 140)** – Johnson concentrates Oldham's couplet (188) Do you but smile, immediately the Beast/ Laughs out aloud, tho he ne'er heard the jest. ***And as their patron....in December sweat.* (l. 142-143)** – The indispensable rhyme 'heat'/'sweat' was used by Oldham

(188) and Dryden (177-8). *Hints:* mentions. *Dog-days:* the period when the Dogstar Sirius rises and sets with the sun (3 July to 11 August); a time of oppressive heat, at least in Mediterranean countries. ***How, when competitors like these contend,(l. 144)*** – This has a reflection of Juvenal's Satire 3: 104-07 –

What confidants our wealthy Romans chose:
And whom I most abhor: to speak my mind,
I hate, in Rome, a Grecian town to find:
To see the scum of Greece transplanted here,

Can surly virtue hope to fix a friend? (l. 145) – Can couse/ rough virtue make a firm friend. ***Slaves that with serious impudence beguile, (l. 146)*** – *Slaves:* in apposition to 'competitors' (*l.*144). *Serious impudence:* shamelessness with a serious expression. ***Your taste in snuff, your judgment in a whore; (l. 149)*** – The line should be enclosed, at least mentally, in parentheses, for 'taste' exemplifies 'trifle', and 'judgment' exemplifies 'vice'. in apposition. ***Can Balbo's eloquence applaud, and swear (l. 150)*** – *Balbo:* from the Latin for stammering; an imaginary character whose name conveys his incompetence as a speaker. ***N.B.*** In his original draft Johnson had written - "Who dwell on Balbo's courtly mien [i.e. looks]". But since Balbo comes from the Lat. *balbus* (stammering), the change to 'eloquence' was clearly an improvement. No individual can be identified. ***He gropes his breeches with a monarch's air. (l. 151)*** – *gropes:* in the obsolete sense of "grasp," "take hold"; Balbo's oratorical stance is standing with his hands on his thighs; *with a monarch's air:* George II's favoured method of showing displeasure at court was to turn his back on the offender while drawing the rear flaps of his coat aside to show his backside. This was known as "rumping." ***They first invade your table, then your breast; (l. 153)*** – 'Invade' has a literal (though extended) sense with 'table', a figurative sense with 'breast'; an instance of zeugma. ***For arts like these preferr'd, ... or betray (l. 153-157)*** – Here Johnson, through the voice of Thales, criticizes the contemporary beurocrates and ministers. who excercise an evil practice of eulogizing the head of the Ministry to get promotion in their offices. Thales says that these art of pretention at first contaminate their statesmanship and, gradually, pollute their soul. The effect of these practices harm their soul and make them venomous for the common men. *Commence (l.157)*: 'to take a new character', Hence 'to turn into' or 'become'. ***Watch the weak hour, and ransack all the heart; (l. 155)*** – Reading the absurd *aulam* in Juvenal 112, and accepting the probably spurious 113, Barten Holyday translated: They'll ransack House and Heart and thence be fear' d. His note explains: 'He will turn his friend's house and all in it, as it were, upside down, so to discover his secrets and keep him in awe.' This was taken over and condensed by Johnson in 154-155. ***"By numbers here from shame or censure free, (l. 158)*** – All crimes are so numerous that they provoke neither shame nor censure; the only crime now is to be poor. *By numbers:* on account of their large numbers. ***This, only this, provokes the snarling muse; (l. 161)*** – Here 'Snarling muse' refers to satire. In classical times the satirist was sometimes referred to as a vicious cur by his opponents and as a trusty watch-dog by his supporters.

This, only this, provokes the snarling muse ....taunt a thousand ways (ll. 161-165): Johnson criticises those satirists who get pensions from the court and praise their Lord and satirise the opponent in with monotonous and repetitive verses. The term 'tattered cloak' referes to their verse also. *Sober:* solemn, with overtones of 'humourless'. *Labours for a joke :* struggles to make a joke. ***Of all the griefs ....insult points the dart:*** struggles to make a joke. Here, Johnson describes the limitation of those satires. He says that for the poor nothing is more sorrowful than a contemptuous jest. He adds that for those generous noble hearts of the poor, nothing is more sorrowful than a verbal attack from the block head or stupid (refering to those satirists). *Brisker:* more lively and alert. *Gen'rous:* noble. *Blockhead's insult:* i.e. an insulting blockhead. *Points:* 'directs' rather than 'sharpens', for sharpening would imply wit.

- **Lines 170-200 :**

"Has heav'n reserv'd, ...insolence no more. (ll. 170-175) – These lines are based on Horace's sixteenth epode, where the poet calls on those who are disgusted with civil war to set forth on 'the encircling ocean' and to seek 'the happy land' and 'the rich islands' which Jupiter has 'reserved' (secrevit) for the righteous. ***No peaceful desert yet unclaim'd by Spain? (l. 173)*** – During these years Georgia was claimed by the Spaniards, who had settled in Florida. *unclaim'd by Spain?:* "The Spaniards at this time were said to make claim to some of our American provinces" [Johnson's MS. note, 1787]. Again, Johnson's discourse, in keeping with the typical British outlook of the time, reverses the actual situation: the British colony of Georgia (est. 1732), and before that traders and settlers from the Carolinas, encroached onto territory long claimed by the Spanish as "Guale"—to say nothing of its native inhabitants, such as the Yamasee and Santee Indians, who had been extirpated by the British after the Yamasee war of 1715. *Seats*: a place to settle; Lat. *sedęs*. *Explore:* search out. ***"This mournful truth...are slaves to gold,(ll. 176-178)*** – Line 177 is justly admired for its massive weight. It must be granted, however, that the logic of the verses is untidy. The sense should be 'worth rises slowly everywhere, but more slowly here'; but in Johnson's syntax 'ev'ry where' goes with 'confess'd', not with 'rises'. ***"Where looks are merchandise,...the favours of his lord.(ll. 179-181)*** – If you want a great man to notice you, you must bribe his servant; cf. Juv. 184-9. Retails: retail: 'to sell at second hand'. ***"Where looks are merchandise (l.181)***– *groom:* a servant of any kind, not necessarily one who looks after horses. ***"But hark! th' affrighted crowd's tumultuous cries (l.182)***– Juvenal's mention of Ucalegon (199), a figure taken from *Aeneid* 2.312, led Johnson to Virgil's description of burning Troy. As the cries of the crowd woke Aeneas in his palace, so Johnson's sleeper is roused from his dream of a palace. Dryden's translation of the passage begins thus:

Now peals of shouts came thundering from afar,
Cries, threats, and loud laments, and mingled war:
The noise approaches, though our palace stood
Aloof from streets, encompassed with a wood.

Louder, and yet more loud, I hear the alarms
Of human cries, distinct, and clashing arms.
Fear broke my slumbers. (397-403)

***Sustain the th' approaching fire's tremendous light; (l.187)**– Tremendous:* terrifying. ***And leave your little ALL to flames a prey; (l.189)**– Little ALL:* an abridgement of Juv. 208-9. ***Then through the world a wretched vagrant roam, (l.190)**–* Another epic expansion of Juv., recalling the fate of Aeneas after the fall of Troy. ***In vain your mournful .... most insult your woes. (l.192-193)**–* These lines show how Johnson could use scholars' lumber to construct a fine couplet. 'In vain' comes from frustra, which was wrongly admitted into the text of Juvenal (210) by certain editors and was mentioned as a variant by others. Johnson rightly read frusta (scraps); *frustra,* being a spondee, is metrically impossible. ***"Should heav'n's just bolts Orgilio's wealth confound, (l.194)**–*In the Middle Ages, the village, was part of the valley community of Lugano. In 1484 it was ravaged by the plague. Juvenal 212-13 has :

My long dependance in an hour is lost:
Look round the world, what country will appear,

***"How virtue wars with persecuting fate; (l.199)**–* The line parodies the false rhetoric of the laureate tribe. ***With well-feign'd gratitude the pension'd band (l.200)**–* Juvenal 215-216 had

In Rome (nor think me partial to the poor)
All offices of ours are out of door:

- **Lines 201-230 :**

Refund the plunder of the beggar'd land. (l.201) – They give him the equivalent of the wealth he has lost -wealth which he had acquired by exploiting the country's poor. ***Dome* (*l.*203)** – massive building. ***The price of boroughs and of souls restore, (l.204)** – The price of boroughs:* the cost of bribing electors in parliamentary elections. *N.B.* Certain small boroughs ('pocket boroughs') were virtually the property, for electoral purposes of wealthy aristocrats who could sell or give the representation to men of their choice. In addition, the ownership of a manor often carried with it the right (called 'advowson') to appoint a clergyman to the local church. 'Restoring the price' means giving back to the landowner enough money to purchase new estates. So the line as a whole refers to the corrupt use of land ownership to influence parliament and church. ***Now bless'd with all the baubles of the great, (l.206)** – Bauble:* 'a thing of more show than use'. ***The polish'd marble, and the shining plate, (l. 207)**–the shining plate*: "Vessels made of silver or gold, possibly plated ones." ***Orgilio sees the golden pile aspire, (l.208)** – Orgilio :* the draft had 'Sejano'. In the mind of the reading public there was a chain of association connecting Verres (the evil governor of Sicily), Sejanus (the powerful favourite of Tiberius whose fall is described in Juv. 10), Wolsey, and Walpole. The evidence from *The Craftsman* and elsewhere is presented by C.B. Ricks, *Modern Language Notes* 73 (1958) 563-8. So it is fair to think of Orgilio, who in v.84 is the counterpart of Juv.enal Verres, as 'a man like Walpole' and of his palace as 'a mansion like Houghton'. For the meaning of Orgilio see note on *l.*84. *Aspire :* 'to rise, to tower.' ***Refund the plunder of the beggar'd land. (l.209)*** – Juvenal, as often, is more sharp and cynical. The rich man, he says, is now suspected with good reason of having set fire to his own house (221-2). According to Fleeman, fire insurance became possible in 1739-the year after the publication of *London. "**Could'st thou resign the park and play content, (l.210)*** – *Park:* e.g. St James's Park and Hyde Park, and fashionable pleasure-gardens like Vauxhall and Ranelagh. ***For the fair banks of Severn or of Trent; (l.211)*** – English rivers far from London; the Trent flows through Lichfield, where Johnson's family lived.***N.B.*** Thales is travelling to Wales, beyond the Severn; Oldham (199) had : "An handsom Dwelling might be had in Kent.

There might'st thou find some elegant retreat, (l.212) – *Elegant retreat:* this does not contradict 'secret cell' (49), for Thales does not say that he intends to acquire such an 'elegant retreat' for himself. ***Some hireling senator's deserted seat; (l.213)*** – *hireling senator:* a Member of Parliament who has been put on the government payroll to secure his vote. ***N.B.*** The M.P. is living in London, where he votes as his patron tells him. ***And stretch thy prospects o'er the smiling land, (l.214)*** – *Prospects:* views. *Smiling:* OED gives 'cheerful', 'agreeable to the sight'; but here it seems to have the added connotation of 'fertile'; in fact the draft had 'fruitful'. the Lat. *laetus* in the first line of Virgil's *Georgics*: *quid faciat laetas segetes* (what he is doing yielded the standing corn of the). ***For less than rent the dungeons of the Strand; (l.215)*** – *Dungeons:* basements. ***There prune thy walks....walk and morning toil. (ll. 216-223)*** – One might contrast this pastoral evocation of the countryside with Johnson's remarks in his "Life of Savage" (1744): "As he [Savage] was ready to entertain himself with future Pleasures, he had planned out a Scheme of Life for the Country, of which he had no Knowledge but from Pastorals and Songs. He imagined that he should be transported to Scenes of flow'ry Felicity, like those which one Poet has reflected to another, and had projected a perpetual Round of innocent Pleasures, of which he suspected no Interruption from Pride, or Ignorance, or Brutality". ***N.B.*** This elevated, and yet tender, way of writing about rural life owes something to Milton; Milton's description of Eve in Paradise Lost 9.427-30:

> ... oft stooping to support
> Each flower of slender stalk, whose head, though gay
> Carnation, purple, azure, or speck'd with gold,
> Hung drooping unsustain'd.

One must also bear in mind the Georgie tradition, which, though it started earlier, received its main impetus from Dryden's translation of Virgil's *Georgics*. Here Thales wants us to see the country in these idealized terms. Rural delights are needed as a contrast to urban horrors. And this may well have been a contrast which Johnson wished to draw at this point in his career. His general view of country life was much more complex. His appreciation of it was based on a thorough knowledge of practical details, and he was by no means blind to its harshness. ***Bower (l.217)***: 'an arbour; a sheltered place covered with green trees, twined and bent', Diet. ***Beds (l.218):*** Hawkins changed this to 'grounds' in 1787, perhaps because 'beds' was thought to be too low. Yet 'beds' is more precise. ***Security (l.222) :*** freedom from both danger and worry. ***"Prepare for death, if here at night you roam (l.224):*** It is reference to Juvenal 3: 272-74. Here, it refers to London. ***"Some fiery fop, with new commission vain, (l.226):*** A fop who has just purchased a commission in the army, and now cannot rest until he kills a man in a duel to prove his valour. ***"Some fiery fop, ... stabs you for a jest.(ll.226-229):*** A reflection of Milton, Paradise Lost 1.500-502:

And when the night
Darkens the streets, then wander forth the sons
Of Belial, flown with insolence and wine.

Fop: 'a man of small understanding and much ostentation',

New commission: he has just been made an officer.

Frolick (l. 228): 'gay, full oflevity, full of pranks'.

"Yet ev'n these heroes, mischievously gay, (l.230): *Mischievously:* in a way involving harm, wickedly. The Dictionary does not give the lighter, more playful, meaning, which seems to be a later development.

- **Lines 231-263 :**

Their prudent insults to the poor confine; (l.233) – They prudently confine their insults to the poor. The adverbial idea of 'prudently' is rendered by an adjective, which is then transferred from 'they' to 'insults'. Both processes are common in Latin poetry. ***Afar they mark the flambeau's bright approach, (l.234)*** – *flambeau:* torch; the rich and powerful rode by night in coaches accompanied by numerous servants and linkboys with torches to light the way. ***Train (l. 235):*** retinue. ***Flush'd as they are ... and golden coach. (l.232-235)*** – Oldham had :

Yet heated, as they are, with Youth, and Wine,
If they discern a train of Flamboes shine,
If a Great Man with his gilt Coach appear,
And a strong Guard of Foot boys in the rere,
The Rascals sneak, and shrink their Heads for fear.

Balmy (l. 237): mild, soothing. ***Midnight murd'rer (l. 239):*** cf. Oldham had 'midnight Padders'. ***Faithless (l. 239):*** the opposite of 'trusty'. ***Plants (l. 241):*** it may be argued that the variant 'leaves', adopted in 1787, rounds off the scene with the murderer's departure; but the reader has to adjust his construction on finding that 'leaves' is a transitive verb. 'Plants', moreover, is a stronger word. ***"Scarce can our fields, such crowds at Tyburn die, (l.232-235)*** – *Tyburn:* the place of public execution until 1783, near the present site of the Marble Arch. Hanging-days, which occurred eight times a year, were observed as public holidays. Oldham had

Then fatal Carts thro Holborn seldom went,
And Tyburn with few Pilgrims was content.

"With hemp the gallow....convoy for the k--g. (l.243-247) – Johnson could have said 'so many are hanged that the executioner is running out of rope', or 'so many are hanged that the fleet is running out of rope', or 'so many are hanged that there won't be enough rope for the king's convoy'. The draft, which did not originally include 244-5, suggests that J. may have intended to choose the third, and strongest, possibility, or at least to combine the first and third. In the end he tried to include all three and so blurred the effect. Juv. (310-11) did not make the same mistake. Schemes: 'The words "project" and "scheme" were anathema to Walpole's Tory critics', Kramnick 194. ***Whose ways and means support the sinking land* (*l.* 245)**–Ways-and-means bills were votes of money for government purposes; Johnson in a note calls "Ways and Means" a "cant [political jargon] term in the House of Commons for methods of raising money." **(*ll.* 246-247) :** Another political shaft. 'Tempting' makes it clear that Johnson is referring to the eight months which George II spent in Hanover with his mistress Mme de Wallmoden from May 1736 to January 1737. This and other visits to Hanover were greatly resented; (It is perhaps over-ingenious, however, to see a verbal play in 'rig' which would connect it with 'riggish'=wanton.) ***Fair justice then, without constraint ador'd* (*l.*250)–** *Without constraint* : the absence of greed and violence made penal laws unnecessary. J.'s contemporaries read about the golden age of Alfred in Sir John Spelman's Lzfe of Alfred the Great, translated and edited by Thomas Hearne, Oxford 1709. ***Held high the steady scale, but dropp'd the sword;* (*l.*251)–** *Deep'd the sword:* the meaning should be 'lowered the sword', which provides a suitable contrast to 'held high the ... scale'. If this is right, Johnson must have not only revived an obsolete verb but also given it a new sense. (The previous sense was 'to plunge or immerse deeply', OED.) Of other suggestions 'dipp'd' is at first sight attractive, but those who have studied J.'s handwriting maintain that his 'dipp'd' would hardly have been corrupted into 'deep'd' by the printer. 'Drop'd' could have been misread and would have provided the right sense. ('Drop'= 'lower' was used in fencing; cf. 'to drop one's guard' in boxing.) In that case, however, we have to exclude the more common sense, viz. 'to let fall'. If 'deep'd' was wrong, it was allowed to stand uncorrected for a very long time. 'Sheath'd', the alteration printed by Hawkins in 178 7, gives an inferior antithesis and is iconographically inept. ***N.B.*** In 1738, this line read: "Sustain'd the balance, but resign'd the sword;" Johnson's only significant change in the 1748 text was to substitute: "Held high the steady scale, but deep'd the sword". The reason for the change appears to be that "resign" went too far; Justice may not make use of her sword, but should not give it up altogether. The word "deep'd," however, hardly makes sense. In their edition, McAdam and Milne conjecture that Johnson wrote "drop'd," (i.e., lowered), which does make sense and could well have been misread by the printer; their emendation is adopted here. ***No spies were paid, no special juries known,* (*l.*252)–** A statute of 1731 had made it possible for either party to a lawsuit to demand a special jury; opponents of the government believed this was a device to win verdicts. *Spies:* Walpole had an extensive network of spies to counteract Jacobitism. See J. H. Plumb, Sir Robert Walpole; the King's Minister, London 1960, index under 'Spies'. Harley also had his sources of information. *Special juries:* under Walpole such juries, chosen from a panel of rich landowners, were used to secure convictions in cases of seditious libel. ***"Much could I add, -- but see the boat at hand, (l.254)–*** At last the boat the Thales is seen. The moment of parting between has arrived at last. Thales says that he could say more on the subject he has been discussing about, but as the wherry is at hand he has to take leave. ***The tide retiring, calls me from the land: (l.255)–*** The retreating tide would carry Thales's boat to his desired land. ***Farewell! -- When youth, ...Thy satire point, and animate thy page." (l.256-263)–*** Before leaving, in hs parting speech, Thales tells his friend that a day will surely come when the poet-friend will be tired and exhausted of his city life,when his youth, health and wealth will deacy, and then the poet would also esacape to the wilds of Kent; and then, Thales comments that, being tired of the corruptions and crimes of the city like him, the poet will also write down his anger in his verses. And then Thales will surely meet the poet leaving his shelter of Cambrian. Thales tells that on that day also he will continue to remain a 'foe to vice'. He with once again exert his rage in virtue's cause. He comments that the poets satire will be a sharp weapon against the vices of London on that day.

Wilds of Kent (l. 257): J. must surely have considered 'banks of Trent' as a parallel to Juv.'s reference to his native *Aquinum*. But that would have meant altering v.211, where he had substituted 'Trent' for Oldham's 'Kent'. So he followed the other course and put 'Kent' here. Since we are dealing with such a strongly explicit poet, it seems improbable that 'the wilds of Kent' was meant to suggest either Canterbury cathedral or the family home of Johnson's friend Elizabeth Carter.

Aid (l.260): Johnson's text of Juvenal (322) had *adjutor* (helper).

Foe to vice (l. 261): Prateus' note on Juvenal's *caligatus* (322) reads: 'equipped like an energetic soldier, certainly a keen foe of vice (acer vitiorum hostis)'. For the satirist as a foe to vice and a friend of virtue, we can refer to Horace, Sat. 2.1.70 and Pope's Imitation 119-22:

> Yes, while I live, no rich or noble knave
> Shall walk the World, in credit, to his grave.
> To VIRTUE ONLY and HER FRIENDS A FRIEND,
> The World beside may murmur, or commend.

Shade: a place of seclusion. Juvenal's 'Umbricius' might possibly suggest 'the man in search of seclusion (umbra)'. Certainly he has nothing to do with the haruspex mentioned by Pliny the Elder (10.6) and Tacitus (Hist. 1.27) and referred to by some of the older commentaries.

Rage (l. 262): in view of 'virtue's cause' and 'exert' it probably means 'zeal' or 'ardour' rather than 'anger'. Fleeman understands it in the more specialized sense of *furor poeticus* or inspiration.

❖ *London*-এর সারাংশের বঙ্গানুবাদঃ

স্যামুয়েল জনসন রচিত "লন্ডন" (১৭৮৪) কবিতাটি লেখা হয়েছিল জুভেনালের তৃতীয় স্যাটায়ারের অনুকরণে, যে স্যাটায়ারে বর্ণিত হয়েছে যে নগরের পাপ ও বিপদ থেকে বাঁচতে আব্রিসিউস রোম (নগর) ছেড়ে কুমীতে (গ্রামে) বাস করতে চলেছে। একটি অনুকরণ সাহিত্য মূল সাহিত্যের গঠনশৈলী ও ভাবনাকে প্রদর্শন করে কিন্তু এর বিষয়বস্তুকে অনুকরণের সময়কালের যুগপোযোগী করে তোলে, অর্থাৎ, এটি রচিত হয় সেই যুগের মত করে যে যুগে কবি নিজে জীবনযাপন করেছেন। এইভাবে, জনসন জুভেনালের রোমকে লন্ডন দ্বারা আর গ্রীকদের ফরাসীদের দ্বারা প্রতিস্থাপিত করেছেন।

নগর ও গ্রামের বিষয়বস্তু এই কবিতার কেন্দ্রীয় ভাববস্তু হয়ে উঠেছে। পাঠকদের সাথে কবিতার প্রথম দশ পংক্তিতেই গ্রাম ও নগরের রূপকের পরিচয় হয়ে যায়। কবি দুঃখ প্রকাশ করেছেন যে তাঁর বন্ধু থালেস [অনেক তাত্ত্বিকই মনে করেছেন যে এই চরিত্রটি দরিদ্র কবি রিচার্ড স্যাভেজ-এর ভিত্তিতে রচিত হয়েছে, কিন্তু জনসন এমন দাবীকে অস্বীকার করেছেন।] "পাপ ও লন্ডন" পরিত্যাগ করে চলে যাচ্ছে শান্ত ও মনোরম "ক্যামব্রিয়া"তে (ওয়েলস্-এ) বাস করতে, "দূরবর্তী প্রান্তরের বিশুদ্ধ বাতাসে শ্বাস নিতে"। শিল্প বিপ্লব সত্ত্বেও এই সময়কালের লন্ডন কলঙ্কিত হয়েছিল চরম দারিদ্র ও সর্বব্যাপী দুর্নীতির দ্বারা। লন্ডন ধীরে ধীরে অবক্ষয় প্রাপ্ত হয়ে তার পূর্বতন গৌরব নগরীর এক খোলসমাত্রে রূপান্তরিত হচ্ছিল। এটি ক্রমাগত তর্ক বিধ্বস্ত হয়ে চলেছিল ইংরেজ রাজসভায় ফরাসীদের ক্রমাগত উপস্থিতি ও ইংরেজ সাগরে স্প্যানিশদের আধিক্যের কারণে। থালেসকে একজন "প্রকৃত ব্রাইটন" হিসাবেও বর্ণনা করা হয়েছে যেহেতু সে ব্রিটেনের স্বাধীণতার অবনতি ও লন্ডনের সংস্কৃতির উপরে ফ্রান্সের প্রভাবের প্রতি বিতৃষ্ণা অনুভব করেছে। জে.পি. হার্ডির মতে "জনসন নগরের নিন্দা করেছেন আর প্রশংসা করেছেন সেইসব কিছুর যা আদর্শগতভাবে এখনও অকলুষিত গ্রাম প্রতিনিধিত্ব করে চলেছে। থালেসের কাছে দুর্নীতিগ্রস্ত রাজধানী এক অপরিচিত ভূ-খন্ডে পরিণত হয়েছে, আর যখন সে এসবের থেকে পালিয়ে যাওয়ার জন্য মনোস্থির করে, সে এক গ্রাম্য অবসরের ইচ্ছার দ্বারা প্ররোচিত হয়নি, বরং তা হয়েছে গ্রামের আদিম বাসিন্দাদের আত্মার সাথে নিজেকে সংযক্ত করার বাসনায়।" তাসত্ত্বেও, যদিও আক্রোশ, ডাকাতি আর দুর্ঘটনা নগরের নিত্য-নৈমিত্তিক ঘটনা হয়ে গিয়েছিল, কথক থালেস চরিত্রটির মধ্য দিয়ে নিজেকে গ্রামের মেঠো পরিবেশের প্রতি আস্থার মত ভ্রান্ত বিশ্বাস প্রদান করেন নি। অতিরঞ্জিতকরণ স্যাটায়ারের একটি পরিচিত পন্থা, আর বোঝাতে চেয়েছেন যে শহরের দোষগুলি গ্রামাঞ্চলের জীবনযাত্রার কঠিন পরিস্থিতির সম্মুখীন হওয়ার চেয়ে অনেক বেশি অসহনীয়।

থালেস যখন তাকে ওয়েলস-এ নিয়ে যাওয়ার নৌকার জন্য অপেক্ষা করছে, সে স্বপ্ন দেখে সেই প্রশান্তিপূর্ণ যুগের আর সেই নিরুদ্বিগ্নতার যা এমন সুখী দৃশ্যমালা প্রদান করে। "ব্রিটানিয়ার গৌরবের" এমন "সুখী দৃশ্যমালা" থালেস ও কথক উভয়কেই ক্ষণিকের সান্তনা প্রদান করে। যদিও "আশা" তাদের উদ্বিগ্নতাকে প্রশমিত করল, তবু তা সেটিকে পুরোপুরি মুছে দিতে পারলনা, আর ফল স্বরুপ কেবল তার বিহ্বলতাকে দ্বিগুণিত করল। সে স্মরণ করল সেই 'বাণিজ্যের কবচ'কে আর সেই 'স্পেনের মৃত্যু'কে। এই সময়কালে, জনমত সাংঘাতিকভাবে স্পেন বিরোধী ছিল কারণ ক্যারিবিয়ান সাগরে তাদের ক্রমাগত বাণিজ্যিক শত্রুতা। স্পেনের নৌসেনাদের দ্বারা ব্রিটিশ জাহাজগুলির উপর আক্রমণ বিশেষভাবে ঘৃণিত হয়েছিল, আর প্রধান মন্ত্রী ওয়ালপোলের যুদ্ধ না করার নীতি,কেবল তার রাজনৈতিক বিরোধী পক্ষেরই নয় বরং গোটা দেশেরই অসন্তোষের মূল কারণ ছিল। একজন সমালোচকের মতানুসারে, স্প্যানিশ নৌসেনাদের আক্রমণ থেকে ব্রিটিশ বাণিজ্য জাহাজগুলিকে রক্ষা করতে না পারার ওয়ালপোলের ব্যথতাকে 'কাপুরুষোচিত' হিসাবে দেখা হয়েছিল আর 'ইংরেজদের সম্মান' বিদ্রুপের পাত্র হয়েছিল।

থালেস প্রতিবেশি নগরের (লন্ডনের) 'অবক্ষয়প্রাপ্ত দিনের' জন্য ভীষণভাবে হতাশ হয়েছিল, যে অবক্ষয় কেবল পাপকর্ম আর স্বার্থসিদ্ধির প্রতি উৎসর্গীকৃত হয়েছিল আর সেই 'জ্ঞানের প্রতি নয় যা ব্যর্থভাবে কষ্টার্জিত হয়েছিল। সে আশা প্রকাম করেছে যে স্বর্গে সে খুঁজে পাবে এক সুখী স্থান যেখানে সততা ও বিবেকবোধ অপমানিত হবেনা সবুজ উইলো গাছের ভিড়ে আর প্রকৃতির আনন্দঘন চিত্রপটে। যদিও থালেস শহর ছেড়ে গ্রামে চলে যেতে উদ্যত হয়েছে, তবু মনে হয় যেন সে বিস্মৃত হয়েছে প্রকৃতপক্ষে গ্রাম বলতে কি বোঝায়- কঠিন কৃষিসংক্রান্ত কায়িক শ্রম, দারিদ্র, আর ক্ষুধা। এখানে, সে গ্রামকে সাজিয়েছে এমন এক চিত্রার্পিত স্থান হিসাবে যেখানে শহুরে মানুষ কেবল প্রকৃতির চিত্রিত রূপ উপভোগ করতে আসে। এখানে কবিতাতে একটা ইঙ্গিত রয়ে যায় যে থালেস গ্রামেও তার আত্মার পরিপূর্ণতা লাভ করতে পারবেনা।

থালেস এর পাশাপাশি নিজেকে গ্রাম্য ভাষা সম্পন্ন মানুষ হিসাবেও অভিহিত করেছে। জনসন প্রণীত অভিধান অনুসারে 'rustic' শব্দটির অর্থ "অশিক্ষিত, অমার্জিত ও কৌশলহীণ"। যদিও থালেস শহরে বাস করেছে, তবুও সে নিজেকে অশিক্ষিত বলে অভিহিত করেছে, কারন সে সেই 'বীরদের মত নয় যাদের লোভ আর অহঙ্কারের সীমা ছিল না আর নিজেদের দেশবাসীর জীবন, সম্পদ ও স্বাধীণতার উপর যারা নিয়ন্ত্রণ স্থাপন করেছিল। সে লন্ডনকে এমন এক স্থান হিসাবেও বর্ণনা করেছে যা ফ্রান্স ও রোমের মত দুর্নীতিস্ত দেশগুলির আশ্রয়দাতা "সাধারণ তীর" হিসাবে কাজ করেছে। সে চায়নি যে এসমস্ত দুর্নীতি গ্রস্ত দেশগুলির 'অধঃক্ষেপ' এসে পোঁছাক "বীরদের দেশে" (লন্ডনে) আর চায়নি তা পরিণত হোক "ফরাসী মহানগরীতে"। থালেস-এর হতাশা এতটাই গভীর যে সে এক "অনাহারে থাকা ফরাসী লোককে"-যে পরবর্তীকালে একজন 'পরজীবী' বলে বর্ণিত হয়েছে- তাকে নরকে গমন করতে বলেছে, যে নরকগামী হয়েছে।'

সে লন্ডনের জীবনের প্রতি পুরোপুরি বিতশ্রদ্ধ হয়ে উঠেছে যেহেতু কোনও অপরাধী আর অনুভব করেনা "লজ্জা" অথবা ভয় পায়না "বিধিনিষেধের" যেহেতু অপরাধের "সংখ্যা" বেড়ে চলেছে লক্ষ্যণীয়ভাবে। একমাত্র যে অপরাধটি এখনও দন্ডনীয় রয়ে গেছে তা হল 'দারিদ্র'। সে স্বর্গকে জিজ্ঞ্যাসা করেছে যে "দরিদ্রদের সহমর্মিতার" জন্য কোন স্থান আদৌ সংরক্ষিত আছে কিনা হতে পারে তা "পথভ্রষ্ট অপচয়" অথবা "অনাবিস্কৃত তটভাগ" কিন্তু তা হবে স্প্যানিশদের থেকে নিরাপদ। সে তার একক কথন শেষ করেছে কবিতার কথকের প্রতি শে-ষপূর্ণ জবাব দানের মাধ্যমে, যে কথক 'পলায়ন করবে আত্মগোপন করতে' কেন্টের অরণ্যে যা মানব বসতি থেকে বহু দূরবর্তী এক স্থান, যখন তারা শহরের 'অশুভতা ও অপরাধ" থেকে ক্লান্ত হয়ে পড়বে। সে তার বন্ধু, কথককে আর পরোক্ষে পাঠককূলকে আবেদন জানিয়েছে "তাদের বিক্ষোভের বহিঃপ্রকাশ ঘটাতে" আর লিখতে ভেদ শক্তিসম্পন্ন স্যাটায়ার নগরের প্রশাসনের বিরুদ্ধে আর "আপনাদের পৃষ্ঠাগুলিকে প্রাণবন্ত" করে তুলতে। এইভাবে, যদি থালেস-এর বন্ধুটি গ্রামে যাত্রাও করে, তা যেন কোনওভাবেই প্রতিবন্ধকতা হিসাবে কাজ না করে আর যেন তারা নিজেদের দায়িত্ব বিস্মৃত না হয়। তারা লেখক হয়ে উঠতে পারে, পরবর্তী প্রজন্মকে অশুভতা আর পাপের বিরুদ্ধে সাবধান করার মাধ্যমে।

❖ A Critical Analysis of *London*:

London, published in 1738, represents Johnson's attempt to satirize the grubby world of London and also to rise above it. The poem is an "imitation" of the third Satire of the Roman poet Juvenal, which probably dates to the first century. In this poem, Juvenal imagines a friend of the poet, named Umbricius, who is sick and tired of the city of Rome and is leaving for the countryside for good. In doing what was called an "imitation" of his classical source, Johnson is not simply translating Juvenal's poem, but updating it, finding modern correlations to the Latin original. Here, London stands in for Rome, "Thales" stands in for Juvenal's friend Umbricius, and the Tuscan countryside to which Umbricius was headed becomes Wales. Exhausted by the filth, crowds, noise of London, and the difficulty of making a living as a writer, Thales (believed by some scholars to refer to Richard Savage, another hack writer who had become a friend of Johnson's) in some ways expresses Johnson's own frustrations. But London itself, published in a handsome folio edition, written in the heroic couplet form that to readers of the 1730s identified the high style of serious poetry, using the form of the imitation to signify its neoclassical aspirations, and hyped in the pages of the Gentleman's Magazine (which published ads for the poem, and also excerpted it), is clearly an attempt to Johnson to get out of hackdom as soon as possible, to become a poet like Alexander Pope, making a good living independent of the whims and tight fists of the booksellers and magazine editors.

The poem also positioned itself as part of the growing opposition to the government of Sir Robert Walpole, who had dominated British politics since taking over as the de facto Prime Minister (there was no such official position yet) in 1721.

Walpole successfully suppressed dissent through a mixture of brutality, bribery, and control of the print media. By the late 1730s, however, attacks on his regime were becoming more open and frequent, prompting new attempts on the part of his government to suppress dissenting voices. In particular, the Stage Licensing Act of 1737 called for theater managers to submit all plays for government approval in advance of performance. Prompted in part by satires against the regime like John Gay's The Beggars Opera (1728) and the satirical afterpieces by Henry Fielding that had been very popular in the mid-1730s, the Stage Licensing Act had a chilling effect on the theater. In particular, the passage of the Act thwarted Johnson's attempt to become a playwright himself. Johnson had arrived in London just that year with a half-finished tragedy in his luggage, a play called Irene that he probably imagined as a vehicle by which he could make a lot of money and gain status as an author. But in the aftermath of the Stage Licensing Act, theater managers became extremely cautious about new plays in general, and Irene was not staged until 1749. By using Juvenal's Third Satire as a point of departure, London manages to critique the Walpole regime indirectly and through coded references, but contemporary readers, particularly those in sympathy with the opposition, were readily able to see how the poem mocked Walpole's reign as corrupt.

Probably because of its political stance, London seems to have sold reasonably well, and Alexander Pope, the most famous poet of the period (and a sympathizer with opposition politics), praised it. But as a vehicle for establishing Johnson's reputation as a significant poet who could make a living off his art it was a dead end. Johnson had to continue to grind out work for hire for another decade and a half. It was not until he achieved fame in the 1750s, first as the author of a Spectator-like series of journalistic essays called The Rambler and then as the editor of the Dictionary of the English Language, which made him a kind of national treasure, since he had single-handedly accomplished for English what it had taken large teams of scholars to do for other European languages. Here, let's read Johnson as eighteenth-century Grub Street's finest product–and its most perceptive critic.

A brief comment on Dr. Samuel Johnson's Satirical Mode in "London"

Dr.Samuel Johnson's 'London' was published in 1738 anonymously as an imitation of Juvenal's 'Third Satire'. Imitation was a poetic form that was practiced by poets in the latter half of the 17th Century like Dryden, with works like 'Preface to Ovid's Epistles' (1680). The form underwent extensive development during the Restoration Period with notable practitioners like Abraham Cowley, John Oldham (Who also has a version of Juvenal's Third) and The Earl of Rochester. By the 1730s, Imitation was a popular contemporary poetic form with Alexander Pope's 'Imitations of Horace gaining immense popularity. Critics like T.F. Wharton have viewed Johnson's employment of the form as a bid for recognition and commercial success, while others have viewed it as a political statement in support of Pope's Tory and Pro-Jacobite convictions.

Dryden had described the imitation as a kind of translation, "where the translator assumes the liberty not only to vary from the words and sense, but to forsake them both as he sees occasion; and taking only some general hints from the original, to run division on the groundwork, as he pleases." Johnson defines imitation in the 'Life of Pope' as "a kind of middle composition between translation and original design, which pleases when the thoughts are unexpectedly applicable and the parallels lucky." A typical deficiency of this form was that it relied heavily on the Classical Literacy of its readers, a deficiency that was recognised by Johnson himself. However, his reworking of Juvenal's original operates as a broader Social and Political indictment of the political setting and social backdrop of England. His project seemed to have struck a chord with the burgeoning population of readers as 'London' was printed in numerous subsequent editions across a variety of journals and magazines. This can be owed to the extremely political and topical nature of 'London' as it was rife with allusions to matters like the Licensing Act of 1737 and The Excise Bill of 1733. Johnson's use of the imitation form as a method of satirising was brilliant as it was able to accommodate topicality with the general tone of the Augustan age. Harriet Raghunathan observes that the classical atmosphere affords a kind of Augustan respectability to the poem which endowed it with weight and universality which made it general rather than merely topical.

Johnson's 'London' was unique in its engagement with both the social and political issues that throttled Britain. Britain, at the time was functioning under the principles of Mercantilism which bestowed regulatory authority unto a government for the purpose of augmenting national prosperity. Mercantilism emerged as a manifestation of Capitalism that had evolved from earlier practices of Proto-Capitalism which were prevalent in the preceding centuries such as Agrarian Capitalism. It was because of a Mercantilist attitude of accumulation that Britain had expanded its influence in the Colonial Marketplace. England under the Ministerial umbrage of Sir Robert Walpole had ascended to the state of a Mercantilist nation. By the 1730s, Britain had emerged as a major colonial power contending with the likes of France and Spain for profit. The commercial ethic that had propelled Britain to this stature had wide ranging social and political ramifications. It was these outcomes that were satirised by Johnson in his work. The ethic of commercial success that propelled the Walpole administration to maintain the Peace treaty with Spain (After the Spanish Wars of Succession), to the disgust of The Opposition (Which had the Tories and a faction of Opposition Whigs) who conglomerated under the broad umbrella of "Patriotism". The members of this group, also broadly known as the Country Party (as opposed to the Court Party) were in support of waging war against Spain as a response to the damage incurred by English ships around the Caribbean. David Nichols Smith alerts us to Johnson's hypocrisy towards the issue of Piracy, Johnson is riled up due to the losses incurred by the British but he remains unperturbed by the perpetuation and condoning of Piracy by the British. Maintaining a peaceful relationship with Spain was viewed as an act of acquiescence by these Patriots. Johnson identified himself as a part of this group at the time and his sentiment echoes in the following Lines from 'London'

"In pleasing Dreams, the blissful Age renew,
And Call Britannia's Glories back to view:
Behold her Cross Triumphant on the Main,
The Guard of Commerce, and the Dread of Spain"

These lines use England's past image as a contrast to its current stance of servility towards the Spaniards. The character of Thales also frequently refers to previous visions of Britain's glory with images of Elizabeth I (and the annihilation of the Spanish Armada at the hands of Drake). Thales constantly conjures up images where England was a dominant force and was unwilling to submit to foreign entities. The image of Henry V's victory over the French also serves as an image to view against Britain's current relationship with the French. Johnson lambasts the import of French culture and affectations in the English circles of power and influence. This mirrors the invasion by the Greeks in Juvenal's original work. Johnson here distinguishes himself drastically from Juvenal. As Wharton observes, Juvenal describes in detail all the latest fashions his parasite Greeks have brought along from harp-strings to sandals, while Johnson uses details in a controlled manner for the dismissal of such values as Johnson's parasites are just seen as "Singing, Dancing and Clapping".

It is the commercial ethic that Johnson links to the Greed and avarice in men which manifests itself as a corrupt Walpolean system, where Walpole takes the place of Verres in Juvenal's original under the name of 'Orgilio', as a veiled attack. Johnson uses a strategy of not naming the targets of his satire openly as Walpole's administration had placed oppressive mechanisms to silence all Opposition to his reign. It is said that Walpole spent around 50,000 pounds (from 1731-1741) in an effort to propagandise everybody through his control over the papers like Gazetteer and Hyp-Doctor. Walpole's efforts to control the work of outspoken writers are what probably lead to the most famous lines from this poem.

"This mournful truth is everywhere confest
SLOW RISES WORTH, BY POVERTY DEPREST"

It was through measures like the Licensing Act of 1737, which required every production to go through the Chamberlain's Men before public viewership that created a festering resentment in the minds of struggling writers like Johnson. These lines are In Capital letters to highlight the pain felt by Johnson as a poet who had his dreams of advancement being abbreviated due to inadequate funds.

He had to quit Oxford and the lack of that degree, which was a result of his financial turmoil which precluded him from attaining smooth advancement. Poverty had become a crime in Mercantile Capitalist societies such as England, the competition had rendered the poor as socially unacceptable. People were judged on the basis of their appearance rather than their "worth" (The sober trader and the Tattered cloak) Writers, much like other people needed money to survive. Writing in the time of Walpole was a highly political activity, most writers who flourished were "Pension'd Bands' who received money from the administration or those who sought refuge under the patronage of Political Umbrellas. In both cases, the work of these writers had to be moulded to suit the agenda of the overarching political force. Johnson refused to compromise the value of his work and suffered the ignominy of living in poverty in a city like London. In 'London, Johnson illustrates the travails of living in a city that was slowly getting overpopulated due to the massive influx of immigrants whose livelihood as small time agriculturalists were destroyed because of the Enclosure Acts. These people fled to London, "dreaming" of brighter futures. With the majority of the nation seeking value in monetary currency, Johnson laments the decline (or possibly the demise) of "Worth". "Worth" is a word is used recurrently in 'London', Johnson seems to have formulated a notion of intrinsic worth that was divorced from positions and privilege in society. He saw the decline of that worth in a society where "worthless" or "un-worthy" people found themselves seated in positions of power due to their monetary influence or sycophancy. To my mind, Johnson seems to highlight a state of constant unhappiness in the existence of man is a mercantilist society. These lines serve as a General Truth, irrespective of its immediate political implications in Walpolean England. The notion of Universality exuded by these lines seems to tie-in with Johnson's larger philosophical idea of having a common human existence that exists for all. This can also be seen in the character of Thales as a character that despises the mechanisms of mercantile capitalism that promote Greed and Corruption and the promotion of unworthy individuals to positions of Authority and respect, still finds himself in the "Want of cheap Reward of empty Praise". The character of Thales now functions as a limited character which can be read in two ways. The first reading of Thales can undermine the entire validity of Johnson's Political Satire, as he is the principal agent through whom the readers awaken to the misgivings of a world "where all are slaves to gold". The second reading can view him as a character who understands the issue with such a world but is radically limited even in his act of subversion by the oppressive force of Capitalism and succumbs to the wants of adulation that do not correspond to "Worth". Other Scholars have also read his hatred for the system as a manifestation of resentment, as he is unable to progress within a system that has satisfied the material needs of even those who he considers less worthy than himself.

The Excise Bill acts as an interesting focal point which is attacked by Johnson, the Bill allowed officials to conduct searches for items like Tobacco, Gin etc. on which the Excise had to be paid. What made this curious was that this form of regulation went against the notions of Private Ownership that is often central to Capitalist Economies. This Bill was severely castigated by the British public and there was widespread unrest on account of the same.

Johnson uses the image of the pastoral to invoke an alternative space to the oppressive atmosphere of London. Thales imagines receding into the beauty and peacefulness of nature where the poet seems to search for a domain which is unspoiled by Greed and Mercantilism. He views the areas of Wales as a space where this is possible (As it has never been invaded by the Anglo-Saxons or the Romans), Johnson seems to search for a space for "True Britons" and like his character the answer seems to have been echoing in the scenery of the pastoral for him. 'London' is littered with vocabulary like 'patriots' and 'true Britons' such vocabulary was extremely popular among the Opposition propaganda against the Walpole administration. Johnson tried to juxtapose the image of the rustic country to counterbalance the ills of the corrupt Urban Society. It is perhaps this vision of an alternative space that links him and other Augustan poets to the Romantic Movement that was to articulate a systemic response to the ills of Industrial and Capitalist societies with the Country and Nature at the centre of its alternative conception. However, it would be specious on our part to extend that argument to conclude that Johnson intended to do the same. His satirical critique of England's social and political interface through the poetic form of Imitation was instrumental in providing him with a platform from where his career as a writer started gaining mileage. While his allusions got him into trouble with the British administration, which released arrest warrants in his name he remained a trenchant critic of the system whilst maintaining his "artistic integrity".

A Comparison between Juvenal's *Third Satire* and Johnson's *London*.

A look at the criticism of Johnson's poetic imagery reveals a mixed reaction. Admittedly, there is support for a negative view from certain literary critics. Yvor Winters calls Samuel Johnson the "master of English prose, but whose poetry appears to have been an acquired language in which he was never entirely at home, with a style of imagery which consists of a kind of coagulation of cliches. Johnson's poetic ineptness is also asserted by another of his biographers, Joseph Wood Krutch, who refers to the imagery in Johnson's *London* with the term "coldness.

London is an imitation of Juvenal's satire. While imitations of the classics had long been a traditional exercise among scholars as well as experienced writers, imitation as a genre and as adopted by Samuel Johnson grew from the popular theory of paraphrase in translation as practiced by Denham and Cowley, From their idea of imitation, it was only a short step to modernize the classical text being translated by altering the scene from Rome to London and by making use of English names of men, places, and customs whenever the parallel would permit. Imitation reached the height of its popularity in the early decades of the eighteenth century, mainly with the work of Pope. Writers quickly realized that the imitation was likely to be the most successful with didactic and satiric poems, and, consequently, most of the imitations are poems in this mode.

Samuel Johnson defines imitation in his Dictionary as a '!method of translating looser than paraphrase, in which modern examples and illustrations are used for ancient, 12 domestick, or for foreign. He finds imitation a sympathetic vehicle for his satiric poetry for several reasons. First of all, he holds the concept of "general nature": if the sins and the sinners of Augustan London are similar to the sins and the sinners of Augustan Rome, then certainly, the terms of castigation may also be similar. Also, Johnson believes that all good poetry deals with the unchanging passions of men. Johnson, in discussing the continuity of thought between modern and ancient authors, insists that the ancients have planted "flowers of fiction in the open road of poetry for the accommodations of their successors" and that these flowers belong to "everyone that has art to pluck them without injuring their colors or their fragrance. " There is some significance in relating Johnson work to Juvenal's satire when pointing out the former's versatility in imagery, since the works of Juvenal have been judged rich in imagery.

Samuel Johnson's *London* is an imitation of the Third Satire of Juvenal, which according to Gilbert Highet is "one of the finest ever written" and "is alive with brilliant epigrams. " 16 When London and Juvenal's Third Satire are compared, a number of interesting facts appear. The adjectives, explosive, exuberant, lively, colorful, attributed to Juvenal's work also fit London. Then too, the structure and some of the ideas are parallel. However, Juvenal's poem runs to 322 lines; Johnson's has only 259. Since Latin is considered a more concise language than English, it may be inferred that Johnson has not felt constrained to give a full or a literal translation of Juvenal's poem. This is the result partially of his ability at condensation and par tially of his deliberate ignoring of parts of Juvenal that did not suit his purpose.

Juvenal's Third Satire takes the form of a dialogue between friends. Umbricius, who is moving away from Rome, pauses to take leave of his friend. Umbricius' reasons for leaving the city form a framework for most of the imagery in the satire. With the first set of images, Umbricius describes the consequences of poverty which he has witnessed. He begins by discussing the difficulties that are in the way of making a living in Rome. Umbricius declares, for instance, that honesty is not rewarded.

The literal translation is: "No man will get my help in robbery, and therefore, to no one do I become an associate: I am treated as a maimed and useless body that has lost the power of its right hands. " Also according to Umbricius, there are the Greeks who edge out the native Romans.

The literal translation inquires: "Must I not flee from purple-clad gentry like these ? Is a man to sign his name before me, and recline upon a couch above mine, who has been brought to Rome by the wind which brings us our plums and our figs?" Finally, Umbricius complains that the poor dependent is universally despised and rejected because money is the only standard by which people are judged: "quantum quisque qua nummorum servat in arca, / tantum habet et fidei" (lines 143-144). ("A man is believed in exact proportion to the amount of cash which he keeps in his strong box. ") Thus, Umbricius decides that there is nothing for him to do in Rome: let others stay who can make compromises.

The second main set of images in the Third Satire details the dangers and discomforts of life in Rome and indicates that life is not worth living there anyway. Umbricius asserts that houses fall down or burn up, crimes disturb the night, traffic disrupts the day. Umbricius pictures what it is like to be jostled by a crowd.

The literal translation states: "A crowd hinders us hurrying in front, and a dense mass of people press in on us from behind: one man digs an elbow into me, another hits with a hard pole; moreover, this one dashes a piece of timber against my head, that one a nine-gallon measure. The discouraging conditions of city life here seem endless, Johnson follows the dramatic framework of Juvenal in picturing the city. The parallel he finds between his London and Juvenal's Rome is credible and, for the most part, authentic enough to attract great attention and approval in his own day. He finds the streets unsafe, both from "relentless ruffiansfr (line 15) and "falling housesJ1 (line 17); l8 he scornsthe fawning Frenchmen rather than the odious Greeks; he deplores the impossible fate of the poor, honest citizen. In notable instances, imagery of the original comes off poorly by comparison with London's: "Haut facile emergunt quorum virtutibus opstat res angusta domiu (lines 164- 165). (It is no easy matter, anywhere, for a man to rise / When poverty stands in the way of his merits"). These lines in Juvenal become "SLOW RISES WORTH, BY POVERTY DEPRESSID (line 177; Johnson's capitals) in London. Johnson's very concise picture achieves a majestically somber note that is quite distinctivė along side Juvenal's. When Juvenal bemoans the fate of a poor man who is denied respect simply because he is poor, he pictures a man ridiculed because of soiled and patched clothing; then the Roman satirist pursues his illustration till it becomesso involved as to lose force:

nil habet infelix paupertas durius in se,
quam quod ridicules homines faczt. "exeat, 'I inquit,
"si pudor est, et de pulvino surgat equestri
cuius res legi non sufficit, " et sedeant hic
lenonum pueri quocumque ex fornice nati;
hic plaudat nitidi praeconis filius inter
pinnirapi cultos iuvenes iuvenesque lanistae. (lines 152 - 158)

The literal translation reads: "Of all the woes of luckless poverty none is harder to endure than this, that it exposes men to riducule. 'Out he goes ! what a shame ! ' says the marshall; 'out of the Knights' stalls, he whose means does not satisfy the law. ' Here let the sons of panders, born in any brothel, take their seats; here let the spruce son of an auctioneer clap his hands, with the smart sons of a gladiator on one side of him and the young gentlemen of a trainer on the other. " Johnson uses the same example of the poor man who is taunted because of his tattered clothing, but brings the details to a head:

Of all the griefs that harrass the distress'd,
Sure the mostbitter is a scornful jest;
Fate never wounds more deep the gen'rous heart,
Than when a blockhead's insult points the dart. (lines 166- 169)

Thus a more succinct image comes into focus.

In the Third Satire, Umbricius advises his friend to leave the thankless city and find a place to live in the country. Here Juvenal in his image of country life calls up some half - belief that has traditionally charmed or comforted men; then he threatens the complacent picture with a piece of wry flippancy.

The literal translation is: "Live as a loving steward of a hoe and a tilled garden, till a hundred vegetarians could feast off its produce. It's quite an achievement in whatever retreat, in whatever place to have yourself master of--well, say one lizard. " Johnson turns Juvenal's sour acceptance of a country life into a picture of pastoral stateliness.

Congenial though the general import of the original may be, the imitation must recognize that a considerable part of satirical complaint has to do with to-day's vexation, with foul weather here and now. Thus, although there are some passages which only need recharging with personal experience, there are others from which the meaning has ebbed. The good imitator will only keep that which either fits as it stands or can be transformed by a turn of wit. Here Johnson's firmness appears. He does, in fact, allow London to attack private vice as a "social poem" in the manner of Juvenal, but his most important imagery reveals the evils of the public acts of the Walpole administration.

Here let those reign, whom pensions can incite
To vote a patriot black, a courtier white;
Explain their country's dear -bought rights away,
And plead for pirates in the face of day;
With slavish tenets taint our poison'd youth,
And lend a lye the confidence of truth. (lines 51-55)

There is no imagery in Juvenal that parallels this picture of political bribery. The political drift to the satire is Johnson's own. Like Juvenal, Johnson exhorts the reader to return to the peace and security of the country; unlike Juvenal, he also urges the reader to return to the courage, strength, and political wisdom of earlier days: "In pleasing dreams the blissful age renew, / And call Britannia's glories back to vieww (lines 25-26). The imagery in London centers upon the virtues of country life and the follies of city life and upon the strength of an earlier government in England and the weakness of Britain's present political system. Some of the images are suggested by the Third Satire; others are completely Samuel Johnson's.

Short Answer Type Questions with Answers

Q. 1. ***When injur'd Thales bids the town farewell,*—Comment on the allusion in the line.**

Ans. This line is quoted from the poem "London" by Samuel Johnson.

There is a persistent tradition that Thales represents Johnson's friend the poet Richard Savage, who was compelled by adverse circumstances to leave London and reside in Wales, but Johnson himself insisted that he did not know Savage at the time he wrote the poem, and that the resemblance was coincidental. In Juvenal, the departing friend is called Umbricius; Johnson enhances the authority of his speaker by giving him the name of the great astronomer and sage of ancient Greece.

Q. 2. ***And, fix'd on Cambria's solitary shore,*–Comment on the allusion in the line.**

Ans. This line is quoted from the poem "London" by Samuel Johnson.

Cambria is Wales, of which St. David is the patron saint. In Juvenal, the poet's friend departs for Cumae, near Naples in southern Italy, the home of the Cumaean sibyl (prophetess).

Q. 3. ***For who would leave, unbrib'd, Hibernia's land,*–Comment on the allusion in the line.**

Ans. This line is quoted from the poem "London" by Samuel Johnson.

It is an allusion from Juvenal 5-9. Here, Hibernia refers to Ireland.

Q. 4. ***Quis ineptæ***

***Tam patiens urbis, tam ferreus ut teneat se?*– Comment on the quotation.**

Ans. This line is quoted from the poem "London" by Samuel Johnson.. It is quoted from Juvenal's Satire 3. The English translation of the quotation is -"Who can endure this monstrous city? Who is so iron-willed he can bear it?"

Q. 5. **When injur'd *Thales* bids the town farewell, – Comment on the quotation.**

Ans. This line is quoted from the poem "London" by Samuel Johnson. Thales corresponds to Juvenal's Umbricius, who leaves for the country in disgust at the life in Rome.

Q. 6. ***Who now resolves, from vice and London far,*–Comment on the allusion in the line.**

Ans. This line is quoted from the poem "London" by Samuel Johnson.

It is an allusion from Juvenal 5-9 which says –"I prefer even the barren island Prochyta to the Subura; for what do we see so wretched, so solitary, that you would not believe that the fires, the constant collapse of tenement roofs, and the thousand dangers of the savage city, not to mention the poets reciting in the heat of August, would frighten you worse?"

Q. 7. ***And, fix'd on Cambria's solitary shore,***
Give to St. David[4] one true Briton more. **– Comment on the allusion of 'Cambria' and 'St. Davis' in these lines.**

Ans. This line is quoted from the poem "London" by Samuel Johnson. Here, 'Cambria' is an ancient name for Wales; "St. David" is the patron saint of Wales.

Q. 8. **Or change the rocks of Scotland for *the Strand*? –Comment on the allusion of 'srand' in the line.**

Ans. This line is quoted from the poem "London" by Samuel Johnson. Here 'Strand' refers to a street in the heart of London.

Q. 9. **And here the fell attorney prowls for prey– Comment on the meaning of 'fell' in the line.**

Ans. This line is quoted from the poem "London" by Samuel Johnson. Here 'fell' means 'Cruel'.

Q. 10. **While Thales waits the *wherry* that contains– Comment on the meaning of 'wherry' in the line.**

Ans. This line is quoted from the poem "London" by Samuel Johnson. Here 'wherry' means 'A narrow river vessel'.

Q. 11. **Struck with the seat that gave Eliza birth, – Comment on the allusion of 'Eliza' in the line.**

Ans. This line is quoted from the poem "London" by Samuel Johnson. Here, Johnson's note, printed in 1787, Eliza refers to "Queen Elizabeth born at Greenwich". Elizabeth I was a heroine for the Opposition to Walpole because of her success against the Spanish. Greenwich on Thames was then "an outlying village" and is now "a district of London". Johnson was lodging at Greenwich when he wrote the poem.

Q. 12. **Behold her cross triumphant on the main – Comment on the allusion of 'her cross' in this line.**

Ans. This line is quoted from the poem "London" by Samuel Johnson. Here 'her cross' refers to England's flag, the red cross of St. George.

Q. 13. **Ere masquerades debauch'd, excise oppress'd, – Comment on the use of the word 'excise' in this line.**

Ans. This line is quoted from the poem "London" by Samuel Johnson.
Walpole's attempt to increase excise taxes in 1733, following on earlier excises and duties passed in 1724 and 1732, prompted a concerted opposition campaign that caused him to withdraw the measure and led to a significant diminishment of Walpole's majority in the House of Commons in the election of 1734.

Q. 14. **Or English honour grew a standing jest. – Comment on the alliusion in this line.**

Ans. This line is quoted from the poem "London" by Samuel Johnson. "English honour grew a standing jest" is an allusion to the peaceful policies of the Prime Minister, Sir Robert Walpole. His opponents in the "patriot" opposition called them cowardly". Walpole's "alleged failure to protect British merchant ships from depredations by Spanish coast guards" was a standard topic of Opposition rhetoric.

Q. 15. Where once the harass'd Briton found repose – Comment on the meaning in this line.

Ans. This line is quoted from the poem "London" by Samuel Johnson. The quoted line states– "The ancient Britons retreated to Wales when the Saxons and other Germanic tribes invaded England".

Q. 16. ***Let —— live here, for —— has learn'd to live.*** **– Comment on the line.**

Ans. This line is quoted from the poem "London" by Samuel Johnson. Fred Springer-Miller has pointed out that this line is a close paraphrase of Boileau: 'Que George vive ici, puisque George y sait vivre' (Satire, I.34), and suggested that 'George,' i.e. George II, be supplied for the blanks.

Q. 17. ***Collect a tax, or farm a lottery, .*** **– Comment on the line.**

Ans. This line is quoted from the poem "London" by Samuel Johnson.

"Tax collecting and 'farming' a lottery (paying a fixed amount to the government to conduct a lottery and keeping the proceeds) were often highly profitable activities".

Q. 18. ***With warbling eunuchs fill a licens'd stage*****– Comment on the use of 'warbling eunuchs' in the line.**

Ans. This line is quoted from the poem "London" by Samuel Johnson. Here 'warbling eunuchs' refers to the castrati (male sopranos) who sang in Italian opera, then fashionable in London]. "The 'warbling eunuchs' of the popular Italian opera had been the object of attack since Addison, partly because the opera was Italian, partly because it was opera, and partly because it was patronized by the court".

Q. 19. ***To such, a groaning nation's spoils are giv'n*****– Comment on the line.**

Ans. This line is quoted from the poem "London" by Samuel Johnson. Here the line refers to "the Plunder of a Land is giv'n".

Q. 20. ***And dare to slumber o'er the Gazetteer;*****– Comment on the line.**

Ans. This line is quoted from the poem "London" by Samuel Johnson. Here, according to Johnson's note, printed in 1787, 'Gazetteer" refers to "The paper which at that time contained apologies for the Court". *The Daily Gazetteer,* est. in 1735, was funded by the ministry.

Q. 21. ***All Marlb'rough hoarded, or all Villiers spent*****– Comment on the allusion of *Marlb'rough* in this line.**

Ans. This line is quoted from the poem "London" by Samuel Johnson.

Here the reference is made to the great general, John Churchill, first Duke of Marlborough (1650-1722), who made an immense financial profit during his campaigns against the French in the War of the Spanish Succession (1702-11)".

Q. 22. ***All Marlb'rough hoarded, or all Villiers spent*– Comment on the allusion of Villiers in this line.**

Ans. This line is quoted from the poem "London" by Samuel Johnson. Here the reference is made to George Villiers, 2nd Duke of Buckingham [1628-87], who wasted a fortune and died in squalor". Villiers is the "Zimri" of Dryden's *Absalom and Achitophel;* also Pope's *Of the Use of Riches* (1732), ll.299-314.

Q. 23. ***The common shore of Paris and of Rome;* – Comment on the allusion of 'shore' in this line.**

Ans. This line is quoted from the poem "London" by Samuel Johnson. Here 'shore refers to "sewer".

Q. 24. ***I cannot bear a French metropolis.* – Comment on the allusion of ' French metropolis' in this line.**

Ans. This line is quoted from the poem "London" by Samuel Johnson. Here 'French metropolis' refers to "a London whose customs imitate French ones".

Q. 25. ***Illustrious Edward! from the realms of day,*– Comment on the allusion of 'Edward' in this line.**

Ans. This line is quoted from the poem "London" by Samuel Johnson. Here 'Edward' refers to Edward III (1312-77). He was famous for his victories over the French [e.g., at Crécy]".

Q. 26. ***Illustrious Edward! from the realms of day,*– Comment on the meaning of the word ' *realms of day*' in this line.**

Ans. This line is quoted from the poem "London" by Samuel Johnson. Here 'realms of day' means Heaven.

Q. 27. ***Behold the warriour dwindled to a beau;* – Comment on the meaning of the word *'beau'* in this line.**

Ans. This line is quoted from the poem "London" by Samuel Johnson. Here 'beau' means Dandy or fop.

Q. 28. ***Or like a gibbet better than a wheel;* – Comment on the meaning of the phrase *'gibbet better than a wheel'* in this line.**

Ans. This line is quoted from the poem "London" by Samuel Johnson. Hanging and breaking on the wheel were the British and French methods of execution respectively.

Q. 29. ***On Britain's fond credulity they prey.*– What is the meaning of the word *'fond'* in this line?**

Ans. This line is quoted from the poem "London" by Samuel Johnson. Here 'fond' means Foolish.

Q. 30. ***And bid him go to hell, to hell he goes.* – Comment on the allusion in this line.**

Ans. This line is quoted from the poem "London" by Samuel Johnson. Here 'fond' means Foolish.

The line refers to a translation of Juvenal by Dryden– "And bid him go to Heav'n, to Heav'n he goes".

Q. 31. ***And lisp the tale of Henry's victories;*** **– Comment on the allusion of *'Henry's victories'* in this line.**

Ans. This line is quoted from the poem "London" by Samuel Johnson. Here the phrase *'Henry's victories'* refers to the victories of Henry V (1387-1422) over the French [e.g. at Agincourt]".

Q. 32. ***And flattery subdues when arms are vain?*** **– Comment on the allusion in this line.**

Ans. This line is quoted from the poem "London" by Samuel Johnson. The line raises a rhetorical question –"And what their armies lost, their cringes gain?"

Q. 33. ***To shake in dog-days, in December sweat.*** **– Comment on the allusion of *'dog-days'* in this line.**

Ans. This line is quoted from the poem "London" by Samuel Johnson. Here the phrase *'dog-days'* refers to "Late summer days when Sirius (the Dog Star) was prominent".

Q. 34. ***Can Balbo's eloquence applaud, and swear*** **– Comment on the allusion of *'Balbo'* in this line.**

Ans. This line is quoted from the poem "London" by Samuel Johnson. Here 'Balbo' is an Italian word for 'slutterer'."There are no grounds for identifying this 'stammerer' with any one speaker".

Q. 35. ***He gropes his breeches with a monarch's air.*** **– Comment on the use of the word *'gropes'* in this line.**

Ans. This line is quoted from the poem "London" by Samuel Johnson. Here 'gropes' is used in the obsolete sense 'to touch with the hand, take hold of, grasp.'

Q. 36. ***This, only this, provokes the snarling muse;*** **– What is meant by the phrase *'snarling muse'* in this line?**

Ans. This line is quoted from the poem "London" by Samuel Johnson. Here the phrase *snarling muse* refers to "The muse of satire".

Q. 37. ***Should heaven's just bolts Orgilio's wealth confound*** **– What is meant by the word *'confound'* in this line?**

Ans. This line is quoted from the poem "London" by Samuel Johnson. Here, 'confound' means 'Destroy'. Regarding the passage that begins with line 194, Johnson's MS. note remarks: "This was by Hitch a Bookseller justly remarked to be no picture of modern manners, though it might be true at Rome."

Q.38. ***The price of boroughs and of souls restore*** **– What is meant by the phrase *'boroughs and of souls'* in this line?**

Ans. This line is quoted from the poem "London" by Samuel Johnson. Here the phrase *'boroughs and of souls'* refers to the fact– Rich and powerful persons often 'bought' and 'sold' parliamentary boroughs. Also they often had the right to appoint clergymen to parishes.

Q. 39. ***Could'st thou resign the park and play content*** **– What is meant by the phrase *'park and play'* in this line?**

Ans. This line is quoted from the poem "London" by Samuel Johnson. Here the phrase *the park and play* refers to "Fashionable walking grounds, such as St. James Park . . . and the theatre".

Q. 40. ***For the fair banks of Severn or of Trent*– What is meant by the phrase *'Severn or of Trent'* in this line?**

Ans. This line is quoted from the poem "London" by Samuel Johnson. Here the phrase refers to "Rivers in the western and northern English countryside".

Q. 41. ***Some hireling senator's deserted seat*– Comment on this line.**

Ans. This line is quoted from the poem "London" by Samuel Johnson. The line refers to "The country house of some peer or MP who has a government appointment in Westminster".

Q. 42. ***Who sleeps on brambles till he kills his man*– What is meant by the phrase *'sleeps on brambles'* in this line?**

Ans. This line is quoted from the poem "London" by Samuel Johnson.
Here the phrase means 'sleeps uneasily, as on thorns'.

Q. 43. ***Afar they mark the flambeau's bright approach*– What is meant by the phrase *'the flambeaux's bright approach'* in this line?**

Ans. This line is quoted from the poem "London" by Samuel Johnson. Here the phrase *the flambeaux's bright approach* refers to the fact–the rich were lighted on their way home by servants or linkboys carrying torches (flambeaux).

Q. 44. ***Scarce can our fields, such crowds at Tyburn die,*– What is meant by the allusion *'Tyburn'* in this line?**

Ans. This line is quoted from the poem "London" by Samuel Johnson.
Here 'Tyburn' refers to "The customary place of execution in eighteenth-century London [till 1783]".

Q. 45. ***Whose Ways and Means support the sinking land;*– What is meant by the phrase *'Ways and Means'* in this line?**

Ans. This line is quoted from the poem "London" by Samuel Johnson.
Here the term 'Ways and Means' is "A cant term in the House of Commons for methods of raising money".

Q. 46. ***To rig another convoy for the k—g.*– What is meant in this line?**

Ans. This line is quoted from the poem "London" by Samuel Johnson. Herebe the phrase 'to rig another convoy for the k—g', Johnson satirizes "George II's frequent visits to his mistress, Amalie von Wallmoden, in Hanover".

Q. 47. ***A single jail, in Alfred's golden reign*– Comment on the allusion of 'Alfred' in this line.**

Ans. This line is quoted from the poem "London" by Samuel Johnson. Here, 'Alfred' referes to Alfred the Great, King of the West Saxons (849-899 CE).

Q. 48. ***No spies were paid, no special juries known,* – Comment on the allusion of 'special juries' in this line.**

Ans. This line is quoted from the poem "London" by Samuel Johnson. Here, the term 'special juries' refers to "Special juries, drawn from a panel of wealthier citizens than ordinary juries—and therefore presumably more in favour of preserving the status quo—were said to be used by the ministry to obtain convictions of Opposition printers and writers for sedition".

Q. 49. ***Thou fly'st for refuge to the wilds of Kent;* – What is meant by the phrase 'wilds of Kent' in this line?**

Ans. This line is quoted from the poem "London" by Samuel Johnson. Here, 'wilds of Kent' is perhaps meaning the Weald (sometimes spelled 'Wild') of Kent, a large wooded area also covering part of Surrey and Sussex..

Explanations

Q. 1. ***Though grief and fondness in my breast rebel,***

Ans. Eightcenth-century literary criticism recognized three types of translation from other languages, principally from Greek and Latin: "metaphrase" (word-for-word translation; what we would call a crib or trot); "paraphrase" (a version that reads well in English, a literary translation), and "imitation." An imitation follows the structure and patterns of thought of the original, but updates the content to the time of the imitation; if the original author were to write his poem here and now, this is what he would write. Thus Johnson substitutes London for Juvenal's Rome, and Frenchmen for Juvenal's contemptible but culturally dominant Greeks. In the 1730s, the leading exponent of imitation was Alexander Pope, whose "Imitations of Horace" used the Latin poet's satires to attack the administration of Sir Robert Walpole, the same target that Johnson scarifies less subtly in this poem. Johnson's 263-line poem is considerably shorter than Juvenal's 322-line original. Some of what Juvenal describes is not applicable to modern London; Johnson selects what suits his purpose and ignores the rest. In one instance, however, the account of Orgilio's recovery from a disastrous fire (194-209), Johnson later admitted that this episode was not appropriate to eighteenth-century England.The poem was first published anonymously in London in 1738. Ten years later Johnson made minor revisions to the text for publication in Dodsley's Collection of Poems. The present text is based on the revised version of 1748. In both versions Johnson printed passages from Juvenal at the foot of the page to show how closely he was imitating the Latin.

Q. 2. Comment on the quotation:

"In pleasing Dreams, the blissful Age renew,
And Call Britannia's Glories back to view:
Behold her Cross Triumphant on the Main,
The Guard of Commerce, and the Dread of Spain"

Ans. These lines are quoted from "London" by Samuel Johnson.

These lines use England's past image as a contrast to its current stance of servility towards the Spaniards. The character of Thales also frequently refers to previous visions of Britain's glory with images of Elizabeth I (and the annihilation of the Spanish Armada at the hands of Drake). Thales constantly conjures up images where England was a dominant force and was unwilling to submit to foreign entities. The image of Henry V's victory over the French also serves as an image to view against Britain's current relationship with the French. Johnson lambasts the import of French culture and affectations in the English circles of power and influence. This mirrors the invasion by the Greeks in Juvenal's original work. Johnson here distinguishes himself drastically from Juvenal. As Wharton observes, Juvenal describes in detail all the latest fashions his parasite Greeks have brought along from harp-strings to sandals, while Johnson uses details in a controlled manner for the dismissal of such values as Johnson's parasites are just seen as "Singing, Dancing and Clapping".

It is the commercial ethic that Johnson links to the Greed and avarice in men which manifests itself as a corrupt Walpolean system, where Walpole takes the place of Verres in Juvenal's original under the name of 'Orgilio', as a veiled attack. Johnson uses a strategy of not naming the targets of his satire openly as Walpole's administration had placed oppressive mechanisms to silence all Opposition to his reign. It is said that Walpole spent around 50,000 pounds (from 1731-1741) in an effort to propagandise everybody through his control over the papers like Gazetteer and HypDoctor. Walpole's efforts to control the work of outspoken writers are what probably lead to the most famous lines from this poem.

Q. 3. Comment:

Here let those reign, whom Pensions can incite
To vote a patriot black, a courtier white;
Explain their country's dear-brought Rights away;
And plead for Pirates in the Face of Day;
With slavish Tenets taint our poison'd Youth,
And lend a Lye the confidence of Truth.

Ans. These lines are quoted from "London" by Samuel Johnson.The most apparent political attack in the poem is on the Robert Walpole's administration. Johnson makes several allusions to particular instances of his times which mark his discontent towards the parliamentary authority under Walpole. Johnson satirizes the the measures of the government , and the corruption which the government was thought to have fostered:

"Here let those reign, whom Pensions can incite
To vote a patriot black, a courtier white;
Explain their country's dear-brought Rights away;
And plead for Pirates in the Face of Day;
With slavish Tenets taint our poison'd Youth,
And lend a Lye the confidence of Truth.

London attacks the excise, the Stage Licensing Act, and political pensions; these last, Johnson feared would led to a system of administration that encouraged sycophancy. Firstly, Johnson criticizes the insecurities of the government and their attempts at suppressing the opposing voices. The reference to "special juries" and "spies" (line 252) in London allude to The Special Juries Act, wherein panels were introduced in 1729 that were used to suppress opposition writings. This reference "licensed stage" hints at the tyranny of Licensing Act of 1737 through which the government sought to control stage performances and prevent satires on Walpole's government. Secondly, while feeling nostalgic about the "blissful age" and Britain's erstwhile "glories", Johnson finds fault with the pusillanimity of Walpole in the face of Spanish depredations ("dread of Spain") evident from The Treaty of Utrecht 1713. However, David Nichol Smith brings to notice the unacknowledged hypocrisy of Johnson's ardent support of the English ships which were pirates and smugglers, not the Spanish. Thirdly, Johnson censures the "debauch'd" Walpole administration which introduced a bill in 1733, increasing "excise" taxes. Also, reference to Walpole as Orgilio is a parallel to Verres in Juvenal's original. Verres was a very corrupt governor of Sicily, against whom Cicero wrote a famous indictment In Verrem. Lastly, Johnson is indignant at the huge amount of personal wealth Walpole accumulated as the Prime minister over years. Open reference to his "Palaces" and "Manors" as a result of his "Thirst of Pow'r and Gold".

Q. 4. ***"This mournful truth is everywhere confest***
SLOW RISES WORTH, BY POVERTY DEPREST"

Ans. It is the commercial ethic that Johnson links to the Greed and avarice in men which manifests itself as a corrupt Walpolean system, where Walpole takes the place of Verres in Juvenal's original under the name of 'Orgilio', as a veiled attack. Johnson uses a strategy of not naming the targets of his satire openly as Walpole's administration had placed oppressive mechanisms to silence all Opposition to his reign. It is said that Walpole spent around 50,000 pounds (from 1731-1741) in an effort to propagandise everybody through his control over the papers like Gazetteer and HypDoctor. Walpole's efforts to control the work of outspoken writers are what probably lead to the most famous lines from this poem.

"This mournful truth is everywhere confest
SLOW RISES WORTH, BY POVERTY DEPREST"

It was through measures like the Licensing Act of 1737, which required every production to go through the Chamberlain's Men before public viewership that created a festering resentment in the minds of struggling writers like Johnson. These lines are In Capital letters to highlight the pain felt by Johnson as a poet who had his dreams of advancement being abbreviated due to inadequate funds. He had to quit Oxford and the lack of that degree, which was a result of his financial turmoil which precluded him from attaining smooth advancement. Poverty had become a crime in Mercantile Capitalist societies such as England, the competition had rendered the poor as socially unacceptable. People were judged on the basis of their appearance rather than their "worth" (The sober trader and the Tattered cloak) Writers, much like other people needed money to survive. Writing in the time of Walpole was a highly political activity, most writers who flourished were "Pension'd Bands' who received money from the administration or those who sought refuge under the patronage of Political Umbrellas. In both cases, the work of these writers had to be moulded to suit the agenda of the overarching political force. Johnson refused to compromise the value of his work and suffered the ignominy of living in poverty in a city like London.

In 'London, Johnson illustrates the travails of living in a city that was slowly getting overpopulated due to the massive influx of immigrants whose livelihood as small time agriculturalists were destroyed because of the Enclosure Acts. These people fled to London, "dreaming" of brighter futures. With the majority of the nation seeking value in monetary currency, Johnson laments the decline (or possibly the demise) of "Worth". "Worth" is a word is used recurrently in 'London', Johnson seems to have formulated a notion of intrinsic worth that was divorced from positions and privilege in society. He saw the decline of that worth in a society where "worth-less" or "un-worthy" people found themselves seated in positions of power due to their monetary influence or sycophancy. To my mind, Johnson seems to highlight a state of constant unhappiness in the existence of man is a mercantilist society. These lines serve as a General Truth, irrespective of its immediate political implications in Walpolean England. The notion of Universality exuded by these lines seems to tie-in with Johnson's larger philosophical idea of having a common human existence that exists for all. This can also be seen in the character of Thales as a character that despises the mechanisms of mercantile capitalism that promote Greed and Corruption and the promotion of unworthy individuals to positions of Authority and respect, still finds himself in the "Want of cheap Reward of empty Praise". The character of Thales now functions as a limited character which can be read in two ways.

The first reading of Thales can undermine the entire validity of Johnson's Political Satire, as he is the principal agent through whom the readers awaken to the misgivings of a world "where all are slaves to gold". The second reading can view him as a character who understands the issue with such a world but is radically limited even in his act of subversion by the oppressive force of Capitalism and succumbs to the wants of adulation that do not correspond to "Worth". Other Scholars have also read his hatred for the system as a manifestation of resentment, as he is unable to progress within a system that has satisfied the material needs of even those who he considers less worthy than himself.

Q. 5. ***Here let those reign, whom pensions can incite.***

To vote a patriot black, a courtier white;.

Ans. These referred lines are quoted from the poem "London" by Samuel Johnson.

"The 'Patriots' were those who opposed Walpole and the Court party ['courtiers']. Pension grants were a common means of influencing M.P.'s" [Brady]. In his Dictionary (1755), Johnson defines "pension" as "An allowance made to any one without an equivalent. In England it is generally understood to mean pay given to a state hireling, for treason to his country" [Smith]. "When Johnson received his own pension [of £300 per annum, in 1762 from Lord Bute's ministry under George III], these definitions, and the 'distant hints and dark allusions' in this poem were turned to account by [John] Wilkes in The North Briton (No. 12, 21 August 1762)"; likewise, Horace Walpole commented on this line in his copy of Dodsley's Collection (1748), "This would have suited Johnson himself latterly" [Smith].

Q. 6. ***And plead for pirates in the face of day;***

Ans. The referred line is quoted from the poem "London" by Samuel Johnson. Here, the 'pirates', according to Johnson's note, printed in 1787, refers to "The invasions of the Spaniards were defended in the houses of Parliament". "The Parliamentary Opposition denounced Walpole's policy of allowing the Spanish to stop and search all ships trading with their American colonies" [Brady]. The unacknowledged hypocrisy of Johnson's "patriotic" rhetoric here is that English ships were the pirates and smugglers, not the Spanish. "Spain had at this time the legal right to regulate the traffic with her American possessions, and the activity with which she enforced the search of English merchant vessels created a popular indignation which was steadily augmented after the affair of 'Jenkins's ear' in 1731 till in 1739 Walpole was forced against his will into a naval war with Spain" [Smith]. Cf. Pope's Epistle to Augustus, l.2, and One Thousand Seven Hundred and Thirty-Eight, ll.17, 18 [Smith].

Q. 6. ***With warbling eunuchs fill a licens'd stage***

Ans. The referred line is quoted from the poem "London" by Samuel Johnson.

Here, according to Johnson's note, printed in 1787, "The licensing act was then lately made"and he also mantions the phrase"our silenc'd stage" (in edd. 1-5, 1787). "The Stage Licensing Act, 1737, required plays to be approved and licensed by the Lord Chamberlain's office before they could be publicly performed" [Greene]. The Stage Licensing Act "had been introduced to silence satire on Walpole's government. But by the date of Dodsley's Collection [1748], Garrick was manager of Drury Lane, and Johnson changed 'our silenc'd stage' to 'licens'd' . . . Professor Donald J. Greene has pointed out that 'warbling eunuchs' on a 'silenced stage' make the best Irish bull Johnson ever committed in print" [Yale].

Q. 7. ***And strive in vain to laugh at H—y's jest.***

Ans. The referred line is quoted from the poem "London" by Samuel Johnson.

"H—y's jest" probably stands for "the Revd John 'Orator' Henley, a public buffoon and a supporter of Walpole" [Greene]; he was "an eccentric preacher noted for his crude jests at the Opposition" [Brady]; Pope called him "Preacher at once, and zany of thy age" (Dunciad III.206) [Yale]. The allusion was earlier identified as directed at "John Lord Hervey (1696-1743), supporter of Walpole and confidant of the Queen" [Smith], but McAdam later accepts the argument in favor of Henley (first made in Donald Greene's The Politics of Samuel Johnson, p.308) [Yale]. "The authority for Hawkins's reading, 'Clodio,' is unknown but . . . 'Clodio,' at least, is in keeping with the non-specific names of Thales, Orgilio, and Balbo" [Yale].

Q. 8. ***No peaceful desart yet unclaim'd by Spain?***

Ans. The referred line is quoted from the poem "London" by Samuel Johnson.

Here, according Johnson's MS. note, 1787, the phrase *unclaim'd by Spain* refers to "The Spaniards at this time were said to make claim to some of our American provinces." Again, Johnson's discourse, in keeping with the typical British outlook of the time, reverses the actual situation: the British colony of Georgia (est. 1732), and before that traders and settlers from the Carolinas, encroached onto territory long claimed by the Spanish as "Guale"—to say nothing of its native inhabitants, such as the Yamasee and Santee Indians, who had been extirpated by the British after the Yamasee war of 1715.

Q. 9. ***There prune thy walks, support thy drooping flow'rs,***

...

And bless thine evening walk and morning toil.

Ans. The referred line is quoted from the poem "London" by Samuel Johnson.

We can contrast this pastoral evocation of the countryside with Johnson's remarks in his "Life of Savage" (1744): "As he [Savage] was ready to entertain himself with future Pleasures, he had planned out a Scheme of Life for the Country, of which he had no Knowledge but from Pastorals and Songs. He imagined that he should be transported to Scenes of flow'ry Felicity, like those which one Poet has reflected to another, and had projected a perpetual Round of innocent Pleasures, of which he suspected no Interruption from Pride, or Ignorance, or Brutality" [Smith]. One might also note the disappointing encounter with the shepherd's life and rustic simplicity in Johnson's Rasselas (1759) and Journey to the Western Islands of Scotland.

Short Essay Type Questions with Answers

Q. 1. Comment on the theme of City and Country life in Samuel Johnson's "London".

Ans. Samuel Johnson's "London" (1784) was written in imitation of Juvenal's Third Satire which describes Umbricius leaving Rome (city) to live in Cumae (countryside) in order to escape from the vices and dangers of the city. An imitation depicts the structure and patterns of thought of the original but modernizes the content to the period of the imitation, that is, it is written in accordance to the time in which the writer lives. Thus, Johnson substitutes London for Juvenal's Rome, and Frenchmen for the Greeks.

The theme of the countryside and the city is central to the poem. The reader is immediately introduced to the trope of country and city in the first 10 lines. The poet "regret[s]" his friend Thales (who by many a critic is considered to be based on the impoverished poet, Richard Savage, but Johnson denied such claims) leaving "vice and London" to live in the calm and idyllic "Cambria" (Wales) "to breathe in distant Fields a purer Air". The city of London was marked in this period by abject poverty, in spite of Industrial Revolution, and widespread corruption. London was slowly degenerating into a shell of the city it once was. It was also haggled by the constant presence of the French in the English courts and Spanish in the English seas. Thales is also described as "one true Briton" as he was disgusted by the decline of British liberty and the cultural influence of France in London. According to J.P. Hardy, "Johnson condemns the city and praises what the still uncorrupted country, ought, ideally, to stand for. For Thales the corrupt capital has become an alien land, and when he resolves to leave to flee it, he is prompted not by a desire of rural retirement, but a willingness to associate himself with the spirit of his country's ancient inhabitants." However, even though "Malice, Rapine, Accident" are common occurrences of the city, the narrator through the character of Thales has not deluded himself into believing in the bucolic atmosphere of the countryside. Exaggeration was a common satirical device, and the poet suggests that the vices of the city make it far more intolerable than the difficulties faced in countryside.

Q. 2. Comment on the Dream of Thales of the 'blissful age' in Samuel Johnson's "London".

Ans. Samuel Johnson's "London" (1784) was written in imitation of Juvenal's Third Satire which describes Umbricius leaving Rome (city) to live in Cumae (countryside) in order to escape from the vices and dangers of the city. An imitation depicts the structure and patterns of thought of the original but modernizes the content to the period of the imitation, that is, it is written in accordance to the time in which the writer lives. Thus, Johnson substitutes London for Juvenal's Rome, and Frenchmen for the Greeks.

As Thales waits for the "wherry" that would transport him to Wales, he "dreams" of the "blissful age" and the "calm" which "such happy scenes bestow". These "happy scenes" of "Britannia's glories" temporarily "soothe" both Thales and the narrator. Even though "hope" assuages their anxiety, it does not completely dissolve them and results only to "double" his "distress". He remembers the "guard of commerce" and that "dread of Spain". In this period, the popular opinion was extremely hostile to Spain because of their continued commercial rivalry in the Caribbean. Attacks on British shipping by Spanish coast guards was particularly resented, and Prime Minister Robert Walpole's policy of not going to war was one of the main grievances, not only of his political opponents but also of the nation. According to one critic, "Walpole's alleged failure to protect British merchant ships from depredation by Spanish coast guards" was seen as seen as "cowardly" and "English honour" was "jest[ed]".

Q. 3. Comment on Thales' dissapointment of the "degerate days" of London in Samuel Johnson's "London".

Ans. Samuel Johnson's "London" (1784) was written in imitation of Juvenal's Third Satire which describes Umbricius leaving Rome (city) to live in Cumae (countryside) in order to escape from the vices and dangers of the city. An imitation depicts the structure and patterns of thought of the original but modernizes the content to the period of the imitation, that is, it is written in accordance to the time in which the writer lives. Thus, Johnson substitutes London for Juvenal's Rome, and Frenchmen for the Greeks.

Thales was so disappointed by the "degenerate days" of the "neighb'ring town" (London), which was devoted only to "vice and gain" and not "science" which "toil[ed] in vain". He wishes heaven would find him a "happier place" where "honesty and sense" would not be "disgraced" with green willow trees ("verdant osiers") and "nature's paintings gay". Even though Thales wants to retire from the city to settle in the countryside, he seems to have forgotten what the countryside actually stood for- hard agricultural labour, poverty and hunger. Here, he envisages the countryside only as a picturesque place where a city bred man came to enjoy the "paintings" of nature. There is a hint in the poem that Thales' dream would not find fulfilment in the countryside either.

Q. 4. Comment on Thales' reference to his 'rustic tongue' in Samuel Johnson's "London".

Ans. Samuel Johnson's "London" (1784) was written in imitation of Juvenal's Third Satire which describes Umbricius leaving Rome (city) to live in Cumae (countryside) in order to escape from the vices and dangers of the city. An imitation depicts the structure and patterns of thought of the original but modernizes the content to the period of the imitation, that is, it is written in accordance to the time in which the writer lives. Thus, Johnson substitutes London for Juvenal's Rome, and Frenchmen for the Greeks.

Thales also refers to himself as having a "rustic tongue". According to Johnson's dictionary, the word rustic means "untaught, inelegant, artless". Even though Thales had been living in the city, he still called himself "rustic", as he is unlike those "heroes" whose greed and pride knew no restraint and had gained control over their countrymen's lives, properties and liberty. He also describes London as being the "common shore" that is the drain of the refuse of other corrupt states like France and Rome. He does not want the "dregs" of these corrupted states to come to the "Land of Heroes" (London) and does not want it to become a "French metropolis." Such is Thales feeling of frustration that he bids a "fasting monsieur"- who has later been described as a "parasite"- to "go to Hell, to Hell he goes."

Q. 5. How does Thales express his dissatisfaction with the life of London in Samuel Johnson's "London"?

Ans. Samuel Johnson's "London" (1784) was written in imitation of Juvenal's Third Satire which describes Umbricius leaving Rome (city) to live in Cumae (countryside) in order to escape from the vices and dangers of the city. An imitation depicts the structure and patterns of thought of the original but modernizes the content to the period of the imitation, that is, it is written in accordance to the time in which the writer lives. Thus, Johnson substitutes London for Juvenal's Rome, and Frenchmen for the Greeks.

He is thoroughly dissatisfied with the life in London as no criminal feels "shame" or fears "censure" as the "number" of the crimes has increased exponentially. The only crime which remains is that of poverty. He asks heaven whether isn't any place "reserved" "in pity for the poor" albeit it be a "pathless waste" or "undiscovered shores" but safe from the Spanish. He ends his soliloquy with a repartee to the narrator of the poem, who would "fly for refuge" to the "wilds of Kent" that is areas which are far from human habitation, when they are tired of the "follies and crimes" in the city. He urges his friend, the narrator and in turn the readers to "exert their rage" and write incisive satire against the administrators of the city and "animate thy page". Thus, even if Thales' friend moves to the countryside, this musnt act as a deterrent and should not forget their responsibility. They can become writers, warning "succeeding times" against vice and folly.

Q. 6. How does Thales' reasons for leaving London signify in Samuel Johnson's "London"?

Ans. Samuel Johnson's London (1748) presents eighteenth century English anxieties about discord and decay through the antithesis of the city and the country. Johnson critiques the pitiful state of the country's capital by commenting on the degeneration that has plagued the society. The poet's despair on his friend's departure from England is emblematic of the loss of all the virtues of a "true Briton" that once characterised the people of the country. The construction of binaries in the poem needs to be critically evaluated to reveal a truer picture of the society that the poet wishes to reform.

Thales' reasons for leaving London and "exploring" foreign lands signifies that the corruption of the city stands for corruption of the country as a whole. Thales is not only leaving London, but seeking refuge in Wales, which discards the earlier image of England as the epitome of civilisation. The complete breakdown of morality is indicated by the phrase, "from Vice and London far". The vices of the city are elaborated throughout the poem, which are then contrasted with the countryside. The "vice" of the city is mainly depicted through the ambition of those in power. This ambition, leading to bribes and unchecked crimes has resulted in the terribly unsafe atmosphere of the city. The countryside, in contrast, is a place where such ambitious men are absent and Thales can find "repose" by living in "poverty" as "once the harassed Briton" did. The phrase "safe in poverty" is interesting, as it condemns the unsafe and chaotic state of the city. The lines providing reasons for preferring the country over the city are immediately followed by the political decisions that the poet condemns. Johnson vents his frustration with Robert Walpole's administration as he mentions the "pensions" which buy the people's "vote" and a true Briton, who is a "patriot", is punished while the corrupt "courtier" is made richer.

Q. 7. How does Johnson criticise the corrupt political scene of London in "London"?

Ans. Samuel Johnson's London (1748) presents eighteenth century English anxieties about discord and decay through the antithesis of the city and the country. Johnson critiques the pitiful state of the country's capital by commenting on the degeneration that has plagued the society. The poet's despair on his friend's departure from England is emblematic of the loss of all the virtues of a "true Briton" that once characterised the people of the country. The construction of binaries in the poem needs to be critically evaluated to reveal a truer picture of the society that the poet wishes to reform.

Besides the city-country theme, the corrupt political scene is a theme that Johnson uses to critique the condition of the city. Johnson grieves over the loss of "one True Briton" to Wales. This entails dwelling on the perversion of truth in fields of literature, drama, politics, and relationship between the ruler and the ruled. The corrupt politicians influence the sort of literature that is written by English writers.

Since such "Lords" do not possess true virtue, their patronage results in "cheap" panegyrics. The perversion of order and harmony is a major theme in English satires and Johnson uses it to show the disruption of class relations. He is critical of the way the "Lord" has to "win" the "groom" by "bribes [and] flattery". This reversal of relations between the ruler and the ruled is a sharp attack on Robert Walpole's practice of giving favours to men and securing political support. Johnson observes with satirical revulsion at how money changes hands between corrupt men and makes the nation a "beggar'd land". In contrast, the countryside is constructed as a "smiling land" which still possesses uncorrupted idyllic beauty. It is also a place where class relations are undisturbed as so Thales can freely "despise the dainties" of the "Lord" whom he serves. The countryside is, therefore, a place where relations between people and their nature remain frozen, while the people in the city have changed for the worse.

Q. 8. Comment on the extended image of Origilio in Samuel Johnson's "London".

Ans. Samuel Johnson's London (1748) presents eighteenth century English anxieties about discord and decay through the antithesis of the city and the country. Johnson critiques the pitiful state of the country's capital by commenting on the degeneration that has plagued the society. The poet's despair on his friend's departure from England is emblematic of the loss of all the virtues of a "true Briton" that once characterised the people of the country. The construction of binaries in the poem needs to be critically evaluated to reveal a truer picture of the society that the poet wishes to reform.

In the extended image of Origilio, Johnson imitates Juvenal's style of commenting on the plundering of the country's wealth by the politicians' greed for "gold". Contrary to this, Johnson likens Thales' person to the country Briton whose "rustic tongue" is not skilled in sophistry that the ambitious men of the city use to feed their ambition. This theme of the city and the country is, however, a poetic construction and does not wholly correspond to the realities of the time. The countryside is not presented as a thriving place where people labour hard to meet out a barely sufficient living. The population of the city of London grew over twenty times with the advancements brought with the Industrial Revolution. These advancements also affected the countryside, and had an adverse impact unlike the city which benefitted greatly. The replacement of manual labour by machinery caused widespread unemployment for the people of the countryside. The people were forced to resort to violence and the countryside was in a state of chaos, which finds no place in Johnson's depiction. In critiquing the city, the poet uses the countryside as a blank slate, as an imagined space which can be construed as a foil to the problems of the city.

Q. 9. How is Walpole's corrupt rule is contrasted with the rulers of the past in Samuel Johnson's "London"?

Ans. Samuel Johnson's London (1748) presents eighteenth century English anxieties about discord and decay through the antithesis of the city and the country.

Johnson critiques the pitiful state of the country's capital by commenting on the degeneration that has plagued the society. The poet's despair on his friend's departure from England is emblematic of the loss of all the virtues of a "true Briton" that once characterised the people of the country. The construction of binaries in the poem needs to be critically evaluated to reveal a truer picture of the society that the poet wishes to reform.

Walpole's corrupt ruling tactics are set against the honourable rulers of the past, being Elizabeth I and the "illustrious" Edward III. The corruption of those in power is extended to the deplorable diplomatic relations that England has made in their rule. The anti-war standpoint taken by the Walpole administration is criticised as it has corrupted English culture and society. As the poet remarks with contempt, the "warrior" has "dwindled into a beau". Johnson is extremely critical of England's political as well as cultural ties with France. The metropolis stands for civility and decorum, which is in conflict with the French who treat England's banks as "shores" or dumping grounds. As the poet apologies for such disturbing details of England's filthy banks, he is engaging with the eighteenth century idea of purging the city of contamination. The idea of the city as a sanitised place which is free from corruption, both in physical and moral terms informs Johnson's critique. The French people who have settled in London are, to the poet, those criminals of France who have fled harsher punishment of their country. The city has become a place that is plagued by robbers and "Lords of the Street" who harass the common man. The city, therefore, is far from being the ideal image of civilisation. This grim image of the city is set against the countryside where Thales can "prune" his walks in a place that has the Edenic semblance of Milton's paradise. Such picturesque "prospects" that Thales expects from the countryside sideline the turmoil that the place was experiencing.

•

Q. 10. Comment on the image country sidein Samuel Johnson's "London".

Ans. Samuel Johnson's London (1748) presents eighteenth century English anxieties about discord and decay through the antithesis of the city and the country. Johnson critiques the pitiful state of the country's capital by commenting on the degeneration that has plagued the society. The poet's despair on his friend's departure from England is emblematic of the loss of all the virtues of a "true Briton" that once characterised the people of the country. The construction of binaries in the poem needs to be critically evaluated to reveal a truer picture of the society that the poet wishes to reform.

The countryside is an imagined space that could give Thales hope of dwelling in "A happier place". Another such space is that of the past which Johnson uses to contrast with the present state of the city. In the standard Neo-classicist strain, Johnson imitates Juvenalian satire that compares the degraded present to a rich past that is now lost. The past as a foil to the present is combined with the antithesis of the city and the country, as the countryside becomes an idealised repository for virtues that the past stands for. The poet separates the past from the present through the nostalgic recollection of England's glorious past. The past, even though far removed from the present, exists in the natural surroundings of the London that

Thales cannot bear to live in. The rivers in poem become the elements that still belong to the past as the Thames evokes "pleasing dreams" of a time when "Britannia's glories" were plentiful. Besides serving the antithesis of the past and the present, the river motif also connects the city and the country. The "fair banks of Severn or Trent" to which Thales wishes to retire stand for the "surly virtue" that he can only hope to find in these luminal spaces between North and South England.

Q. 11. How does Thales' depature excite reaction in the poet in Samuel Johnson's "London"?

Ans. Samuel Johnson's London (1748) presents eighteenth century English anxieties about discord and decay through the antithesis of the city and the country. Johnson critiques the pitiful state of the country's capital by commenting on the degeneration that has plagued the society. The poet's despair on his friend's departure from England is emblematic of the loss of all the virtues of a "true Briton" that once characterised the people of the country. The construction of binaries in the poem needs to be critically evaluated to reveal a truer picture of the society that the poet wishes to reform.

Thales's departure excites mixed reactions in the poet, as in the very first line he says that he is struggling with the conflicting emotions of "grief and fondness". This reflects the problem the poet faces in living in a city that he has come to despise. He admires the decision of his friend, but at the same time he knows he is unable to take the same step. As J.P. Hardy observes, Rome cast a "spell" on Juvenal as he could not leave it despite having condemned the city in his satires. In this imitation of Juvenal's satire, Johnson expresses similar discontent with the state of the city, but cannot find an escape which his friend has supposedly found. The fact that the city and the countryside cannot be water-tight binaries is evident from the oxymoron phrases in the poem. These phrases occur while describing both, the country virtue and city vice. The "rustic grandeur" that the poet mourns as lost in England's past is a problematic expression of the virtuous country Englishman whose simplicity accounts for a sort of "grandeur". Contrary to this is the city coxcomb. The feminine vanity of the "fop" is satirised as it is used with "fiery" to note his vain pretentions to manly valour. Another oxymoron that qualifies Johnson's stance against the city is "gaudy vassals" as the "Lords" buy fealty to rule a nation they are "plundering". While such phrases support the indictment of the city, the ones concerning the countryside show an unresolved contradiction. The "surly virtue" which Johnson lauds is not a true representation of a country dweller and the "safe poverty" in which he lives is most atrocious to him.

Johnson's London is a poem of its time as it combines the energies of satire with Neo-classical stress on order, harmony, and the need to preserve England's integrity. In condemning the city of London however, Johnson fails to give a true picture of the English countryside and makes it almost a metaphor for the virtue he cannot find in the city.

Q. 12. Comment on Johnson's use of pastoral image in "London".

Ans. Johnson uses the image of the pastoral to invoke an alternative space to the oppressive atmosphere of London. Thales imagines receding into the beauty and peacefulness of nature where the poet seems to search for a domain which is unspoiled by Greed and Mercantilism. He views the areas of Wales as a space where this is possible (As it has never been invaded by the Anglo-Saxons or the Romans), Johnson seems to search for a space for "True Britons" and like his character the answer seems to have been echoing in the scenery of the pastoral for him. 'London' is littered with vocabulary like 'patriots' and 'true Britons' such vocabulary was extremely popular among the Opposition propaganda against the Walpole administration. Johnson tried to juxtapose the image of the rustic country to counterbalance the ills of the corrupt Urban Society. It is perhaps this vision of an alternative space that links him and other Augustan poets to the Romantic Movement that was to articulate a systemic response to the ills of Industrial and Capitalist societies with the Country and Nature at the centre of its alternative conception. However, it would be specious on our part to extend that argument to conclude that Johnson intended to do the same. His satirical critique of England's social and political interface through the poetic form of Imitation was instrumental in providing him with a platform from where his career as a writer started gaining mileage. While his allusions got him into trouble with the British administration, which released arrest warrants in his name he remained a trenchant critic of the system whilst maintaining his "artistic integrity".

Q. 13. Comment on Johnson's criticism on both political and social issues of London in his poem "London".

Ans. Johnson's 'London' was unique in its engagement with both the social and political issues that throttled Britain. Britain, at the time was functioning under the principles of Mercantilism which bestowed regulatory authority unto a government for the purpose of augmenting national prosperity. Mercantilism emerged as a manifestation of Capitalism that had evolved from earlier practices of Proto-Capitalism which were prevalent in the preceding centuries such as Agrarian Capitalism. It was because of a Mercantilist attitude of accumulation that Britain had expanded its influence in the Colonial Marketplace. England under the Ministerial umbrage of Sir Robert Walpole had ascended to the state of a Mercantilist nation. By the 1730s, Britain had emerged as a major colonial power contending with the likes of France and Spain for profit. The commercial ethic that had propelled Britain to this stature had wide ranging social and political ramifications. It was these outcomes that were satirised by Johnson in his work. The ethic of commercial success that propelled the Walpole administration to maintain the Peace treaty with Spain (After the Spanish Wars of Succession), to the disgust of The Opposition (Which had the Tories and a faction of Opposition Whigs) who conglomerated under the broad umbrella of "Patriotism". The members of this group, also broadly known as the Country Party (as opposed to the Court Party) were in support of waging war against Spain as a response to the damage incurred by English ships around the Caribbean. David Nichols Smith alerts us to Johnson's hypocrisy towards the issue of Piracy, Johnson is riled up due to the losses incurred by the British but he remains unperturbed by the perpetuation and condoning of Piracy by the British. Maintaining a peaceful relationship with Spain was viewed as an act of acquiescence by these Patriots. Johnson identified himself as a part of this group at the time and his sentiment echoes in the following Lines from 'London'

> "In pleasing Dreams, the blissful Age renew,
> And Call Britannia's Glories back to view:
> Behold her Cross Triumphant on the Main,
> The Guard of Commerce, and the Dread of Spain"

Poetry	ELEGY WRITTEN IN A COUNTRY CHURCHYARD -Thomas Gray

❖ **An Introduction to Thomas Gray :**

Born in the Cornhill district of London in 1716, Gray was the son of Dorothy Antrobus Gray, a milliner, and Philip Gray, a scrivener. Gray's father was a mentally disturbed and violent man who at times abused his wife. Gray attended Eton School from 1725 until 1734, when he entered Cambridge University. He left Cambridge in 1738 without taking a degree, intending to study law in London. However, he and childhood friend Horace Walpole embarked on an extended tour of Europe. The two separated in Italy in 1741 after a quarrel, and Gray continued the journey on his own. He returned to London later in the year, shortly before his father died. Gray then moved with his mother to Stoke Poges, Buckinhamshire, and began his most productive period of poetic composition. In 1742 Grey wrote his first major poem, "Ode on the Spring," which he sent to his close friend Richard West—unknowingly on the very day of West's death from tuberculosis. In the next three months Gray wrote "Ode on a Distant Prospect of Eton College," "Hymn to Adversity," and "Sonnet on the Death of Mr. Richard West." It is believed that he also worked on "Elegy Written in a Country Churchyard" during this time, though this poem was not published until 1751. Gray returned to Cambridge at the end of 1742 and received a Bachelor of Civil Law degree the next year. Gray lived at the university for most of the rest of his life, but he never took part in tutoring, lecturing, or other academic duties; instead he pursued his studies and writing, taking advantage of the intellectual stimulation of the setting. In 1757 Gray was offered the position of Poet Laureate, but he declined it. He moved to London in 1759 to study at the British Museum and remained there for two years. He read widely and earned a reputation as one of the most learned men in Europe. Except for regular trips back to London and elsewhere in England, Gray stayed in Cambridge from 1761 until the end of his life. In 1768 Gray was named Regius Professor of Modern History at Cambridge, an office he held until his death in 1771.

❖ **An Introduction to *Elegy Written in a Country Churchyard!*:**

Thomas Gray's "Elegy Written in a Country Churchyard" was first published in 1751. Gray may, however, have begun writing the poem in 1742, shortly after the death of his close friend Richard West. An elegy is a poem which laments the dead. Gray's "Elegy Written in a Country Churchyard" is noteworthy in that it mourns the death not of great or famous people, but of common men.

The speaker of this poem sees a country churchyard at sunset, which impels him to meditate on the nature of human mortality. The poem invokes the classical idea of memento mori, a Latin phrase which states plainly to all mankind, "Remember that you must die." The speaker considers the fact that in death, there is no difference between great and common people. He goes on to wonder if among the lowly people buried in the churchyard there had been any natural poets or politicians whose talent had simply never been discovered or nurtured. This thought leads him to praise the dead for the honest, simple lives that they lived.

Gray did not produce a great deal of poetry; the "Elegy Written in a Country Churchyard," however, has earned him a respected and deserved place in literary history. The poem was written at the end of the Augustan Age and at the beginning of the Romantic period, and the poem has characteristics associated with both literary periods. On the one hand, it has the ordered, balanced phrasing and rational sentiments of Neoclassical poetry. On the other hand, it tends toward the emotionalism and individualism of the Romantic poets; most importantly, it idealizes and elevates the common man.

❖ **A Summary of *Elegy Written in a Country Churchyard!*:**

Lines 1-4 : In the first stanza, the speaker observes the signs of a country day drawing to a close: a curfew bell ringing, a herd of cattle moving across the pasture, and a farm laborer returning home. The speaker is then left alone to contemplate the isolated rural scene. The first line of the poem sets a distinctly somber tone: the curfew bell does not simply ring; it "knells"—a term usually applied to bells rung at a death or funeral. From the start, then, Gray reminds us of human mortality.

Lines 5-8: The second stanza sustains the somber tone of the first: the speaker is not mournful, but pensive, as he describes the peaceful landscape that surrounds him. Even the air is characterized as having a "solemn stillness."

Lines 9-12: The sound of an owl hooting intrudes upon the evening quiet. We are told that the owl "complains"; in this context, the word does not mean "to whine" or "grumble," but "to express sorrow." The owl's call, then, is suggestive of grief. Note that at no point in these three opening stanzas does Gray directly refer to death or a funeral; rather, he indirectly creates a funereal atmosphere by describing just a few mournful sounds.

Lines 13-16 : It is in the fourth stanza that the speaker directly draws our attention to the graves in the country churchyard. We are presented with two potentially conflicting images of death. Line 14 describes the heaps of earth surrounding the graves; in order to dig a grave, the earth must necessarily be disrupted. Note that the syntax of this line is slightly confusing. We would expect this sentence to read "Where the turf heaves"—not "where heaves the turf": Gray has inverted the word order. Just as the earth has been disrupted, the syntax imitates the way in which the earth has been disrupted. But by the same token, the "rude Forefathers" buried beneath the earth seem entirely at peace: we are told that they are laid in "cells," a term which reminds us of the quiet of a monastery, and that they "sleep."

Lines 17-20 : If the "Forefathers" are sleeping, however, the speaker reminds us that they will never again rise from their "beds" to hear the pleasurable sounds of country life that the living do. The term "lowly beds" describes not only the unpretentious graves in which the forefathers are buried, but the humble conditions that they endured when they were alive.

Lines 21-24 : The speaker then moves on to consider some of the other pleasures the dead will no longer enjoy: the happiness of home, wife, and children.

Lines 25-28 : The dead will also no longer be able to enjoy the pleasures of work, of plowing the fields each day. This stanza points to the way in which the "Elegy Written in a Country Churchyard" contains elements of both Augustan and Romantic poetry. Poetry that describes agriculture—as this one does—is called georgic. Georgic verse was extremely popular in the eighteenth century. Note, however, that Gray closely identifies the farmers with the land that they work. This association of man and nature is suggestive of a romantic attitude. The georgic elements of the stanza almost demand that we characterize it as typical of the eighteenth century, but its tone looks forward to the Romantic period.

Lines 29-32 : The next four stanzas caution those who are wealthy and powerful not to look down on the poor. These lines warn the reader not to slight the "obscure" "destiny" of the poor—the fact that they will never be famous or have long histories, or "annals," written about them.

Lines 33-36 : This stanza invokes the idea of memento mori (literally, a reminder of mortality). The speaker reminds the reader that regardless of social position, beauty, or wealth, all must eventually die.

Lines 37-40 : The speaker also challenges the reader not to look down on the poor for having modest, simple graves. He suggests, moreover, that the elaborate memorials that adorn the graves of the "Proud" are somehow excessive. In this context, the word "fretted" in line 39 has a double meaning: on the one hand, it can refer to the design on a cathedral ceiling; on the other hand, it can suggest that there is something "fretful," or troublesome, about the extravagant memorials of the wealthy.

Lines 41-44: The speaker observes that nothing can bring the dead back to life, and that all the advantages that the wealthy had in life are useless in the face of death. Neither elaborate funeral monuments nor impressive honors can restore life. Nor can flattery in some way be used to change the mind of death. Note here Gray's use of personification in characterizing both "flattery" and "death"—as though death has a will or mind of its own.

Lines 45-48: The speaker then reconsiders the poor people buried in the churchyard. He wonders what great deeds they might have accomplished had they been given the opportunity: one of these poor farmers, the speaker reasons, might have been a great emperor; another might have "waked ... the living lyre," or been a great poet or musician.

Lines 49-52 : The poor were never able to fulfill their political and artistic potential, however, because they were uneducated—they never received the "Knowledge" that would enable them to rule and to create. Instead, "Penury," or poverty, "froze the genial current of their soul." That is, poverty paralyzed their ability to draw upon their innermost passions—the very passions that could have inspired them to become great poets or politicians.

Lines 53-56 : In a series of analogies, Gray observes that the talents of the poor are like a "gem" hidden in the ocean or a "flower" blooming in the desert. Just as an unseen flower in the desert is a "waste," Gray suggests, the uneducated talents of the poor are also a "waste," because they remain unused and undeveloped.

Lines 57-60: The speaker then compares these poor, uneducated people to three of the most famous and powerful people of the previous century: John Hampden, a parliamentary leader who defended the people against the abuses of Charles I; John Milton, the great poet who wrote Paradise Lost and who also opposed Charles I; and Oliver Cromwell, Lord Protector of England from 1653 to 1658. The speaker suggests that buried in this churchyard might be someone who—like Hampden, Milton, or Cromwell—had the innate ability to oppose tyranny, but never had the opportunity to exercise that ability.

Lines 61-64: This person, the speaker reasons, with the proper education and resources, might have "commanded" the government as well as any great political leader. Note, however, that Gray gives us two ways in which to consider this power. On the one hand, a great ruler can receive applause and can ignore "threats of pain and ruin." A great leader can "scatter plenty," can offer prosperity, to a grateful nation. But on the other hand, if one governs, one is, in fact, exposed to dangerous threats. And simply governing to receive "applause" suggests a shallow and self-serving motive. Moreover, "scattering plenty" implies that the wealth of a nation can be squandered by its rulers. Gray may be suggesting that having power is not as desirable as it seems. Note that the final line of this stanza is enjambed; it continues into the following line—and in this case, the next stanza.

Lines 65-68 : The first line of this stanza continues the thought of the previous, enjambed line. It abruptly reminds us that the impoverished conditions of the poor "forbade" them from becoming great rulers. Gray underscores the abrupt shock of this idea by abruptly interrupting the flow of the line with a caesura. Building on the idea of the previous stanza, the speaker notes that if poverty prevented the country laborers from acquiring the "virtues" of great and powerful people, it also prevented them from committing the "crimes" often associated with those people—and especially with those people who hold political power. In particular, it prevented them from engaging in the bloody activity associated with the British Civil War.

Lines 69-72 : Because these farm laborers were not in positions of power, the speaker reasons, they never had to ignore their own consciences. Nor did they sacrifice their artistic talents (the gift of the "Muse") to "Luxury" or "Pride."

Lines 73-76 : The speaker continues his praise of the simple life of common people. They are "far from the madding crowd" of city and political life. "Madding" here can mean either "maddening" (that is, the source of madness or insanity) or it can mean "mad" (that is, the crowd is itself hatefully insane). In either case, the common country people were removed from this insane world; as a result, they never "strayed" into the immoral acts of the powerful. Instead, they kept steadily to their simple but meaningful lives.

Lines 77-80 : The speaker then reminds us that these common people are, in fact, long dead. He notes that even if they were not powerful or great, and even if they do not have an elaborate memorial of the sort mentioned in line 38, they still deserve homage or tribute. At the very least, he suggests, an onlooker should "sigh" on seeing their graves. Note here the multiple meanings we can attach to the word "passing." It can refer to the onlooker, who is simply walking or "passing by" these graves. It can mean "in passing"—that someone seeing these graves should take just a moment out of their busy lives to remember the dead. And "passing" itself is a euphemism for death. In a way, then, Gray is suggesting that there is no difference between the person "passing" by the grave and the person who has "passed" away—another reminder that all will eventually die.

Lines 81-84 : Instead of "fame and elegy," the people buried here have modest tombstones, which display only their names and the dates of their birth and death. These common people were not famous, and no one has written elaborate elegies or funeral verses for them. Still, the very modesty of their tomb-stones testifies to the nobility and "holy" nature of their simple lives. As such, they provide an example not so much of how life should be lived, but how its end, death, should be approached. The term "rustic moralist" here is open to interpretation. It may refer to anyone who is in the countryside thinking about the meaning of death. But more likely, it refers to the speaker, who is himself moralizing—preaching or contemplating—about the nature of both life and death.

Lines 85-88 : The speaker reasons that most people, faced with the prospect of dying and ultimately being forgotten, cling to life. Note Gray's use of paradox in line 86: "this pleasing anxious being." On the one hand, "being" or living can be "anxious," filled with worries. On the other hand, just being alive— when faced with death—is itself "pleasing" or pleasant. The speaker is suggesting that even the troubles and worries of life are enjoyable in comparison to death.

Lines 89-92 : The dead rely on the living to remember them and to mourn for them. The speaker suggests that this need is so fundamental that even from the grave the buried dead seem to ask for remembrance. In fact, as line 92 suggests, the dead actually live on in our memories.

Lines 93-96 : In this stanza, the speaker addresses himself. He reasons that since he himself has been mindful of the dead, and has remembered and praised them in this poem, perhaps when he is dead someone will remember him. This person, he reasons, will necessarily be a "kindred Spirit," someone who is also a lonely wanderer in the country, meditating on the nature of death. The speaker then goes on to imagine his own death: he envisions this "kindred Spirit" seeing his (the speaker's) grave and wondering about his life and death.

Lines 97-100 : In the next five stanzas, the speaker imagines how an old farm laborer might remember him after his death. If, the speaker speculates, the "kindred Spirit" sees the speaker's grave and wonders about it, perhaps an old man might offer to describe the speaker. The old man would say that the speaker was often seen wandering about the countryside at dawn. Presumably, he was frequently out all night—as, no doubt, he has been in this very poem.

Lines 101-104 : At noon, the old man continues, the speaker would frequently stretch out under an old tree at noon, and stare at a nearby brook.

Lines 105-108 : The old man would have observed that the speaker's moods were changeable: sometimes the speaker would wander about in the nearby woods, "smiling scornfully" and talking to himself; other times, he would appear depressed; then again, sometimes he would look as though he were in anguish. Perhaps, the old man speculates, the speaker had been "crossed in hopeless love."

Lines 109-112 : The speaker continues to imagine this old man remembering him after his death. The old man would have noticed one morning that the speaker was absent: he was not in any of his favorite spots. Likewise, the old man would remember, the speaker did not appear the following day.

Lines 113-116 : The third day, however, the old man and his friends would have seen the speaker's body being carried to the churchyard for burial. (The speaker, then, is imagining himself buried in the very graveyard he once used to wander by.) The old man invites this curious passerby, or "kindred Spirit," to read the speaker's epitaph. Note the reminder that the old man is uneducated: he cannot read, although the passerby can do so.

Epitaph:

Lines 117-120 : The last three stanzas are, in fact, the speaker's epitaph; the way in which the speaker imagines his epitaph will read. Through the epitaph, the speaker asks the passerby (and the reader) not to remember him as wealthy, famous, or brilliantly educated, but as one who was "melancholic" or deeply thoughtful and sad.

Lines 121-124:

The speaker asks that we remember him for being generous and sincere. His generosity was, in fact, his willingness to mourn for the dead. Because he was so generous, the speaker reasons, heaven gave him a "friend"—someone who would, in turn, mourn for him after his death. This friend is unnamed, but we can deduce that it is any "kindred Spirit"—including the reader—who reads the speaker's epitaph and remembers him.

Lines 125-128 : The speaker concludes by cautioning the reader not to praise him any further. He also asks that his "frailties," his flaws or personal weaknesses, not be considered; rather, they should be left to the care of God, with whom the speaker now resides. The poem, then, is an elegy not only for the common man, but for the speaker himself. Indeed, by the end of the poem it is evident that the speaker himself wishes to be identified not with the great and famous, but with the common people whom he has praised and with whom he will, presumably, be buried.

❖ **Word notes and Annotations:**

Stanza 1-3 :

The curfew tolls- there is the ringing of the curfew bell. **N.B.** In England, after the Norman Conquest , a code was introduced to ring a bell at eight o'clock in the evening for putting off the fireplace of every house. That bell was designed as the curfew [from French coluvir (to cover) and feu (fire)].The ringing of the curfew was, however, introduced not as a measure of supression, but in the interest of the people to have protection against fire. *The knell of parting day-*the end of the dayy (day light) that is passing away. *The curfew tolls...day-*the ringing of the curfew bell announces the end of daytime and the beginning of night. **N.B.** 'Knell' actually refers to the ringing of the church bell at the death of a person. here the curfew is likened to the knell (that is the death-bell) of the day. This is a fine case of the metaphor. *The lowing herd-* the bellowing herd (possibly oxen). 'Low' is a loud sound produced by the cattle, generally oxen and cows. This refers to the herd of oxen returning from the field with lowing sounds. *Wind slowly...lea-* winding up their course in a slow pace across the open field. **N.B.** The movement of the herd is slow, because of the exhuastion in the field throughout the day. *The ploughman...weary-* the ploughman walks heavily towards his home, tired of his hard labour in the field. *Weary way-* the 'way' is not 'weary' but the 'ploughman', who plods the way, is. **N.B.** An instance of the transferred epithet. *And leaves...to me-* the darkness of evening settles down all over and the poet finds himself all alone in the darkness of the descending night (in the country churchyard.)

The first stanza presents a quite common place country scene. Daylight is fading. The tired ploughman is returning home with his tired herd, lowingloudly. Gradually darkness descends and settles totally, ending the daytime.

*Now fades...on the sight-*there is the continuation of the description of darkness, descending and settling all over. The last, lingering light of the day (actually twilight) passes away. *And all the air-*the entire atmosphere. **N.B.** A note of exaggeration is noted. A case of the hyperbole. *A solemn stillness holds-* a majestic silence seems to prevail all over. *Save-* the silence prevails, except. *Where the...droning flight-* the dull, humming sound of the beetles incourse of their circular flight. *Drowsy tinkling-*tinkling sound coming from the bells of the drowsy sheep. **N.B.** There is the transferred epithet in 'drowsy tinkling'. Here the sheep in the fold are, drowsy, and, 'tinkling' is not. There is also the Onomatopis in 'tinkling' (the sound echoing the sense). *Distant fold-*the sheep kept in the fold, situaterd at a dstance. **N.B.** 'Fold' is an enclosed place where sheep are kept. Here 'fold' is substituted for the sheep that are in the fold. This is a case of the metonymy (the container for the thing contained.)

After darkness comes silence that is profound, and disturbed only by two sounds- the humming sound caused by the wheeling beetles and the tinkling sound of the bell tied to the neck of tghe sheep feeling drowsy.

Save that from- there is another interruption to the perfect stillness of the whole surrounding. *Ivy-mantled tower-* the tower is covered with ivy creepers, as if wearing a mantle of the same. **N.B.** A case of the metaphor- an implied comparison between two unallied objects- mantle and ivy. *The moping...complain-* this is the cause of the interruption.There is heard a shrill cry from a grim-looking owl, that seems to complain to the moon. *Of such as* -the cause of the complaint. *Wand'ring...bower-* flying close to her secluded nest. *Molest her..reign-* violate the privacy of the owl's secluded nest where this has been living with an absolute authority.

N.B. This is a kind of romantic imagination. The poet well fancies, in a romantic vein, the reason for the owl's cry. This is, perhaps, because of the violation of its exclusive privacy in its secret bower where some intruders seem to have disturbed. As the owl is a night-bird, the poet also fancies that this is complaining to the moon.

Stanza-4 :

*Beneath the rugged elms-*under those bare elm trees. *That yew tree's shade-* under the shade of a yew tree. *Where heaves...heap-* amid thhe decaying piles of mounds. *Each in his...laid-* each of them lies buried in his narrow grave. **N.B.** There is a periphrasis (a round-about expression) in 'for ever laid' in the sense 'dead.' *The rude...sleep-* the ignorant forefathers of the village lie dead (are in 'eternal sleep').

The descrfiption of the graves of tghe rude forefathers of the hamlet in the country churchyard is precise but graphic. These are situated under the barren elm trees and the shade of a yew-tree amid the mouldering heap of earth.

Stanza 5-7 :

The breezy...Morn- the pleasant fragrant wind blowing in the early morning. *The swallow ...straw- built shed-* the twittering of the swallows from their nest made of straw. *The cock's ...clarion-* the loud cry of the cock. *The echoing horn-* the echoes of the horns of the hunters at a distance. *NO more...bed-* will no more awaken them from their lowly bed under earth.

The implication is here very clear. The humble villagers, when they were alive, used to wake up as the pleasing, fragrant morning wind blew of them, the swallows twittering in their nests, the cocks lloudly cried, or the echoes of the hunters' horns at a distance could be heard. But now they are all dead and lie buried under the ground.Nothing of those elements would any more awaken them from their eternal sleep.

From them...shall burn- no brightly burning fire-palce would greet their home-coming. **N.B.** This is a fine instance of the hyperbaton or inversion in which the grammatical order of words is inverted. The normal order is- "The blazing hearth shall no more burn for them". *Busy house-wife-*the mistress of the house, engaged in her domestic duty. *Ply her...care-* attending to her domestic duty, as her husband was returning from the field after the hard work oof the day. *No children....share-* they would no more be greeterd by the loving prattle of their children, trying to vie with one another to have the first kiss from their fathers. **N.B.** Gray presents here a simple yet llloving scene of domesticity. This marks the universality of his poem.

Oft did the...field- the effort of their sickles succeeded often often in having a good harvest. *Their furrrow...broke-*their ploughs could succeeded to break the hard lland for the purpose of tilling. What the poet means to say is that they tilled often well to gain good harvests. *How jocund...afield-* they went to work in their field with their animals in a joyous spirit. **N.B.** They were not weary of their work, but rather loved the same. *How bowed....sturdy stroke-* they could hew down the trees for the purpose of cultivating the soil.

The poors tillers of the village worked hard to cleanse annd dig the fields and sow and harvest the seeds. The poet here speaks of the humble but useful toil of the poor villagers.

N.B. Gray celebrates here the warmth of life, no matter whether the persons concerned are rich or poor.What matters most is the spirit of life that cares for no high birth, physical beauty, or wealth.

Stanzas 8-9 :

Let not Ambition...etc.- Gray appeals to the men of ambition and grandeur. They should not slight the pooor villagers who lived and died unknown in their humble but useful toil, much ignored destiny. The short and simple story of those pooer people must not be taunted or belittled by them.

Gray's sympathy for the poor and the ignored and his warning against the rich and proud are distinctly heard here.

Ambition-men of ambition. **N.B.** A case of the synecdoche (abstract) for the concrete ..Useful toil- *labour that is productive.* Homely joys- common and simple pleasures of domesticity *Destiny obscure-* unrecognised fortune. *Let not ambition... obscure-* the poet forbids ambitious people to refrain from mocking the humble but productive toil, the plain yet sincere joys and the little known career of these poor people.

Nor Grandeur hear -nor the the people of grandeur. *Grandeur*-of pomp and splendour. The poet means the persons of pomp and splendeur. Another instance of the synecdoche (the abstract for the concrete). *Disdainful smile-* contemptous smile; a sarcastic attitude. *The short...poor-* the life-story of the poor people whose living is nothing eventful and long. *Nor Grandeur...etc.-* In the same way, the poet appeals to those who prone to pompous and grand liviing not to be contemptuous of the short ans simple way of living of the poor.

The boast of heraldry- the glory of high birth that mmakes people vain and boastful. *The pomp of power-* the grand demonstration of power and authority. *All that...e''er gave-* whatever may be attained- glory, admiration, fame, or anything else--by the graces of beauty and the resources of riches.

Gray muses on what on what ultimately comes to man's high heredity, pervasive power, matchless beauty and immense riches. Highh birth, power and authority, captivating beauty and inexhaustible wealth may be possessed, enjoyed and even exhibited by those who are fortunate. But that is no reason why they should slight or despise the poor villagers, with their plain uneventful stories of life and with no name or fame to exhibit or propagate..

Awaits alike..etc- This is what Gray wants to preach and propagate. Each of these privileges of the fortune-high birth, great power, rare beauty and opulent riches. *Th' inevitable hour-* the inevitable hour; the certain hour of death which is inviolable. **N.B.** An instance of the periphrasis.

What the poet means is that everything-high birth, pompous power, unparallelled beauty and immense riches- is equally destined to face inevitable and invincible death. *The paths...to the grave-* one of the immortal lines in English poetry and contains much of the lesson of life. Of whatever man may feel proud or boastful-his heredity, power, beauty, or riches-, he cannot avoid death. Death is invincible, irrestible, and touuches all-the rich and the poor, the learned and the ignorant. Whatever gory man may enjoy from his good fortune, his end is certain in death. His acts and achievements, his aspirationsd and attainments, all havetheir culmination in the grave. His glorious life ends in the gloomy grave wherein his body is interred after his inevitable death.

Stanzas 10-11 :

Nor you,ye proud- the poet refers to the proud -those who are proud of heredity, power, beauty, or wealth. *Impute to these the fault-* should find fault with those poor people; those proud men ust not put blame on those poor people. *If Mem'ry o'er ...raise-* if no memorial is raised over their graves by those who want to retain their memory. *Mem'ry-*those wo want to have memory of the dead. This is another specimen of the synecdoche. *Their tomb-*Their grave. *trophies raise-* erect memorials as the signs of the memory of the dead. *Where-* whereas (the poet wants to mean even 'where'). *Long drawn aise-*long passages. The poet actually means long passages or corridors inside the church premises. *Fretted vault-* arched roof, ornamented with carvings.

The poet is speaking of the interior of the church buildig with its long passages and arched roof, decorated with engraings.

*The pealing anthem-*the high-pitched prayer song in praise of the dead. *Swells ...praise-* the prayer song, in praise of the dead, attains higher pitches gradually.

Gray presents another picture the interior of the church enriched with high architectural skill and high-sounding sacred songs for the dead who lie buried therein. What he means is that it does not matter if those poor villagers had not the privilege to be buried iside the church, highly decorated and made solemn by high-sounding prayer notes.

Gray's point is that there is no difference between the humble burial place in the churchyard and the high and solem ones inside the church, for death is the same unsparing truth every where.

*Storied urn-*urn, engraved with the life-story of the man. It was the usual custom to keep the ashes of the dead in some costly, deorated urs *Animated bust-* life-like statues of the dead.

Its masion- original body; i.e., the deadbody. **N.B.** A case of periphrasis. *Can storied ...breath-* the poet now answers why te proud and powerful persons must not despise the uble graves of the poor villagers, for not having ay memorial erected o teir graves. After all, much carefully worked out and retained urn or well executed life-like statues of the dead cannot bring back life to one who is dead. The dead man cannot be restored to life by ay means, however artful and expensive this may be. *Honour's voice-* words of honour, high tributed, of course paid to the dead. *Provoke-*stir,activate, make alive. *The silent dust-*the dead person. Human ody has come from the dust. *Can Honour ...dust-* is it possible to restore life to the man who is paid high complments or tributes in his praise? Of course, the answer is obvious and in the negative.

Flatt'ry- words of flattery to the dead.*Soothe-*appease, please.*The dull...Death-* unresponsive, turned deaf ears of death.

The poet wants to mean that no words of flattery can stir life ito a dead person and make death responsive to the appeal for life. Death is definite and unchanging and nothing can bring back the life that is gone.

The stanza records an ualterable fact about death. Death is cold, callous and cruel, and spares none and once it toches one, the effect is beyond any change or recall.

It is to be noted that the whole stanza contains a rhetorical nterogation (questions, carrying ovious answers to the same.)

Stanzas 12-14 :

*Perhaps-*this is no certainty, but the humanitarian poet's fancy. *In this neglected spot-* the unattended, slighted place of the country churchyard. *Is laid-* is buried. *Some heart-* some person of a strog heart. **N.B.** Synecdoche (the part for the whole) *Once pregnant* - that was inflamed once. *With celestial fire-* with some sublime heavenly ispiration.*Some heart...fire-* the poet mses on the suppressed possibility of some of the rude forefathers of the hamlet. Some of them might have been a heavenly inspired prophet. *Hands-*the hands of a strong man. (another instance of the syecdoche-a part for the whole). *The rod of empire-* the authority over an empire. *Might have swayed-* might have cotrolled or ruled. *Hands...swayed-* some of the poor villagers might be strong enough to rule and command an empire. *Waked to ecstasy-*enlivened to an ecstatic joy. *The living lyre-* the tune of the lyre that seemed almost alive. *Waked to...lyre-* some poor villagers might possess the skill of great music-maker to provide ecstatic pleasure with the tune of his lyre.

N.B. Gray muses on what those ignorant poor villagers might have been in a favourable situation. There might have been among them an inspired prophet, a powerful emperor, or an enchanting musician. But that could not be in a repellant situation.

*But Knowledge to their eyes-*the poet emphasises how the door of knowledge was kept totally shut to the rude fore-fathers of the hamlet. *Her ample page-* sufficient store that knowledge has. *Spoils of time-* that is taken away by time. *Did ne'er unroll-* war never opened. *But Knowledge...unroll-* knowledge is imagined as a book that is enriched with the passage of time. But that sufficiently opulent book of knowledge was opened to the poor villagers who remained ignorant, deprived book of its blessing. **N.B.** 'knowledge' is here personified. *Chill Penury-* oppesive poverty. *Repressed...rage-*Their high, or noble ideal was ruthlessly repressed. *Genial current-*

instinctive flow. *Froze the ... soul-* the spontaneity of their intuitive urge was arrested and constricted in the repellent circumstances of their lives.

N.B. 'Penury' an abstract idea, is given the attribute of a living being in the verb 'repressed'-anothedr case of *Personification.*

The poet sadly relates how their learned desire or noble zeal perished in the hard and incongenial situation of their loives. The ample belssing of knowledge, enriched every year, was denied to them. Their acute poverty suppressed and destroyed their intuitive inspiration and entusiasm. They coukd not be what they might have been in a coongenial condition.

The poet's sympathy for the poor, unfortunate villagers is all distinct here. The humanist is Gray here comes out.

Full many a ...etc.-From the tale of the circumscribed lot of the poor villagers, denied of the light of knowledge and thrashed by the chilliness of penury, the humanitarian poet noow turns to the obscure fortune of those unfortunate down-trodden, poverty-stricken masses of people who have neither advantage nor opportunity in their lives to stimulate and actuate what might have been possible for them. He laments sadly on the misfortune of the poor victims of a hard and repressive situation that forces them to waste and wither away their latent talent. From the individual rude forefathers of the hamlet, Gray passes into humanity-the sad tragedy of the socially ignored and wronged humanity, with whom he is found to be in full sympathy.

Full many a ...etc. Gray takes instances from the world of Nature to substantiate his sad musing on the unfortunate rude forefather of the hamlet. *Full many .... serene-* he refers to good many pearls of pure and quite sparkle of much worth and value. *The dark...bear-* such pure and pregnant pearls remain concealed and unknown in the invisible, unfathomed bottom of the boundless ocean.Those gems, no doubt of much value and elegance, remain hidden , unseen, ignored because of the very condition (the deep depth of the ocean) in which they arc.

Full many a ...etc.- Gray's second analogy is also from nature. He speaks of fair and fragrant flower, blooming in deep and desolate deserts, with none to attend to and admire. Such flowers fade away, unnoticed, unacknowledged and unwept. *Full many ...blush unseen-* a good many flowers bloom and fade in a dreary and desolate situation and thereby waste their sweetness of colour and scent, without any appreciation or admiration from any one.

Gray's analogies are extensive and appropriate. The poor unfortunate people, rudely deprived of the much needed opportunities or necessary advantages, are compared to the valuable gems lying under the unfathomed ocean or the lovely flowers blooming in the unfrequented desert. The latent talent of those people grow sterile and stale in the oppressive and hostile circumstance of life, just as the worth of the valuable gems under the sea or the beautiful flowers in the desert remain unrecognised and unaapreciated in an adverse situation.

Stanza 15-18 :

Some village Hampden- a person as spirited and bold as Hampden might be possible among the poor villagers, John Hampden of Buckinghamshire, a cousin of Cromwell, opposed the tax, imposed by Charlles I, without the sanction of Parliament. *The little tyrant* - the small landlordm, using oppression on his poor tenants. *Some village...withstood-* as John Hampden fearlessly defined and opposed the tyranny of Charles I, who had levied ship money, with out the approval of Parliament, some poor villager, bold and spirited enoughj like him, would have protested against the unjust action of the tyrannical landlord of his little field.

Gray wants to indikcate the possibility of some poor villager to defy and oppose the cruel tyranny of the landlord under whom he might have to work.

Some mute inglorious Milton- the poet turns to another aspect of their possible talent.. There might have been among the poor villagers, some person, possessing a rich poetical talent that could not come out. In a situation, suitable for cultivating that talent, that could not come out. In a situation, suitable for cultivating that talent, that very villager might have been as gifted a poet as John Milton, the immortal Muse in English poetry.But that could not be. Milton in him could not speak out and his poetic gift had no oportunity for revealing itself. So that possible Milton in them remained mute and inglorious. *Some Cromwell-* Gray speaks of another possible attainment of the poor villagers, lying buried in the country churchyard. Some of them might prove to be as strong and capable a leader as Oliver Cromwell, who led the civil war against the tyrannical King, Charles I, and brought about the fall of the monarchial power in England, Gray's point is to emphasize the possibility of such a poor villager to be as finished a politician as Oliver Cromwell, if provided with proper privileges and scopes. *Gultless of his country's blood-* Cromwell was guilty of causing bloodshed in the country, but the possible Cromwell among the poor villagers would not have indulged in the unnecessary acts of bloodshed like him. **N.B.** Gray is fgound to give vent here to the strong prejudice against Oilver Cromwell in the eighteenth century. His political sagacity, patriotic fervour and Puritanic zeal were discarded in that age and he was looked down upon as a bloody power-monger, responsible for immense bloodshed in the country.

N.B. Gray muses on what the rude forefathers of the hamlet might have been in the changed circumstances, providing them with the opportunity for cultivating their untrimmed gifts. They might have been in that case spirited and defiant agitators against tyranny, injustice and cruelty, like John Hampden, immortal and glorious poets, like Milton, or mighty political leader, like Cromwell, without remaining guilty of shedding blood of their countrymen. But their talent, whatever might be its manifestation, withered away for want of nurture and opportunity. So Hampden remained inactive in them, Milton among them was all mute, and Oliver Cromwell could not not emerge from them.

The applause...to command- it might have been possible for some of them to be an eloquent parliamentarian, drawing audience and admiration. The eloquence of a powerful orator to keep the listeners spellbound and under command might have been the attainment of some of them.*Then threats...despise-* some of them might be heroic and fearless enough to treat scornfully any threat of pain or destruction from any quarter. *To scatter plenty...land-* some of them might have made their country plentiful and properous by benevolent functions. *Read their history...eyes-* some of them could have the satisfaction to perceive the spontaneous appreciation of their feats in the very look of their countrymen.

Gray continues his sad reflection on the misfortune of the poor villagers, buried in the country churchyard. Some of them might have the potency or gift of an eloquent orator to win applauses from the attentive senate. Some of them, too, might have the heroic spirit to defy and despise the threats of pain and dangers. Some of them could have made their lannd happy and prosperous to receive commendation from the very appreciative look of their countrymen.

But they could not be what they might been because of their misfortune that did not allow them to fully utilize and expoit their hidden possibility. Naturally, they remained all unknown, unexpressed, the rejected scum of society.

*Their lot forbade-*Their circumsribed lot prevented them (from what they might have been-a great poet, an inspired prophet, or a mighty politician). *Nor circumscibed ...crimes confined-* but that was a blessing in disguise. Their poor lot had a two-fold effect on them. It , no doubt, marred their possibities, stinted their qualities and capabilities. At the same time, that restrained the possible criminality in them and stopped them from any moral degeneration or criminal temptation. *Forbade to ...a throne-* their circumscribed lot kept them in check from any indulgence to crime or wrong, suvh as to usurp the royal power by a heinous act of murder.

N.B. Gray is here referring to the common vices of ambitious men, aspiring after power and authority.

*And shut the gates...amnkind-*they did not turn cruel, tyrannical and merciless in their lust for power or greed for gold. They did never learn how to stain their virtue or morality by entertaining dishonourable plans and unholy acts.

The struggling pangs- the pain that struggles within. *Conscious truth to hide-* to hide the truth of which one is conscious. *The struggling...to hide-*the poet speaks of the innocence of those effort to hide some truth known to them. In short they were not guilty of any kind of pretence or hypocrisy. *To quench-*to put out. *The blushes-* the blushes caused by the feeling of shame. *Ingenuous shame-* the feeling of shame that is instinctive. *To quench..shame-* the innocent poor villagers were ignorant of the art to put out the sense of shame that instinctively comes for an act of wrong. The poet wants to emphasize the purity of the poor mind that was not affected by any suppression of the instinctive sense of shhame for an act of moral wrong.

The shrine of...Pride- the temple of luxury and pride. The poet actually mmeans the high places of luxury and pride, that is the persons who are proud and live in immense luxury. *Or heap the shrine ...the Muses flame-* the poet wants to show the honest nature of the poor villagers who lie buried in the country churchyard.They nnever degenerated and debased themselvews by writing verses, flattering rich and proud persons. **N.B.** Gray refers to the common practice of a good many poets of the time to write poems, heaping exaggerated and extravagent pariases on their rich and proud patrons.

Gray brings out how their circumscribed lot prevented the poor villagers from turning shameless pretenders and flatterers.

Stanzas 19 :

Madding crowd- people madly engaged in the various pursuits of life for name and fame, riches and power, honour and glory. *Ignoble strife-* the strife of life for power, wealth and dignity and the mean strategy, adopted in the same for success. Such a strife is ignoble, sordid. *Far from...strife-* these poor villagers live far from the mad pursuit of various people, engaged in ignoble strives to have power, riches and glory. *Their sober wishes-*Their restrained virtuous objectives. *Never learned to stray-* didnot know how to deviate from their normal, peaceful life. *Cool sequestered vale of life-* their mode of living is compared to a quiet, lonely valley. **N.B.** This is a happy instance of the figure of speech metaphor. *The kept...their way* -they well retained a quiet and contended living in common occupations and humble joys.

Gray relates here the calm, peaceful life of those rude forefathers of the hamlet, who did never deviate from their simple and humble living annd kept themselves scrupulously aloof from the ognoble pursuits of ambitious men, maddened by the lure of riches and rank, power and domination.

Stanzas 20-23 :

Yet even- even then. The poet implies that even then those poor dead. *These bones-* these dead bodies (bones for bodies, a part for the whole-the synecdoche) . *From insult to protect-* to save the burial place from treading under feet by a stranger. *Some frail memorial-*some kind of weak, rather poorly constructed memorial.*Still erected nigh-* yet raised close at hand.

The poet points out that some sort of memorials, rather weak and poorly constructed, are even then raised over the burial ground of those poor villagers, lest their burial palces may be insulted by trampling under feet by strangers. *With uncouth rhymes-* the verses inscribed on the memorials are ill-composed and unhappy. *Shapeless sculpture deck'd-*adorned with rather unsatisfactory sculptural work.

The poet admits that on those frail memorials are carved some ill composed verses and ill shaped sculptural designs.

Implores the passing...of a sigh- those frail memorials, according to the poet, do serve the purpose of drawing some attention from the persons, happen to pass by. Gray implies that those memorials mmake a chance passerby aware of the graves of the of the unknown villagers and draw the instinctive homage to them from him or her with a sigh of sorrow for the dead.

Their name, their years,...etc.- The poet mentions the engravings or inscriptions on those frail memorials. These contain the names and the ages of the persons buried , engraved by the illiterate villager poet. *The place of ...supply-* these inscriptions, however, serve the purpose of announcing their existence and of expressing some lamentation for them. *Many a ...strews-* some scriptural texts or instructive quotation from the Holy Bible, too, are engraved on those humble, ill-shaped tombstones. *She strews-* scattered by the Muse, the goddess of poetry. **N.B.** 'She' here stands for the 'Muse', the poetic inspiration, and not the village poet, who made those inscriptions.

That teach- that instruct, that inspire, 'That' is the instructive 'holy text' engraved.. *The rustic moralist to die*-the poor villagers, who had the ethical realization that death is the inviolable truth of life and to be accepted steadily as the basic reality of human existence.

Gray here compliments the ignorant, poor deads for their moral sense to take death, as imevitable and unavoidable to life, without any fear or grief.

For who, to dumb forgetfulness...etc.- The poet now goes to explain the need for erecting those frail and uncouth memorials. After all no human being wants to be absolutely forgotten after his or her death. *To dumb...prey*- to be a victim of utter oblivion, of whom nothing is remembered or spoken. *This pleasing anxious*- the pleasurable sensation even in anxiety (a case of the oxymoron-contradictory words are juxtaposed). *Being e'er resign'd*- ever given up or surrendered.*This pleasing anxious...e'er resign'd*- there is no one to give up willingly the anxiety of being remembered by his or her rrelations, as that has a sense of pleasure. **N.B.** Gray rightly brings out the instinctive human desire to remain alive in the memory of the living world after death. His study of human psychology is keen and admirable.

Left the warm precincts...lok behind- there is no living being, ready to quit this warm, cheerful realm of life, without remembering and recalling its happy, pleasant memories. The poet here refers to another natural human instinct to look back fondly and wishes to linger at the livig world that the dying man is to leave soon.

Gray emphasizes here that no dying man wishes to be totally forgetten by the living world with with he has so long been associated.Such a man rather wishes to have his memory retaied affectionately by those whom he is leaving behind.

On some fond breast- on the breast of some affectionate friend or relation.. *The parting soul*-The dying man.. The dying man wishes to repose on the breastof some affectionalte relation or friend. What such a man longs for is the touch of affection. *Some pious drop*- sincere drops of tear. *The closing eye*-the dying person. **N.B.** A case of Periphrasis.*Some pious...requires*- at the approach of death the dyig man craves for some affectionalte touch, for some sincere tears of sorrow. *Even from the tomb*- even when the person is dead and buried.. *The voice ...cries*-the same natural desirefor remembrance is active. *e'en from the tomb...Nature cries*- even after a person's death and burial, the keen desiire in him or her to be remembered by the living world remains all active. *E'en in..wonted fires*- even the ashes of the dead, retained as a memory, seems to possess the intense desire for remembrance in the living world.**N.B.** Gray seems to reflect on the intensity of the interest of a dying man or woman in the world that he or she is to leave soon.There is an instinctive urge in him or her to enjoy affection or sympathy from his or her dear or near ones. He or she is equally eager to be remembered by the living world after his or her death.

Stanzas 24-29 : *For thee*- the poet refers to the unlettered muse-the village poet. *Who, mindful...dead*- the village poet remained attentive to those poor villagers, lying buried, without any trophy of honour.*Dost in...relate-* he has expresses the short and simple account of the unhonoured dead in the uncouth inscriptions on their frail tombstones..*If chance..lead-*if accidentally, while remaining all by himself in his contemplation.*Some kindred spirit-* some perso of the same nature of the village poet. *Inquire thy fate-* want to know of the life-story of the village-poet.

For thee...thy fate- the poet speaks of the village poet, who took labour and pain to inscribe on the tombstones of the poor villagers, the scrappy details about their name, age and some scriptural text. Of the very village poet, some stranger, while loitering all by himself in a contemplative mood, may mmake some enquiry.

*Haply some...may say-*some very old inbitant of the village may, however, acquaint the stranger with the life-story of that village-poet.*Oft have...dawn-* the poet was often seen in the time of the early dawn. *Brushin..away-* he was found moving very hastily brushig aside the dews on the lawn.*To meet ...lawn-* his purpose was to reach the top of some high land to see the rise of the sun.

Gray traces how the village poet started his day. He qickly moved across the dewy mmeadow to see sunrise from some highland.

*There at the ...nodding beech-*under the shade of that bending beech tree, standing close at hand. *That wreathes...so high-* the big roots of that tree are found to form some awkward wreathes at a height. *His listless ...stretch-*The village poet would stretch his body quietly at noon time. *And pore upon..babbles by -* he continued to look at the babbling brook that flowed by. 'babbles' -a case of the onomatopia.

The poet next mentions how the village poet passed his noontime. He lay under the shade of the big, old nodding beech tree quietly and watched steadily the brook that babbled by.

Hard by yon wood- very close to that nearby forest. *Now smiling...as in scorn-* he was found to smile occasionally as in a scorn. *Muttering his wayward fancies-* whispering indistinctly his thoughts in course of his loitering. *He would rove-* he could be found loitering rather idle-minded. *Now drooping...woe-wan-*he looked depressed, sad and pale. *Like one forlorn-*just like one who was all alone. *Or crazed with care-*he appeared also much pressed with cares and worries. *Or crossed...love-* or like one, shocked in frustrated love.

Gra shows the aimless, rather depressed and melancholy worn mode of living of the village poet who was found to loiter and mutter casually, with his pale, sad and care-worn appearance. The village poet was no joyous, warm-hearted personality at all.

One morn...hill- one morning the old rusic could not see the village poet in his usual haunt at the hill top wherefrom he used to watch sunrise. *Among the...tree-* he could not be seen in his favourite spots- the dewy lawn and the old beech tree. The village poet was no more seen brushing with his hasty steps dews away the lawn or lying quiet under the beech tree and watching steadily the brook that babbles by. *another came-* one more day came. *Nor yet...trill-* he was not found by the side of that babbling brook. *Nor up...was he-*he couldnot be seen, too, in his usual haunts- the lawn of hs loitering and the forest of his wayward fancies.

Gray now refers to the sudden disappearance of the village poet from his customery haunts. He could not be seen where he had usually been-in the dewy lawn, in the woodland, under the beech tree, or by the side of the flowing stream.

The next- the next day. *With dirges due*- with dirges, sung appropriately. *In sad array*- in a funeral procession. *Thro'...borne*- his dead body was carried through the path, leading to the churchyard. *Approach...aged thorn*- the poet refers to the tombstone, erected over the village poet's grave and the epitaph inscibed thereon. *Approach and read*- this is said to the stranger. *For thou canst read*- for he is an educated man. *The lay*- the simple poem, here the epitaph. *Grav'd on the stone*-engraved on the tombstone. *Beneath...thorn*- under the old hawthorn tree where the village poet was buried.

So the village poet died. His body, taken in a funeral procession, was buried in the churchyard under an old howthorn tree and a tombstone was raised, with an epitaph inscribed on the same.

N.B. The village poet, as presented by Gray, was simple, rather melancholy-minded fellow, who took immense interest in the poor unattended destiny of the rude fore-fathers of the hamlet. Some sort of the rustic poet's nature and temper in supposed to have been traced in Gray's personal life.

Stanzas 30-32 : *The Epitaph*- the inscription on the tomb-stone in the commemoration of the dead. The last three stanzas form the epitaph, and this is supposed to be Gray's own epitaph, written by himself.

Here rests...earth- the poet lies buried here with his head reposing on thhe lap of the mother earth. *Lap of earth*- earth is personified. *A youth...unknown*- the young poet could not attain fame or fortune. He could neither be rich nor famous. *Fair science*-this is a case of the personification. Here ''science' means 'education', *Frown'd not* - favoured. **N.B.** A case of Litotes. *Humble birth*-birth in a humble family. *Fair science...humble birth*- though born of a poor family, he was not deprived of the favour of education, *i.e.,* not an ignorant person. *And melancholy...own*- he was all prey to melancholy-minded youth. *Large was bountry*- his gift (of sincerity and sympathy for the poor) was immense. *His soul...sincere*- hs nature was sincere. *Heaven did...send*- he was properly compensated by God with His blessing for his goodness and sincerity in feeling and action for the poor villagers. *He gave to misery*- he was liberal in his gift to miserable or wretched men. **N.B.** 'Misery' means a miserable person. A case of the synecdoche (abstract for the concrete). *(All he had), a tear*- all that he could possess-the tears of sympathy. *He gain'd ....a friend*- God proved to be his friend, and that was all he could desire from im. He did not want any fame or fortune from Him. *No farther...abode*- The poet prefers to shut out all analyses and evaluations of his merits and drawbacks.. Let not the dead be subjectedto any unnecessary scrutiny of worth or limitation. *There ...God*- he has his repose now in the bosom of God, with all his qualities and frailities, for the final judgement from Him Who was his Father and God. The epitaph ends in an ideal Christian note definitely didactic.

❖ *Elegy Written in a Country Churchyard*-এর সম্পূর্ণ বঙ্গানুবাদঃ

সন্ধ্যার ঘন্টাধ্বনি সূচিত করল বিদায়ী দিবসের অবসান লগ্ন,
শব্দতোলা মেষের দল বক্রপথে হেঁটে আসে তৃণভূমি পথ ধরে
কৃষকটি ক্লান্ত অবসন্ন পদক্ষেপে ফিরে চলে বাড়ির দিকে,
আর রেখে যায় অন্ধকারে এই জগতকে আর আমাকে।

এখন দৃষ্টি থেকে ঝাপসা হয়ে আসে আলোকিত নিসর্গ শোভা,
আর গোটা বাতাস জুড়ে বিরাজ করছে থমথমে নিথরতা,
শোনা যায় কেবল গুবড়ে পোকার ভনভনে আওয়াজে উড়ে চলা।
আর মেষের গলার ঘুমপাড়ানী ঘন্টার টুং টাং দূরের আস্তাবলে।

শোনা যায় অদূরের আইভি লতা জড়ানো মিনারের মাথায়
বিষন্ন প্যাঁচাটি চাঁদের কাছে জানায় অভিযোগ
এমনভাবে যেন, তার গোপন কুঞ্জবনের কাছে আসা যাওয়ায়,
অপমানিত করেছে তার আদিম একক রাজত্বকে।

ঐ অসমতল এলম্ গাছের নীচে, ঐ ইউগাছের ছায়ায়,
যেখানে দেখা যায় বহু আদলের মাটির ঢিপির সারি,
প্রতিটি সংকীর্ণ কক্ষে চিরতরে শায়িত রয়েছে,
এই ছোট গ্রামটির অশিক্ষিত পূর্বপুরুষগণ ঘুমন্ত অবস্থায়।

সকালের সুগন্ধিত নিঃশ্বাস সহ বাতাসের ডাক,
খড়ের বাসা থেকে ভেসে আসা সোয়ালো পাখির ডাক,
মোরগের তীক্ষ্ণ ডাক, অথবা প্রতিধ্বনি তোলা শিঙার আওয়াজ,
আর জাগিয়ে তুলবেনা তাদের অতিসাধারণ কবর শয্যা থেকে।

তাদের জন্য আর অগ্নি সংযোজিত হবেনা অগ্নি কুন্ডে,
অথবা ব্যস্ত গৃহবধূ সারবে তার সান্ধ্য যত্নের কর্ম কান্ড ;
কোন শিশু দৌড়ে এসে অস্ফুটবাক্যে জানাবেনা তার পিতার প্রত্যাবর্তনের কথা,
অথবা আর তার হাঁটু জড়িয়ে ধরবেনা ঈর্ষা জাগানো চুম্বন লাভের আশায়,

তাদের কাস্তে প্রায়শই প্রদান করেছে ফসলের ফলন্ত
তাদের লাঙল কঠিন মাটির ঢেলাকে চূর্ণ করেছে :
কি আনন্দঘন ভাবে তারা তাদের দলবল সহ মাঠে যাত্রা করেছে ?
তাদের কঠিন আঘাতে কিভাবে নত হয়েছে অরণ্যরাজি !

উচ্চাকাঙ্খা যেন ব্যঙ্গ না করে তাদের প্রয়োজনীয় শ্রমের,
তাদের ঘরোয়া আনন্দের, আর দুবোর্ধ ভাগ্যের ;
না যেন আতিশয্য উপেক্ষার হাসি নিয়ে না শোনে
হতদরিদ্র সংক্ষিপ্ত ও সাধারণ ঘটনাপঞ্জী।

বংশগৌরবের অহঙ্কার, ক্ষমতার দম্ভ,
আর সকল সৌন্দর্য, আর যা কিছু সম্পদ হয় প্রদত্ত,
অনিবার্য ক্ষণটির অপেক্ষা করে একইভাবে।
গৌরবের পথ কেবল গিয়ে মেশে কবরেই।

না তুমিও, ওহে অহঙ্কারী, এতে সংযোগ করনা ত্রুটি,
যদি তাদের কবরের উপর কোনও ফলক স্মৃতি দ্বারা উত্থিত না হয়,
যেখানে গীর্জার দীর্ঘ সরনী বেয়ে আর কারুখচিত গম্বুজ আদলে
উচ্চ ধ্বনিত মৃতের প্রার্থনা সংগীত উথলে তোলে শংসাগীতি।

নথিযুক্ত মৃতের ফলক, অথবা আবক্ষ মূর্তি কি পারে,
বিদায়ী নিঃশ্বাসকে ফিরিয়ে আনতে তার আবাসস্থলে?
পারে কি সম্মানসূচক স্তুতির কণ্ঠ প্ররোচিত করতে নীরব ধূলিকে,
অথবা মিথ্যা স্তুতি স্বান্তনা দিতে মৃত্যুর শীতল বিবর্ণ শ্রবণকে?

হয়ত এমন অবহেলিত স্থানেই শায়িত রয়েছে
এমন কিছু হৃদয় যারা দৈব অগ্নির উত্তাপ ধারণ করেছিল,
ছিল হাত, যারা সম্রাটের শাসনদন্ড আন্দোলিত করতে পারত,
অথবা পারত জীবন্ত বীণায় উদ্দীপনা জাগাতে।

কিন্তু জ্ঞান তাদের সামনে নিজের যথাযোগ্য পৃষ্ঠাগুলিকে
সম্পৃক্ত যা ছিল সময়ের ক্ষয় লিপিতে কোনওদিন করেনি উন্মোচন ;
শীতল অনটন তাদের মহত আগুনকে চাপা দিয়েছিল,
আর নিথর করেছিল তাদের আত্মার বৃদ্ধি সহায়ক স্রোতস্বিনীকে।

বিশুদ্ধ উজ্জ্বলদ্যুতি সম্পন্ন বহু রত্নরাজিকে
মহাসাগরের অন্ধকার নিস্তরঙ্গ গুহা লুকিয়ে রাখে ;
বহু ফুল ফোটে আর ঝরে যায় অলক্ষ্যেই,
আর হারায় তার মিষ্টতা মরুবায়ুর শুষ্কতায়।

কোনও গ্রাম্র হ্যাম্পডেন, যে, অসম সাহসী বুকে
তার মাঠের ছোট্ট স্বৈরাচারিতাকে সহ্য করেছিল,
কোনও মূক গৌরবহীণ মিলটন হয়ত এখানে করছে বিশ্রাম,
রয়েছে কোনও ক্রমওয়েল যে নিজ দেশের রক্তপাতের অভিযোগ থেকে মুক্ত।

শ্রবণশীল মন্ত্রীবর্গের হর্ষধ্বনিকে নির্দেশ প্রদানকারী,
যন্ত্রণা আর ধ্বংসের শংকাকে উপেক্ষাকারী,
হাস্যরত প্রান্তরে সপ্রচুর সম্পদ বন্টনকারী,
আর জাতির চোখে লেখা রয়ে যেত যাদের ইতিহাস।

তাদের ভাগ্য বাধা দিয়েছিল, কেবল পরিস্থিতিতে বন্দী করেনি তাদের,
তাদের সমৃদ্ধিশীল গুণাবলীকে, বরং আটকে ছিল তাদের অপরাধকেও ;
বাধা দিয়েছিল হত্যালীলার পথ বেয়ে সিংহাসন আরোহনে,
আর মানবতার প্রতি দয়া প্রদর্শনের দ্বার রূদ্ধ করতে,

সংগ্রামশীল দীর্ঘশ্বাস সচেতন সত্যকে করতে লুক্কায়িত,
স্বাভাবিক লজ্জার লাজুক হাসিকে নিবৃত্ত করতে,
অথবা আভিজাত্য আর অহঙ্কার আকরের স্তুপ গড়ে তুলতে
কাব্যিক অনুপ্রেরণার ধূপকে প্রজ্জ্বলিত করে।

পাগল জনকূলের ইতর সংগ্রাম থেকে অনেক দূরে,
তাদের সংযত ইচ্ছাগুলি কখনও পথভ্রষ্ট হওয়ার শিক্ষা পায়নি।
জীবনের শীতল বিচ্ছিন্ন সরনী বেয়ে
তারা বজায় রেখেছিল তাদের শোরগোলহীন যাত্রাপথ।

তবু এমনকি এই মৃত অস্থিগুলিকে অসম্মান থেকে রক্ষা করতে
কিছু দুর্বল স্মৃতি সৌধ অলক্ষ্যে হয়েছে উত্থিত,
নিরক্ষর ছন্দ আর অবয়বহীণ ভাস্কর্যের সজ্জাসহ।
এক দীর্ঘশ্বাস সহ শ্রদ্ধার্ঘ করে বয়ান।

তাদের নাম, বয়স, রচিত হয়েছে নিরক্ষর কবির দ্বারা,
স্থানটিকে প্রদান করে খ্যাতি ও শোকজ্ঞাপন :
আর বহুবিধ পবিত্র কথা আশেপাশে ছড়িয়ে রাখে সে,
যা গ্রাম্য নীতিবিধকে মৃত্যুর কথা শেখায়।

কারণ কে আছে, যে মূক বিস্মৃতির শিকার হতে চায়,
এমন তৃপ্ত উদ্বিগ্নতায় চির সমর্পিত হতে
ছেড়ে যায় এমন উষ্ণ দিবসের সীমারেখা,
না ফিরে তাকিয়ে অন্ড়ত একবার যাওয়ার আগে?

কোন প্রিয়জনের বক্ষে বিদায়ী আত্মা রাখে বিশ্বাস,
বন্ধ হয়ে আসা চোখ চায় পবিত্র কয়েক ফোঁটা অশ্রু মোচন ;
এমন কি কবরের সৌধ থেকে প্রকৃতির কণ্ঠ কেঁদে ওঠে,
এমনকি আমাদের অস্থিভস্মেও বেঁচে থাকে তাদের প্রবৃত্তিগত আগুন।

তোমার জন্য, অখ্যাত মৃতের প্রতি আগ্রহী যে,
এই পংক্তিগুলিকে তাদের কৌশলহীণ কাহিনী রয়েছে বর্ণিত ;
যদি সুযোগ, একাকী ভাবনায় বয়ে নিয়ে আসে,
কোন সমমনোস্ক মন জানতে চাইবে তোমার ভাগ্যকে,–

সম্ভবত কোন পক্ককেশ বৃদ্ধ গ্রামবাসী হয়ত বলবে,
প্রায়শই আমরা দেখেছি তাকে ভোরের সূচনা কালে
দ্রুত পদক্ষেপে শিশির দু'পায়ে মেখে চলে যেতে
পর্বতের মাথার প্রান্ড়রে সূর্যের মুখোমুখি দাঁড়াতে।

সেখানে নত শাখা বিশিষ্ট বীচ ছায়াতলে
যা নিজের আদিম বিস্ময় জাগানো শিকড়গুলি পেঁচিয়ে তোলে,
তার ক্লান্ত দেহ দৈর্ঘ্যকে মধ্যাহ্নে সে করে শায়িত,

চিন্ড্রমগ্ন ভাবে তাকিয়ে থাকে নদীর ভাসমান বুদবুদে।

অদূরের অরণ্যের ধারে, হাস্যরত এখন যেন কোনও শ্লেষে,
ভ্রাম্যমান গৃহে ফেরার পথে ফিসফিস করে বলা ভাবনায়।
এখন ঝুঁকে আছে, চিন্তামগ্ন বিষন্নতায়, এক নিঃসঙ্গ মানুষের মত,
অথবা অতি উদ্বিগ্নতায় বিহ্বল হয়ে, বা আশাহত ভালোবাসায় হতাশ হয়ে।

'এক সকালে আমি অভাব অনুভব করেছিলাম তার চিরাচরিত পাহাড়ে,
টিলার গায়ে আর তার প্রিয় গাছের কাছে ;
এল অন্য একজন; নদীর পাশে তা নয়,
প্রান্তরেও নয়, না সে ছিল অরণ্যেও :

এরপরে বিলাপ সঙ্গীতসহ শববাহী মিছিলে
ধীর গতিতে গীর্জার পথ ধরে তাকে দেখলাম বয়ে নিয়ে যেতে :-
এগিয়ে এস আর পড়ে নাও (কারণ তুমি পড়তে পারো) সেই সামান্য বচন
খচিত যা বৃদ্ধ হাউথর্ণগাছের নিচের পাথরে।

সমাধি স্তম্ভলিপি

এখানে মাটির কোলে মাথা রেখে বিশ্রাম নিচ্ছে
ভাগ্য আর খ্যাতি যার কাছে অজানা এক যুবক :
সৌজন্যের বিজ্ঞান তার সাধারণ কূলপরিচিতিকে করেনি ব্যঙ্গ,
আর বিষন্নতা নিজ লগ্নে তাকে করেছে চিহ্নিত।

তার মহত্ব ছিল বিশাল, আর আত্মা ছিল নিবেদিত,
দৈব করেছিল ক্ষতিপূরণ যেমন বৃহৎ মাপে প্রেরণ করেছিল :
সে প্রদান করেছিল বিষন্নতাকে (যা কিছু ছিলতার) এক ফোঁটা অশ্রু,
সে পেয়েছিল স্বর্গ থেকে (যা ছিল তার সর্বান্তকরণ চাওয়া) এক সখা।

আর চেওনা তার গুণাবলীর উদ্ঘাটন করতে,
অথবা চেওনা তার মৃত বিশ্রামাগার থেকে তার দুর্বলতার বিশ্লেষণ করতে
(সেখানে তারা একই রূপে কম্পমান আশা নিয়ে করে বিশ্রাম,
তার পিতা আর তার ঈশ্বরের সাথে)।

❖ A Critical Analysis of *Elegy Written in a Country Churchyard* : Gray Expresses the Sympathy for the Common Man

An Elegy Written in a Country Churchyard is a poem by Thomas Gray, first published in 1751. Gray may, however, have begun writing the poem in 1742, shortly after the death of his close friend Richard West. In this poem Gray has changed the form of writing an elegy; it is the first elegy that mourns the death not of great or famous people, but of common men who remain unknown and unrecognized. Gray also attempts to show that all 'the paths of glory lead but to the grave.' By implication, the futility of all human ambition and aspiration is hinted at. The contrast between the lives of the rich and the poor, or the privileged and the unprivileged is also highlighted in the poem. He shows how the poor are not in a position to enjoy the luxuries and joys of life in this world. Their poverty proves an obstacle in the path of their progress. But this poverty is a blessing in disguise. If it does not allow people to rise higher, it also restrains them from doing evil, by limiting their power to do so. The rich, on the other hand, possess the power and means to do well to themselves and the world, but they also have powers to do mischief and bring destruction on innocent people.

Introduction:

Thomas Gray was one of the most important poets of the eighteenth century. He was born on December 26, 1716 in London. He was the fifth of twelve children; all the others died in infancy. His father was Philip Gray, a scrivener and exchange broker who treated his wife with extreme cruelty. He refused to educate the lad, and the expense of Gray's education was borne by his mother. In 1727 or thereabouts, he was sent to Eton College, where he formed lasting friendships with Horace Walpole, son of the Prime Minister, Richard West, son of the Lord Chancellor of Ireland and Thomas Ashton, nicknamed "Plato." In December of 1743, he took the degree of Bachelor of Civil Law (LL.B.) at Cambridge, but never practiced. In 1748 he began a philosophical poem on The Alliance of Education and Government. (Clark Sutherland Northup, 1911)

Perhaps Gray was the most learned man in Europe. He was equally acquainted with the elegant and profound parts of science, and not superficially but thoroughly. He knew every branch of history, both natural and civil and had read all the original historians of England, France, and Italy. Criticism, metaphysics, morals, and politics formed a principal part of his plan of study; voyages and travels of all sorts were his favourite amusement; and he had a fine taste in painting, prints, architecture, and gardening. He was also a good man, a well-bred man, a man of virtue and humanity. But His strength and courage gradually declined until in May, 1771, he was attacked by gout of the stomach and at 55, he died. He was buried beside his beloved mother at Stoke Poges churchyard, the scene of the "Elegy".

Samuel Johnson was the first of many critics to put forward the view that Gray spoke in two languages, one public and the other private, and that his private language—that of his bestknown and most loved poem, "Elegy Written in a Country Churchyard" was too seldom heard.

2. Gray's Productivity - Poems

Gray is widely considered the most important English poet of the mid-eighteenth century and he was a major figure in the transition from the Neo-classical to the Romantic style in English letters. His famous poems are: Ode on a Distant Prospect of Eton College, Ode on the Death of a Favourite Cat, Drowned in a Tub of Gold Fishes, Ode on the Spring, Hymn to Adversity, Sonnet on the Death of Mr. Richard West, The Progress of Poesy, The Bard, A Long Story, Ode on the installation of the Duke of Grafton, Ode to Mary Magdalene and Hymn to Ignorance. In 1754, his incomplete Ode on Vicissitude, was found after his death in a diary .But he is primarily remembered for his greatest masterpiece, Elegy Written in a Country Churchyard - one of the best known and most beloved poems in English literature.

3. Elegy

Greek origin word elegy is the poetic expression of sorrow or mournfulness, which is usually associated with death. It has the tone of mourning and it is a song of lamentation. It was usually written to mourn the death of a friend or a dear and near one. Expressive both of personal grief and of preoccupation with universal concerns, it often combines the particular and the general, the emotional and the intellectual, to create the fusions of great poetry. In the words of Coleridge, an elegy "is the form of poetry natural to a reflective mind".

There is quite a difference in the writing of today's Elegies and Ancient Greece. Elegies from Ancient Greece were not written about death, but written about one's "true love." (Túrner) At that time, the term denoted a particular rhythmic pattern rather than specific subject matter. The most famous Latin love-elegists, Propertius, Tibullus, and Ovid became models for poets of the English Renaissance, who used humor, irony, even slotted narratives into a poem and still called it elegy. They also composed funeral elegies of the type with which modern readers are familiar. Propertius wrote many of his elegies to his lover Cynthia, the prosperous member of ancient Greek society.

Until the 16th Century, the definition of elegy becomes a poem that is somber and melancholy in tone. 'Shed No Tears' is a poem that adheres to the definition of elegy. It is somber in tone and is a tribute to someone who has passed, but lives on in the heart of the writer. But at that time, elegy was only written on the death of celebrated and famous persons. Milton's *Lycidas* on the death of his friend Edward King and Tennyson's In Memoriam at the death of A. H. Hallim are the celebrated elegies. Walt Whitman wrote the famous elegy *O Captain! My Captain!* As a tribute to slain President Abraham Lincoln and P.B. Shelley's *Adonais* mourns the death of John Keats.

But Jonathan Swift's elegy was quite different from others. His "A Satirical Elegy on the Death of a Late Famous General" was written in 1722 upon the death of the English general John Churchill, the Duke of Marlborough, who had a checkered diplomatic and military career. Among these, Elegy Written in a Country Churchyard by Thomas Gray as a tribute to his friend and fellow poet, Richard West and "When Lilacs Last in the Dooryard Bloom'd" by Walt Whitman are the two most popular examples of elegy. (Swift, 1765)

4. Objective Mourning

Gray's elegy like other elegies of Milton, Shelley, Tennyson or Arnold is also a song of lamentation and mourning. But it is objective mourning whereas in the elegies of other poets the mourning is too personal. Though written to commemorate gray's friend, Richard West, the poem expresses grief over death in general. But he reflects upon death, the sorrows of life, and the mysteries of human life with a touch of his personal melancholy. And he honors the potentially great people who live and die in obscurity. In this context, Swinburne said "elegy as a poem of high perfection and universal appeal to the tenderest and noblest depths of human feeling", and remarked as an elegiac poet, gray holds for all ages, his unassailable and sovereign station. In fact, due to the new form of the elegy and both its theme and poetic techniques, its popularity has transcended the limits of time and place. It deals with the theme of death and the transitory quality of all worldly glory and human achievements. It also deals with the lot of common men on this earth. These universally appealing themes contributed much to the enduring popularity of the poem. The melancholic note of the poem is in keeping with the poetic taste of Gray's age and it enhances its appeal.

It has been widely read and admired in all places and in all times. Grierson and Smith regard it as the most widely known poem of the 18th century along with Oliver Goldsmith's Deserted Village. And it is probably still the most popular and the best loved poem in the English language. It has been translated into a large number of languages like Greek, German, Hebrew, Dutch, Spanish, Russian, Latin, Italian, Japanese etc.

5. A Representative of the Impersonal Class of Elegies

Gray's elegy is the best representative of the impersonal class of elegies. Here the poet doesn't lament at the death of a particular person; he mourns in a general manner for the lot of man. it mourns the death not of great or famous people, but of common men. The poet sees a country churchyard at sunset, which impels him to meditate on the nature of human mortality. He considers the fact that in death there is no difference between great and common people. He goes on to wonder if among the lowly people buried in the churchyard there had been any natural poets or politicians whose talent had simply never been discovered or nurtured. This thought leads him to praise the dead for the honest, simple lives that they lived.

Gray did not produce a great deal of poetry; the Elegy Written in a Country Churchyard however, has earned him a respected and a well-deserved spot in literary history. The poem was written at the end of the Augustan Age and at the beginning of the Romantic period, and the poem has characteristics associated with both literary periods. On the one hand, it has the ordered, balanced phrasing and rational sentiments of Neo-classical poetry. On the other hand, it tends toward the emotionalism and individualism of the Romantic poets; most importantly, it idealizes and elevates the common man. He provided a bridge between the Neo-classical style of his time and the Romantic era of John Keats.

6. Interest in the Life of Humble People

In this funeral elegy, Gray shows a keen interest in the life of humble people and village craftsmen. These poor, and insignificant people who lie in the churchyard, have in death, become equal to the most famous and prosperous men of all times: death comes to all men. He is able to express how all must die, and it does not matter if one is rich or poor, a noble or a commoner, or a poet or a politician. He is also able to elevate the common man with the elegy as a tool and his own freedom in the use of word power and poetic style. (Be, 2008)

There is little originality or novelty of thought or sentiment expressed in the Elegy. It expresses the feeling for the common man, which everybody has.

The poet's views about death as an inevitable fact of life are quite common. The presentation of the contrast between the destiny of the rich and the poor is based on conventional views. The thought about fame and obscurity, human ambition and pride are quite old too. The Elegy abounds in what Tennyson calls 'divine truisms that make us weep'. However, Gray has lent great force to these common thoughts and truisms through his unique expression and has done it so beautifully, that they have become universally appealing. The commonest man finds the Elegy echoing his own feelings and sentiments. The poem transcends the limits of time and place, and appeals to people everywhere and in all times.

7. An Elegy Written in a Country Churchyard: The Paths of Glory Lead But to the Grave

Gray's "Elegy" is one of the best-known poems about death in all of European literature. The poem presents the reflections of an observer, who passing by a churchyard out in the country, stops for a moment to think about the significance of the strangers buried there. Scholars of medieval times sometimes kept human skulls on their desktops, to keep themselves conscious of the fact that someday they, like the skulls' former occupants, would die; from this practice we get the phrase memento mori, which we say to this day to describe any token one uses to keep one's mortality in mind.

According to Douglas Bush "the Elegy is a mosaic of traditional motifs, classical and modern." The dominant theme of this poem is death. It deals with the death of the rude forefathers of the village, death as a common occurrence in the world and the anticipated death of humans which means a cessation of life's simple pleasures. The forefathers of the village are lying buried in the ordinary graves, beneath the rough alms and yew-trees. The graves are on the turf and very small. The ancestors of the villagers were buried long ago. Now they sleep forever in their decaying graves which look like heaps of earth only. Gray reflects not only on the untimely death of young people, but also on the death that comes after a normal life span. Gray talks of youth who might be the poet himself, or his friend West, in whose memory the poem has been written. In fact the shadow of death constantly hovers over the poem.

Gray's elegy begins with the creation of the late evening atmosphere of gloom and melancholy, suitable to an elegy. The poet sits alone in the country churchyard. The darkness is increasing all around and the cattle are returning home for rest. The bell has tolled, the curfew hour is on, indicating the end of day's business. The moping owl, the bird of ill-omen, hoots. The whole poem is filled with images and phrases of despair. The description of the rustic poet also gives a gloomy picture of his life. Thus the pall of death dominates the poem.

In the third stanza of the elegy the poet describes, "Save that from yonder ivy-mantled tower, the moping owl does to the moon complain," which demonstrates the night is approaching because owls come out in the darkness of night or death, it also signifies the wealthy people because of the mention of the 'ivy-mantled tower'. This undoubtedly and naturally demonstrates the death of the forefathers and the men being put to rest within their tombs. Also, the use of the term fore-fathers seems to indicate that these men were from various walks of life - farmers, politicians, fathers, from both classes, rich and poor.

The poet sees a country churchyard at sunset, which impels him to meditate on the nature of human mortality. The poem invokes the classical idea of memento mori (Memento Mori: The sun sets by the side of the churchyard, making the narrator to ponder over the ultimate fate and nature of human mortality. The narrator tries to bring out the fundamental difference between the great and common man when all lay side by side in their narrow cell. The idea is invoked from a Latin phrase memento mori which states to all mankind, "Remember you must die") (Essencz, 2013), a Latin phrase which states plainly to all mankind, "Remember that you must die." The speaker considers the fact that in death, there is no difference between the great and the common people. He goes on to wonder if among the lowly people buried in the churchyard, had there been any natural poets or politicians, whose talents had simply never been discovered or nurtured. This thought leads him to praise the dead for the honest, simple lives that they lived.

Then in the fourth stanza, Gray uses the churchyard scene to invoke important images: the strength of the elms, death as symbolized by the graves and the comfort provided by the yews giving shade to the bodies that sleep. The poet begins by reflecting on the death of the humble and the lower class.

Gray has the ability to demonstrate the individual and the emotional issues behind death and dying, and also to elevate the common man. In stanza five, he expresses how these forefathers will no longer be roused from their lowly beds by the breeze of the morning, the swallow twittering, or the cock echoing. They are dead and gone forever. He then highlights the fact that it does not matter if one is rich or poor. In stanza nine he writes:

> The boast of heraldry, the pomp of power
> And all that beauty, all that wealth e'er gave
> Awaits alike the inevitable hour.
> The paths of glory lead but to the grave.

These lines vividly portray the factual truth that death comes to all - the wealthy and the poor. Death doesn't make any distinctions between the high and low. It is an unavoidable event in everyman's life. Death waits even for those who are proud of their noble birth, wealth, social importance and beauty. So, proud and ambitious people should not hate these poor rustic people.

They lead simple lives which they spend in useful work. Death comes to all and so the poet concludes that all paths, however glorious, lead only to the grave.

He compares the activities of the rich. It is likely that they would treat with contempt the short and simple history of the poor. Gray asks them not to be proud of themselves because they were ambitious and had achievements to their credit. Despite all their richness, pomp, power and rank, all persons are to die one day. Death closes all. Gray tells them not to be proud of their big monuments over their graves, while the poor have no such things. The poet laments that it is not the mistakes of the poor that they did not have any such monuments over their grave yards. All monuments built in their honour and words spoken in their praise after their death cannot make them come back to life. Death levels every one and there are no distinctions in the grave yard.

Then in stanza eleven he queries, "Can storied urn or animated bust/Back to its mansion call the fleeting breath?" Even those that live in mansions, have wealth beyond what the poor can dream of, still die and fall to "the silent dust" as he states in line three. Similarly speeches in honour of the rich dead and the language of flattery cannot please the ears of the dead or restore them to life.

But nobody wants to leave this world as a prey to 'dumb forgetfulness .The poet expresses the dead man's nostalgic feeling for the world and his desire to be remembered and honoured after his death in stanzas twenty-two and twenty-three. Life is made up of both pleasure and pain, yet no one wants to die, no one has ever left the bright and happy enclosure of this world without casting one longing lingering look behind. Even the poor when they die wish to be remembered long after their death:

For who to dumb Forgetfulness a prey
This pleasing anxious being e'er resign'd,
Left the warm precincts of the cheerful day,
Nor cast one longing, ling'ring look behind?

From this elegy, we feel that every dying man desires some dear person to shed tears on his death in his memory with affection, and also desires to be remembered with love and sympathy after his death. Even in the ashes of the dead man, there are the sparks of a craving for love and sympathy of his fellow beings, which is natural in man. The poet describes the fate of himself and he says that now he is intent on honouring the obscure villagers who are dead, and after his death he himself would be buried in just such a humble place.

He mentions how he was quite an unknown person and did not earn any name or fame. He was by nature gloomy. But he had a kind heart and was sincere. He was sympathetic towards those who suffered. Hence he is sure that God would have sympathy for him. It is just possible that accidentally some poet, having feelings similar to his own and inspired by a meditative cast of mind, may happen to come to his grave, and enquire about his fate.

Thus death seems to have overpowered the poet while he was writing about the death of the rustic forefathers of the village and pointing out their desire to be remembered after death. Lyly Glazier believes "each rude forefather of the hamlet has become a type for mankind. There is thus a double for every man in the poem -- the poet observer who is every man still alive and reflecting about death, and each rude forefather, who is every man already dead and underground. They merge together later in the poem, when the poet suddenly projects himself into his own grave and from there reflects about his own hopeless desire for immortality."

At last, Gray points out both the advantages and disadvantages of death. If it deprives man of his chances to become great and renowned and do good to others, it also restrains him from acts involving cruelty, selfishness and violence. In a way, therefore, death is good for man.

8. An Elegy Written in a Country Churchyard: Sympathy for the Common Man –Representative of Sentimentalism

Carl J Webber remarks "Thomas Gray is the pioneer literary spokesman for the ordinary man, the patron saint of the unknown soldier.... Gray's rude forefathers were also the forefathers of Wordsworth's Wagoner, Michael and Peterbell."

Gray is the representative figure of sentimentalists. With a classical precision and polish, the poet shows a keen interest in the English countryside and a sincere feeling of the life of common people. Sentimentalism came into being as the result of a bitter discontent among the enlightened people with social reality. The sentimentalists continued to struggle against feudalism, but they sensed at the same time the contradictions in the process of capitalist development. Dissatisfied with reason, sentimentalists appealed to sentiment, to the human heart. They turned to the countryside for its material, and showed great sympathy for the poverty of village people.

The poem may be called an elegy on the premature death of the talents and energies of the poor. Another mark of Gray's originality is that instead of addressing it to the rich, great or privileged men, he addresses this poem about common man, to common men and seeks to elicit a sympathetic response for their common lot.

This Elegy is remarkable for its humanity and its concern for the lot of common human beings on this earth. It may be put alongside Keats's Ode to a Nightingale, which deals with the lot of man on this earth. Although it hints at the inevitability of the end of all human glory and the futility of power, wealth, ambition and pride, it is mainly concerned with the destiny of the common man and seems to lament the loss and waste of so much talent and energy of the poor because of lack of opportunity.

Some of the poor rustics might have become inspired poets or great rulers or statesmen, but poverty stood in the way of the development of their inborn powers. They had no opportunity of using the mental gift with which god might have endowed them. They are not in the position to enjoy the luxuries and happiness of life in the world their poverty proves an obstacle in the path of their progress. Yet the poet says this poverty is a blessing in disguise, because if it does not allow the people to rise higher, it also restrains them from doing evil, by limiting their power to do so. The rich, on other hand possess the power and means to do well to themselves and the world. But they also have the powers to commit mischief, and do bring destruction to innocent people.

Gray seriously thinks about poor or common people, so in stanza eight, he admonishes saying, let not ambitious people look down with contempt and ridicule upon their useful labours, their simple and homely joys, and humble lives of these villagers; let not people, who are great and majestic, hear with a contemptuous smile, the brief and simple life history of these poor people. According to him, all the pride and glory and power associated with beauty, pomp and wealth is transitory and awaits the final doom.

He advises the upper classes, those that are full of ambition, grandeur, power, nobility, and pride, exhorting them not to mock the poor for their simplicity, or for not having elaborated statues on their graveyard memorials. For the great men, after their burial, the loud and solemn sound of the song sung by the choir, in praise of the departed, raises high through long passage, and the arched ornamented ceiling of the church. The poor are born with the same natural abilities as members of the upper classes. The contrast between the rich and the poor, the great and the humble, is referred to in these stanzas. The difference between the rich and the poor is illusory, so far as death is concerned. Death is a great leveler:

Nor you, ye Proud, impute to These the fault,
If Memory o'er their Tomb no Trophies raise,
Where through the long-drawn aisle and fretted vault
The pealing anthem swells the note of praise

Gray thinks of the poor villagers who are lying buried. His heart is full of sympathy for them. He laments for the rustic who died un-honoured, unwept and unsung. The sentiment expressed is universal. He writes of the poor villagers and mankind in general. These rustic people when alive led a very simple life. They were not ambitious. They did not commit the crime which ambitious people commit in order to become rich, but in the end everything is reduced to dust.

However, if these poor people were restrained from becoming great and famous, and their powers of doing good were held in check, their capacity for harming others was also limited by their inability to do much in life. Their fate confined their crimes or forbade them to ascend the throne by violent methods or gaining any other advantage through cruel means. These people did not have to hide the truth or suppress feelings of shame, or foster luxury and pride through flattery.

In the same way, the poet presents a view about the overpowering of life by death, in stanza twelve, which makes any human achievement by the poor people impossible. The dead people buried in the churchyard had much potential for development. If chance had been given, they might have become great men, great politicians, and great poets. But these humble people never got the chance to open the vast book of knowledge which is full of the collective wisdom of the wise men of all ages. Cruel poverty chilled their enthusiasm and prevented their soul from finding expression in noble deeds and sentiments.

In spite of this, the poet compares the dead rustics of the village to the bright gems and pearls that lay hidden and unseen in the depths of ocean. They are akin to the beautiful flowers that bloom in the jungles, but fade away unseen and unrecognized and diffuse their sweet fragrance unnoticed and unenjoyed. Similarly, the humble villagers with great capacities died unknown in obscurity for want of suitable opportunity. The elements of comparison bring the divine love that Gray had for his village and for the people who lived there. Very few poetic compositions are able to touch the soul with a caliber of this range! Like in stanza thirteen:

Full many a gem of purest ray serene,
The dark unfathom'd caves of ocean bear:
Full many a flow'r is born to blush unseen,
And waste its sweetness on the desert air.

In the nineteenth stanza of the elegy, the poet describes the life led by the dead forefathers. According to him, they never tried to give up the quiet tenor of their life which was lived in aloofness from the maddening struggles of people in this world. They continuously enjoyed a peaceful course of life in the quite seclusion and peace. The poet thus points to the unambitious life of the poor as contrasted with the life of the rich and great, whose lives are usually full of ambitions, luxury and hectic activities. The poor never cherish high aspirations or ambition and do not hanker after fame and prosperity, because everybody is doomed to death. And, before death, all people are equal. There is no distinction of class in death.

The poet proceeds to think about the simple and poor persons who are buried in this grave yard. He is pained to think that they do not live any more. Their wives kept the fire burning for them and worked hard. When they used to return from their work in the evening, their children would run up to them, lisping their names and eager to have their kisses. They used to harvest the corn, plough the furrow, drive their team of oxen to the field and cut wood with strong axes. All these activities have come to an end for them now. No such happy event would happen anymore.

Gray expresses sympathy with the lot of the common people who lived far away from the madding crowd and spent their days in huts and cottages. He exhorts the proud and ambitious people not to laugh at the simple life and the obscure destiny of the poor. He tells them that they are much like the poor, since they also have to die one day and leave all their glory, wealth and luxuries in this world. The poem lays emphasis on the transitory state of all human glory and the emptiness of all boasts of power and wealth. It also points out the inevitability of death. Gray seems to impress upon us the idea that being poor is not altogether a matter of misfortune. The poor are fortunate in that they do not have to shut the gates of mercy on their fellow beings as the great men choose to do.

Thomas Gray's poem An Elegy Written in the Country Churchyard does not lament the death of a particular person, but feels for the lot of common man. It shows the critical situation of poor people and also the social and economic injustice happening in their lives. Gray very clearly expresses the fact and tells the living upper class people that ultimately it does not matter what glory they achieve, or how elaborate the eulogy upon their tombstones. Death is inevitable. It comes to all and at the end they will also die just like the poor.

It is not a record of personal loss, but is a collection of serious and painful reflections by the side of a village church-yard containing a number of decaying graves. His mourning is not for the famous, the wealthy or the powerful, but for the ordinary people buried in the churchyard. He wonders what they could have become and praises their simple and virtuous lifestyles. Dr. Samuel Johnson, who otherwise was a strong critic of Gray, said of this poem: "the churchyard abounds with images which find a mirror in every mind and with sentiments to which every bosom returns an echo". The poet's sympathy for the low and the downtrodden is clearly brought out in the poems Gray's "Elegy" isn't just about death, and it isn't just doom and gloom. It's about the fear of being forgotten after you're gone. Gray looks at the graves of common folks, and instead of just shrugging and figuring that their lives were not worth remembering, he takes the time to think about what made them tick. And apparently this poem hit a sympathetic chord within the eighteenth-century readers.

There is also a fact that through this poem Gray raised the voice of democratic sympathy much before the French or the American Revolution, aiming at the ideas of liberty, equality, and fraternity. He may be said to have inspired the democratic sentiments of Wordsworth who, much later, wrote about poor rustics like Michael, the leech gatherer and the wagoner. Gray often gets interpreted as a kind of turning point from the more formal poetry of the 18th century, with its emphasis on rich and famous people, to the more loose, free-form poetry of the Romantics, which focused more on everyday folks.

The later Romantic poet Percy Bysshe Shelley was an admirer of the poem and influenced by it, as was Thomas Hardy, who knew the poem by heart. At the end of the century, Matthew Arnold, in his 1881 collection of critical writings, said, "The Elegy pleased; it could not but please: but Gray's poetry, on the whole, astonished his contemporaries at first more than it pleased them; it was so unfamiliar, so unlike the sort of poetry in vogue." In 1882, Edmund Gosse analyzed the reception of Gray's poem: "It is curious to reflect upon the modest and careless mode in which that poem was first circulated which was destined to enjoy and to retain a higher reputation in literature than any other English poem perhaps than any other poem of the world written between Milton and Wordsworth." An anonymous review of Gray in the 12th December 1896 issue, the Academy claimed that "Gray's 'Elegy' and Goldsmith's 'Deserted Village' shine forth as the two human poems in a century of artifice." This elegy presents a faithful account of the human condition on this earth, and if that condition turns out to be gloomy, Gray is not to be blamed for this. To him goes the credit for pointing out not only the obscurity of life of the poor, but also their good luck in having escaped, through death, the acts of cruelty and violence that they might have committed had they lived longer.

An Elegy Written in a Country Churchyard moves from a meditation in a particular place upon the graves of the poor, to a reflection on the mortality of all humankind and on some of the benefits of being constrained by poverty. The poem alludes to the wish of all people not to die and to the ways in which each is remembered after death. Gray concludes by imagining his own death and how he hopes to be remembered. He finally concludes that he wants the same as the common, ordinary people he has written about.

Gray finished writing "Elegy Written in a Country Churchyard" in 1750 and published it in 1751. There is substantial amount of personal baggage behind the poem as the poet's mother, aunt and Richard West, had all died in the years it took Gray to finish the poem.

"Elegy" immediately catapulted the writer into the ranks of the most renowned poets of his age and many believe that Gray would be counted among the best of his time even if he had written nothing but the "Elegy". The poem was praised by almost all of his contemporaries. Samuel Johnson in the Lives of English Poets notes that the "Elegy" abounds 'with images which find a mirror in every mind, and with sentiments to which every bosom returns an echo.' Much later, Tennyson echoed him, applauding the poem for its "divine truisms that make us weep."

Gray was rather shy of publicity and did not like to attract attention to himself. One of the most well known anecdotes in this regard is Gray's refusal to take up the position of the poet laureate of England which was offered to him after the death of Colley Cibber (1671 -1757). The position was ultimately taken up by William Whitehead (1715-1785). His acute self consciousness about the possible reception of his works in the literary 'marketplace', among other factors, made him reluctant to publish his writing. It is not surprising to learn "Elegy Written in a Country Churchyard then that Gray would not have published the "Elegy" had the circumstances not forced him to do so. In February 1751, the publisher of the Magazine of Magazines wrote to Gray informing him that he had obtained a copy of the "Elegy" and that he was planning to publish it. In order to prevent the publication of this unauthorized version Gray requested Walpole to have the poem printed by Robert Dodsley (1704-1764). The "Elegy" was published anonymously on 15 February 1751 just before the Magazine's pirated version of it.

Gray was critical of the success that this work brought him. He believed that the acclaim he was receiving for his poem was only because it fit the current vogue for graveyard poetry. He had hoped that his later Pindaric Odes, "The Progress of Poesy" and "The Bard" would be able to surpass the success of the "Elegy". These lyrics were published by Walpole under his printing-press at Strawberry Hill, Twikenham but at best they received a mixed response. The Odes turned out to be far more sophisticated pieces than the readers were used to and it was with much discontent that Gray agreed to add footnotes to them in subsequent editions. In the light of these observations one can conclude that Gray's diffidence to publish is actually an assertive artistic move. It embodies his critique of the mercantile ethos which dominates the contemporary literary sphere. His active correspondence with friends reveals that he was never the hermit scholar that he is made out to be. He chose not to involve himself with a world where artistic merit was losing out to forces of commercialization.

In 1768 he returned to Cambridge as the professor of modern history. In his later years Gray spent most of his time as a solitary figure devoted to scholarly pursuits. He died in 1771 at the age of 55 years and was buried alongside his mother at St. Giles Churchyard at Stokes Poges, Buckinghamshire. This was the churchyard that is believed to have been the inspiration for the "Elegy".

The etymological origin of the word elegy can be traced back to the Greek 'elegeia' meaning lament. In classical literature, elegy or elegiacs simply meant poems written in the elegiac couplet (or distchs). They were used for a variety of subjects including love, war and beauty. For example, Ovid, or Publius Ovidius Naso (43 BC – AD 17/18), the celebrated poet of Augustan Rome, most well known for his Metamorphosis, wrote witty, amorous poetry exclusively in the elegiac couplet during the early phase of his career. These poems are: Amores, Heroides, Ars amatoria, and Remedia amoris. Elegies were written for, but not confined to, commemorative purposes. It is only from the sixteenth century onwards that they are limited to mournful verses written on the death of a dearly departed. Alfred Lord Tennyson's In Memoriam which he wrote on the death of his friend Hallum in 1849 is perhaps the most well known today. Other poets who wrote elegies include John Donne (1572-1631) (Elegy XIX: "To His Mistress Going to Bed"), John Milton (1608-1674) (Lycidas), and Edward Young (1683-1765) ("Night Thoughts"). Thus, when Gray decides to write an elegy he has a host of literary ancestors to contend with. It is not surprising to know then that the poem is brimming over with literary allusions. Gray touches various writers including Dante, Shakespeare and Milton, among a few. Suvir Kaul in his study of the poem calls it, "an echo-chamber of a poem" (279). These literary predecessors also end up being eulogized in the elegy. But Gray's innovation lies in his decision to not limit his elegy to any specific individual. His subjects are the various nameless/ faceless villagers who have succumbed to eternal obscurity: "Each in his narrow cell forever laid/The rude forefathers of the hamlet sleep" (15-16). This gives his lyric a universal scope, greater breadth and validates his meditative musings about the dilemma of human existence. The speaker understands that death is the greatest leveler of all, unlike fame and success, death does not discriminate between people based upon their material wealth. It embraces one and all and its effects will not be undone by even the mightiest: "Can storied urn or animated bust/ back to its mansion call the fleeting breath?"(41-42). The very first line of the poem: "The curfew tolls the knell of parting day" (1) uses the double image of the dying day (signaled by the curfew bells) and the death of another nameless villager (announced by the knell) to establish the inescapable pervasiveness of death. What makes Gray's poem unique is that despite his acceptance of death, including his own, he does not take recourse to exaggerated lugubriousness. He uses the knowledge of the frailty of human existence to reflect upon various issues such as life and death, social inequalities, poetry, and most importantly, memory and its limits.

"Elegy" is also sometimes seen as a part of what is known as the 'Graveyard School' of poetry of the eighteenth century. Its major proponents included Robert Blair (The Grave, 1743), and Edward Young ("Night Thoughts", 1742–45). This kind of poetry focused upon mournful ideas and drew the attention of its readers towards the brevity of life and the inevitability of death. These poems often also attempted to evoke the horror of death's physical manifestations. The earliest example of this kind of poetry is by Thomas Parnell in his Night-Piece on Death (1721). Although "Elegy" evokes similar ideas, it also transcends them.

ROLE OF MEMORY IN THE 'ELEGY"

As noted above, one of the central ideas in the poem is related to the role of memory and remembrance. Gray was the fifth of twelve children in his family but he was the only child who survived past childhood. Therefore the idea of preserving the memory of those who cannot speak for themselves might have been especially valuable for the poet. The unnamed speaker is intent on preserving the memory of the humble villagers whose narratives will otherwise be dropped from the annals of history: "...who to dumb Forgetfulness a prey," (85). Memory is the only way for ordinary mortals to achieve immortality and defeat the obscurity effected by time and death:

On some fond breast the parting soul relies,
Some pious drops the closing eye requires;
Ev'n from the tomb the voice of nature cries,
Ev'n in our ashes live their wonted fires. (89-92)

The desire to be remembered is common to all humans. This commemoration is achieved through the act of writing. Poetry is the most long lasting relic of remembrance and it enables the speaker to preserve the memory of the villagers. Its effect is better than that of any urn or bust or grave. Memory and memorials (such as the epitaph and "Elegy"), unlike wealth and power, can defeat death. As Howard D. Weinbrot puts it, 'the "Elegy" is not concerned with a choice of life and death, but a choice of eternity.' (538) But Gray doesn't stop at saving the villagers from oblivion, he wants the same for himself. His desire is that his name too be preserved in the memory of others, specifically- the inhabitants of the village as well as the travelers passing by in the future. The speaker in the poem is not just a disinterested observer after all. Hence, through the "Elegy" Gray achieves dual commemoration: the speaker immortalizes the villagers and the 'hoary-headed swain' reciprocates the gesture for the speaker.

Commemoration is crucial to the poem's structure, particularly given that the poem ends with an epitaph. However, his desire to be remembered is of a special kind. He wants also to be remembered as a poet. Thus, in a way remembrance is not evoked only for the humans but for the poem itself. Gray's use of meta-poetic elements in the "Elegy"- such as in the lines "Dost in these lines their artless tale relate" (85) - should be considered in this regard. This self reflexive exercise is a testimony of Gray's poetic skill, but it also belies the anxiety of a poet uncertain about the reception and survival of his poems, and the difficulty of finding ideological kinship with readers in an increasingly commercialized literary market. The multiple points of focus create a tension with the poem which is belied by its tone of melancholic preponderance.

PORTRAYAL OF THE VILLAGERS

The speaker identifies himself with the rustics. The poet's claim that he can/

does empathize with the modest villagers is what gives his speech legitimacy. He presents himself as an outsider to the world of fame and fortune, the city. In the eighteenth century London had become the centre of all literary, scientific and intellectual activity. There was an unprecedented migration towards cities which were rapidly developing as centers of commerce. The distancing of the speaker from the city is an important stance. It is a move as much physical as it is ideological. Sensibility in "Elegy" affords the speaker and those like him an alternative world order where 'ambition' and 'glory' do not reign supreme. The poet's sympathy aligns him with the lot of the villagers and bolsters his critique of the city life and its ethos. For the readers of the "Elegy", especially contemporary readers, their ability to sympathize with the marginalized made them feel distinct from and superior to, others around them. This sense of a shared bond of finer/nobler emotions between poets and the readers of the literature of Sensibility was important. Therefore, although the idea of Sensibility is based upon an inclusive ideal of communal living it could also at times become exclusive and exclusionary. However the speaker's identification with the villagers is by no means absolute. On a closer look one realizes that his attitude towards the villagers is ambivalent.

In the "Elegy", the villagers are the subject of the poetic gaze. The speaker is like an elevated observer. When the poem begins the poet's panoramic eye is seen assessing the landscape as well as its inhabitants. This objectification of the villagers is problematic. He identifies himself with the villagers but it is obvious that he acts as the spokesperson for them. The villagers have no agency, the only villager who has speech in the poem is meant to ultimately talk about the poetic persona. The use of words like 'mute', 'rude', 'unlettered' and 'noiseless' in association with the villagers points towards the fact that he after all has the greater knowledge and poetic authority. The speaker articulates his concern for the impoverished state and thwarted potential of the villagers but it never quite reaches its logical end – the critique of power relations in society. Poetic sympathy is not bolstered by condemnation of the power relations which results in the unequal distribution of wealth in society. Questions have always been raised about the authenticity of the sympathetic impulse driving the cult of sensibility. Does this sympathy translate into concrete action for the emancipation of the downtrodden? Keith's observation sums up the objections to this aspect of the sensibility 'Part of what has been seen to corrupt the literature of sensibility is the way it directs the reader to gaze upon, and therefore objectify, the sufferer. Robert Markley describes this phenomenon as the "theatrics of virtue," where readers, characters, speakers, or audiences gaze on scenes of another's suffering, participating in a submerged sadism' ("Poetry, Sentiment and sensibility" 127). Also the relation between the villagers and the speaker in "Elegy" is not as straightforward as it might seem on the surface. The speaker's sympathy is tempered by the suggestion that the innocence and goodness of the villagers is intact because they are untouched by the lure of lucre. Rather than any sense of inherent morality their virtue is a result of ignorance. The poem is, as if, a double edged sword. Moments such as these force us to see "Elegy" as more than a poem about softer emotions of sympathy and sensibility. It prevents us from settling too comfortably in any certainty about the meaning of the poem.

MELANCHOLY

Melancholy had become one of the ideas central to the process of poetic creation in the eighteenth century. Many works were written about and around it and it was also the subject of much debate. Such was the pervasiveness of melancholy that some even believed it to have become the national ailment of the time. However, melancholy as the poet talks about it in "Elegy" can also be seen as a positive value, a necessary precondition for the poetic process as it spurs him towards reflection. This form of melancholy was seen in earlier works especially Miltons' Il Penseroso. It is both a positive emotion in so far as it propels him to feel for his fellowmen, but at the same time it also leads to his isolation from those around him. The speaker is an inside-outsider even in the village community. He does not completely belong anywhere, although the degree of alienation from the city dwellers and the rustics varies. Through him we know about others but we are never directly told about his inner feelings or psychological turmoil. Gray's letters reveal that he believed himself to be suffering from 'white melancholy'. The epitaph's inscription 'And Melancholy marked him for her own,' is true for both the speaker persona and the poet Gray himself. For Gray melancholy was not only a form of poetic self fashioning but a lived reality. Gray lived a secluded, solitary life in Cambridge, choosing to not associate with the hustle of the city life.

Gray's reticence to publish ('unmanly timidity' as some have put it) his works including the "Elegy" is not simply because of his retiring disposition. Critics like Linda Zionkowski have traced it back to material reasons such as the changes taking place in the print industry. Ever since the Licensing Act expired in 1695 the face of the print industry changed drastically. No longer were works screened before publication, there was greater freedom for writers with checks limited to post publication charges of libel. With a new class of both writers and readers entering the market the older notions about the classicism of literary works were eroded. Every work that was published could be 'bought' and dissected by any number of readers all of whom had varying degrees of expertise and education. According to Gray, even the aristocracy was at fault for the current degradation of literature because they had abnegated their responsibility of promoting arts and protecting writers by acting as patrons. It is this collective failure which gives birth to Gray's disillusionment and skepticism. In his correspondences Gray disdains this mercantile attitude, 'I promised him [Dodsley] an equal weight of poetry and prose: so since my return hither, I put up about two ounces of stuff.' ("Bridging the Gulf" 331-32) In other words Gray' unwillingness to associate with the public word is a personal form of critical distancing that he adopts. Personally, he preferred to write for an intimate audience of friends. Many of his works circulated in manuscript form or through letters where he was certain that the audience reading his works would be discerning and sophisticated. Hence, the alienated speaker of the "Elegy" can be read in terms of Gray's reluctance to associate himself with the market mechanism, 'the "Elegy" mystifies this alienation, transforming it from an aspect of commodified print to a feature of the sensitive poet's temperament' ("Bridging the Gulf" 340). In another essay titled "Gray, the Marketplace" Zionkowski notes how the changes in the print culture were accompanied with changes in the way the writer was perceived by the public, 'critics and writers ...frequently began to associate masculinity and cultural power with commercial success, while characterizing poet's detachment from the market as infantile, or effeminate, dependence upon others' ("Gray, the Marketplace"592). Thus Gray received mixed response from contemporary readers and writers due to his reluctance to publish his works. More than once he was regarded as 'timid' or effeminate.

Gray wrote two versions of the "Elegy". The first one was completed in 1746 (now known as the Eton manuscript) but it was not published. It is the second version, finished in 1750 that we know about today. In this version Gray brings in the very powerful image of the epitaph which also functions as a turning point in the poem. The epitaph is important not just as a memorial of the dead but it also becomes the literary device through which the reader's response to the speaker persona is manipulated ('soul sincere'). We form our opinion of the speaker based on what we read we read about him in the epitaph.

Therefore, the "Elegy" is a far more self conscious piece than any simplistic reading of it as a poem of sensibility would suggest. Its rich inter textual allusions, moral truisms and auditory images are part of a very self conscious poet's craft. All its tensions and paradoxes must be taken into account to fully appreciate it as a work of art.

STRUCTURE OF THE 'ELEGY'

Thomas Gray's Elegy Written in a Country Churchyard makes readers ponder about what truly happens after they die. Will they be remembered by loved ones with smiles and tears of joy? Or detested by all of mankind? Gray's poem uses a simple four line stanza mixed with an ABAB rhyming pattern, placing stress on a template of certain syllables to allude to the dark capacity of human nature mixed with the potential to do good deeds. Alongside this rhyming pattern, Gray uses heavy symbolism from the literal environment to emphasize a complex idea of death and mortality, while also using comparisons to real life objects that are simple to understand. Finally, the simple word choice, capitalization, and personification of Death — and other emotions — are used to both simplify and simultaneously add depth to the meaning of each word.

Elegy Written in a Country Churchyard uses a simple, yet effective, ABAB rhyming pattern in four line stanzas. The simplicity of this pattern is ironic when contrasted with the deep meaning of the poem. As with most poems, there is a more complex substructure with stresses on certain syllables on every line. This stressing pattern can be seen very prominently: "The struggling pangs of conscious truth to hide, / To quench the blushes of ingenuous shame," (Gray lines 69-70). There are light tongued words at the start of every line such as 'to', 'the', and 'if'. Yet the start of the second word is always a heavy mouthed sound using letters that use a heavier tongue and the back of the throat to pronounce. The stresses on the words are in an alternating pattern between softly mouthed sounds. Gray uses this mixture of light and heavy syllables to emphasize the light and darkness every human being possesses.

The lighter syllables make the tongue come forward, closer to the exit of the mouth. This action shows that on the outside every person is trying to be praiseworthy and put on a fabricated, lighthearted smile — a smile that is made when the word 'the' is mouthed. The heavier words can only be made using the lungs like a 'guh' sound, a noise that can only be made using an internal body part. With this steady and relentless pattern found throughout the entire poem, Thomas Gray ironically adds structure while continuing to address the darkness found inside all human beings.

Gray uses the environment within the poem to conjure up a serene landscape that is starting to change into a darker, ghostly terrain. He does this to show how the very base of humanity can quickly morph into darkness. This begins almost at the very beginning of the poem: "Now fade the glimmering landscape on the sight, / And all the air a solemn stillness holds" (Lines 5-6). The very earth that the speaker is standing on is quickly blackened as the sun sets, symbolizing the very core pillars of mankind growing dark. In addition, within the poem, comparisons are made to simple images that represent deep complex emotions:

Full many a gem of purest ray serene
The dark unfathomed caves of ocean bear:
Full many a flower is born to blush unseen,
And waste its sweetness on the desert air. (Lines 53-56).

By making these simple comparisons, Gray is sayinging that internal darkness is on the ground floor of the physiological hierarchy. The meaning of the comparison above is that many people have the potential inside themselves to benefit humanity in the best of ways, yet never get a chance due to the "unfathomed caves of ocean bear" (54).

Finally, Gray personifies the emotions by capitalizing them. This simple technique is used to bring that idea of darkness to life within the reader's mind. With line 36, "The paths of glory lead but to the grave," this gives an overarching structure and warning within the poem. Every emotion that is personified and capitalized can be traced to a need for glory, such as Honour, Knowledge, and Pride, for this simplicity allows for a clearer warning to be given. The diction allows readers to comprehend the fear of darkness that is found within everyone:

Can storied urn or animated bust
Back to its mansion call the fleeting breath?
Can Honour's voice provoke the silent dust,

Or Flattery soothe the dull cold ear of Death? (Lines 41-44)

No matter what social class a person is, no amount of honor, pride, or flattery can convince Death to spare a life. This stanza completely disintegrates all social, monetary, and rank boundaries.

This poem's message is a warning that darkness is within every single person regardless of status, yet this darkness has only as much power as a person allows it. Each person has the power to change humanity for the best or worse depending on their desires.

Neo-classic and romantic characteristics of 'Elegy Written in a Country Churchyard

Elegy Written in a Country Churchyard', one of the five most famous elegies in English literature, is written by Thomas Gray who was the poet of the transitional period between Neo-classic and Romantic. For this reason, he was influenced by both the literary ideals of these periods. In this poem, we see that he follows some of the characteristics from each of romanticism and neo-classicism. At the side of use and presentation of language, he, we can consider, maintains the neo-classic ideals, and at the side of theme and setting, it is romantic. So, this elegy is very important in both theme and style, out of the most famous elegies. Now, we will see how Gray has mingled both the characteristics.

At first we will discuss the neo-classic characteristics of the poem:

The language and the poets emotion in the period are restrained in various literary rules. The neo-classic writers are attentive to make their work perfect-perfection of style is their belief to write poetry. In 'Elegy Written in a Country Churchyard', the whole poem of 128 lines falls into 32 stanzas. Each stanza contains the same style – each of the line is iambic pentameter. Again, his emotion is also restrained in each stanza.

In neo-classical literature, personification is frequently seen. In the same way, we, in this poem, see that Gray uses many abstract words like the living persons, and often places them as the subjects of the verbs. There is a capital letter at first of each of them. For instances- Ambition, Grandeur, Memory, Honour, Flattery, Knowledge, Penury, Luxury Pride, Muse, Forgetfulness, Nature, Ashes, Youth, Fortune, Fame, Science, Melancholy and Misery. We can mention the first stanza of the poem epitaph –

Here rests his head upon the lap of Earth
A Youth to Fortune and to Fame unknown.
Fair Science frowned not on his humble birth,
And Melancholy marked him for her own.

Or,

Can Honour's voice provoke the silent dust
Or Flatting sooth the dull could ear of death?

Addressing by apostrophe is another technique of neo-classic literature. In this poem; we also see apostrophe-

Nor you, ye proud impute to these the fault............

Or.

For thee, who, mindful of the unhonoured dead......

Or,

Approach and read (for thou canst read) the lay....

Moralizing is very common in neo-classism. In this poem, the poet moralizes that: the rich city people should not mock at the poor village people and should not be proud of their high birth and position, beauty and wealth, because the ultimate fate of every man is same. All have to go to the grave. The most famous line of the poem is 'The paths of glory lead but to the grave' Harmony is maintained in neo-classic literature. This elegy is circular to the poets himself- he begins with his own self and ends with his own epitaph-but contains other things also- the poor forefathers of the village, contrasting with the rich city people- so this poem is a symbol of complete harmony.

Now, we will discuss about the romantic elements of the poem:

At first, subjectivity is the most important element in romantic literature. In the same way, we see that the poet ends the first stanza- begins the poem-with the subjective word 'me'-

'And leaves the world to darkness and to me'

Again, he ends this poem with his own epitaph that will, in future, be read beside his grave. So this poem is circular from/with subjectively to subjectivity.

The main theme of the poem is death we can consider to be the romantic element. Here, at the first stanza, the 'parting day'(evening) and the 'darkness' are the symbols of the death. Then the poet mentions about death of the forefathers of the village, and at last the thought of his own death.

Nature is the vital element of romanticism. In this poem, from beginning to end, the poet's description possesses nature. Then, village is the symbol of nature, and he shows the superiority of the village and villagers. Moreover, his most of the imageries are taken from nature. For example,

The lowing herd wind slowly over the lea
The plowman home ward plods his weary way

Besides, there are owl's complaint, twittering of swallow, loud and shrill crowing of cock, the echoing horn of the hunt man and so on. Here one thing can be mentioned that in neo-classic literature nature was almost absent. For instances, in the 'Rape of the Lock' written by pope, representative of the age, nature was absolutely absent.

Again, the poet is standing in such an atmosphere where silence and loneliness that are the romantic elements exists.

From beginning to the end, the mode of the poem is melancholic which is also a romantic characteristic. Even, Gray uses some symbols of melancholy, such as- 'elm tree', and 'yew-tree'.

In fine, it can be said that, Thomas Gray very brilliantly mixes both the neo-classic and romantic characteristics in this poem. Though it is essentially a subjective work, it has a universal appeal to the readers. Because, the main theme of the poem is such a thing that must come in every man's life. Besides, every man wants to be remembered after his of her death. For this reason, this elegy is important and different from other famous elegies.

Meditation on Death:

Gray's "Elegy" is one of the best-known poems about death in all of European literature. The poem presents the reflections of an observer who, passing by a churchyard that is out in the country, stops for a moment to think about the significance of the strangers buried there. Scholars of medieval times sometimes kept human skulls on their desktops, to keep themselves conscious of the fact that someday they, like the skulls' former occupants, would die: from this practice we get the phrase memento mori, which we say to this day to describe any token one uses to keep one's mortality in mind. In this poem, the graveyard acts as a memento mori, reminding the narrator to not place too much value on this life because someday he too will be dead and buried. The speaker of the poem is surrounded by the idea of death, and throughout the first seven stanzas there are numerous images pointing out the contrast between death and life. After mentioning the churchyard in the title, which establishes the theme of mortality, the poem itself begins with images of gloom and finality. The darkness at the end of the day, the forlorn moan of lowing cattle, the stillness of the air (highlighted by the beetle's stilted motion) and the owl's nocturnal hooting all serve to set a background for this serious meditation. However, it is not until the fourth stanza that the poem actually begins to deal with the cemetery, mentioned as the place where the village forefathers "sleep." In the following stanzas, the speaker tries to imagine what the lives of these simple men might have been like, touching upon their relations with their wives, children, and the soil that they worked. They are not defined by their possessions, because they had few, and instead are defined by their actions, which serves to contrast their lives with their quiet existence in the graveyard. This "Elegy" presents the dead in the best light: their families adored them and they were cheerful in their work, as they "hummed the woods beneath their steady stroke." The speaker openly admits that they are spoken of so well precisely because they are dead, because death is such a terrible thing that its victims deserve the respect of the living. In line 90, the poet explains, "Some pious drops the closing eye requires," explaining that the living should show their respect for death with their sorrow.

The "Elegy Written in a Country Churchyard" can be read as a journey of recognition, conceived in dusk and worked out—not in a miasma of depression—but in the light of a symbolic self-destruction. The poem contains a drama of identification with the buried farmers of the village of Stoke Poges; however, this identification yields the poet a brief delivery from his rather narrow life. Moreover, the development of the poem has a quasi-heroic quality, for it grows out of a shorter early version that is a more emotionally distanced study of man's final destiny. When Thomas Gray returned to the Eton manuscript of the "Elegy," he filled the new ending with far more intimate feelings.

The poem opens with the speaker's evocation of the world immediately around the graveyard; it then focuses on a plowman, who "homeward plods his weary way." As if at home in the oncoming darkness, Gray clearly includes himself in the poem in stanzas that are full of a mournful music; suddenly, the verbs take on an almost independent energy: the turf "heaves" as the poet observes the graves as "many a mould'ring heap." As will be later developed, this heaving of the earth suggests a kind of life within.

A series of vital images follows as if the quiet, celibate scholar perceived the farmers' lives in moments of dreamy wistfulness. In spite of the need to point out that the cheerful aspects of the laborers' mornings exist for them no more, the speaker describes elements of dawn: "breezy," "twitt'ring," "the cock's shrill clarion." There follows a series of pictures of a very different end of day than Thomas Gray could know: the "blazing hearth," the "busy houswife," children, and their climbing of the farmer's knees. Finally, stanza seven depicts the farmer's daily life:

Oft did the harvest to their sickle yield,
Their furrow oft the stubborn glebe has broke;
How jocund did they drive their team afield!
How bow'd the woods beneath their sturdy stroke!

These verbs evidence virile strength; they portray a celebration of physical power in that stroke that bows the woods. This may have been merely an idealization of everyday life, but it does touch on what could have been a psychological problem for Gray; it evokes the pride that rises from earning one's own way.

Gray's fellowship at Cambridge gave him a life-long tenure for a somewhat elegant—if narrow—scholarly existence. He was never required to teach and never delivered a lecture. Clarence Tracy asserts that Gray "lived for years on public patronage" and goes on to say that "his friend, Mason, made it a virtue in him that he never dirtied his mind with any intention of earning his living." Tracy also quotes Mason as saying his "life was spent in that kind of learned leisure, which has only self-improvement and self-gratification for its object."

Gray's biographer, Ketton-Cremer, suggests, "the man of reading and reflection often feels an envious admiration for the man of physical skill." However, Gray modulates any such response into an identification—as well as a defense of the farmers against the putative disdain of the upper classes. When he honors the simple graves of the poor, he points out that the "storied urn" and "animated bust" of the aristocrat cannot bring back the dead, as if in an urgent exhortation of the prosperous— or that side of Thomas Gray that has enjoyed a life of leisure.

Gray goes on to suggest the possibility that here may lie "some heart once pregnant with celestial fire," but "chill Penury repress'd their noble range" because they lacked the good fortune of having an education. The farmers, then, were left in pastoral innocence like the famous flower "born to blush unseen." The poem is now near its first ending, which is preserved only in the Eton manuscript of Gray's "Elegy." Here, perhaps somewhat self-consciously, Gray implies that learning, worldly power, and leisure could do little but corrupt:

The thoughtless World to Majesty may bow
Exalt the brave, & idolize Success
But more to Innocence their Safety owe
Than Power & Genius e'er conspired to bless
And thou, who mindful of the unhonour'd Dead
Dost in these Notes their artless Tale relate
By Night & lonely Contemplation led
To linger in the gloomy Walks of Fate
Hark how the sacred Calm, that broods around
Bids ev'ry fierce tumultuous Passion cease
still small Accents whisp'ring from the Ground
A grateful Earnest of eternal Peace
No more with Reason & thyself at Strife;
Give anxious Cares & endless Wishes room
But thro' the cool sequester'd Vale of Life
Pursue the silent Tenour of thy Doom.

"As the swain describes it, Gray's Romantic crisis becomes a self-immolation, a brief escape from his life, for he has moved on to a fearful insight: it is as if Gray and the deceased farmers share a complex species of mortality where the vital dead are more alive than the living speaker feels he is."

A close look at Starr and Hendrickson's rendition of the sixth line of the Eton manuscript excerpt shows an alteration to the word "their" from the original "thy." Of course, this "thy" might have been meant only to refer to the narrator of the poem as he possessed the poem—but it may very well have indicated a deeper involvement as if Gray were briefly identifying with the dead in a melancholic assessment of what his life had become.

The moment of ambiguity between whether "thy" referred only to the tale or to the life of the narrator is resolved when Gray struck out "thy" and rewrote "their," for the line now seems to concern no one except the dead farmers. However, the brief scratchings remain to suggest that the "Elegy" was for his own existence and that he had briefly included himself among the dead.

When he was much younger, Gray had written a four-line Latin fragment, "O lachrymarum Fons—O fountain of tears." Starr and Hendrick-son's translation is: "O fountain of tears which have their sacred sources in the sensitive soul! Four times blessed he who has felt thee, holy Nymph, bubbling up from depths of his heart." This is a moving evocation of the ability to feel as if reaching out to the self's own source of tears; moreover, it suggests an earlier psychological breakthrough in response to depression. While Ian Jack asserts that Gray dropped the original four-stanza ending of his "Elegy" because "it preached a Stoic attitude to life that he could not accept," it is as likely a conjecture that the new ending was yet another breakthrough in understanding for Gray, since it formed an escape from the depressing aspects of merely pursuing what he called "the silent Tenour of thy Doom" (Eton ms. 88).

R. W. Ketton-Cremer has demonstrated Gray's depression; it seems likely to infer an etiology of that condition in "his father's brutality to his mother" and in Gray's subsequent dependence on his mother. David Cecil points out "by the easygoing University regulations of those days he could go on residing in the college free, for as long as he wanted." Cecil also quotes one early letter to a friend saying, "When you have seen one of my days, you have seen a whole year of my life. They go round and round like a blind horse in the mill, only he has the satisfaction of fancying he makes progress, and gets some ground: my eyes are open enough to see the same dull prospect, and having made four and twenty steps more, I shall now be just where I was."

When Gray took up the Eton manuscript to write the ending with which readers are familiar, the farmers are the ones who keep to the "sequester'd vale of life"—and keep "the noiseless tenor of their way." This last word, "way," is, of course, a significant change from Gray's term for himself in the earlier version: "of thy doom" (Eton ms. 88). Moreover, his new understanding is accompanied by a second major surge of energy:

Far from the madding crowd's ignoble strife,
Their sober wishes never learn'd to stray;
Along the cool sequester'd vale of life
They kept the noiseless tenor of their way.

Later, Gray united himself with the farmers and all mankind in tremendously original lines:

For who to dumb Forgetfulness a prey,
This pleasing anxious being e'er resign'd,
Left the warm precincts of the chearful day,
Nor cast one longing ling'ring look behind?
On some fond breast the parting soul relies,
Some pious drops the closing eye requires;
Ev'n from the tomb the voice of Nature cries,
Ev'n in our Ashes live their wonted Fires.

Dr. Johnson said of the two stanzas that contain the ashes line, "I have never seen the notions in any other place; yet he that reads them here, persuades himself that he has always felt them" (Ketton-Cremer). The poet means to suggest that life is still speaking from the buried ashes—yet whose ashes are these? They are those of the safe dead, yet they also form a melancholic, personal estimation of the poet—alive but in the ashes of an entombed self.

When Gray asserts, "Ev'n from the tomb the voice of Nature cries," he must feel the strength of a tremendous moment of human projection; his living soul is speaking for the abstraction, Nature. Then, the idea is reinforced with, "Ev'n in our Ashes live their wonted Fires." In the "our" of this line, Gray achieves a kind of emotional closure and becomes more nearly one with the ironically vital dead.

Perhaps it is at this exact moment of desperate recognition that he becomes "the central figure of the poem and occupies that place until the end" (Ketton-Cremer). At any rate, in the next line, Gray speaks of "thee," who relates these lines. Of course, the "me" of the beginning of the poem and the "thee" here are the same being, for

Gray suddenly distances his spirit from his everyday self. Moreover, this objectification of the soul is Gray's chance to take the whole journey of imagination— and the poem becomes his elegy, "his storied urn" as Cleanth Brooks suggests.

Gray then invokes a "hoary-headed Swain" who would by chance ("haply") describe the poem's speaker, now depicted as a rather romantic youth, who is seen as pale and wandering, possibly "craz'd with care, or cross'd in hopeless love." Frank Brady suggests that "the swain's description of the narrator" shows that the narrator's "life is apparently unproductive and unfulfilled." Then, the Swain is to tell the reader, who is suddenly referred to as a "kindred Spirit," that the narrator is dead! He then invites the reader to read the narrator's epitaph, where an offering of the soul to God is recorded. We must understand that Gray— as narrator—has imaginatively entered the local society and has been long known to the swain, who is the second living farmer in the poem. In fact, he is the older parallel of the earlier rustic who "homeward plods his weary way." That previous figure may have given Gray the first intimation of the farmer's warm reception at home as this imaginary swain yields Gray his escape from mere static contemplation.

The poet has now managed to stage a symbolic death so that his epitaph can be read in the churchyard. It is an unusual conception that allows Gray to break through the natural terror of dying in order to forge a relationship between a fear of death and an acceptance of that death. As the swain describes it, Gray's Romantic crisis becomes a self-immolation, a brief escape from his life, for he has moved on to a fearful insight: it is as if Gray and the deceased farmers share a complex species of mortality where the vital dead are more alive than the living speaker feels he is. Their very ashes contain a fire of life that the speaker senses he is missing, and, thus, they are the object of his sympathetic projection.

Perhaps Gray's personal sense of a buried life can be best approached from the end of the epitaph in which we are earlier told that "Melancholy mark'd him for her own":

> No farther seek his merits to disclose,
> Or draw his frailties from their dread abode,
> (There they alike in trembling hope repose)
> The bosom of his Father and his God.

His frailties are undefined, but they are seen as existing along with his merits in a trembling condition lodged in "the bosom of his Father and his God." It is a strange view of eternal love that reposes the deceased one's attributes only in trembling hope—forever. Indeed, it is depressing, for it pictures God as a stern, judgmental father who holds this split youth (merits and frailties) in eternal abeyance like a bird in winter.

Gray's "Elegy," then, is as much about depression as it is about other species of entombments. Moreover, three years before his death in 1771, in the "Ode for Music," Gray once again referred to melancholy:

> Oft at the blush of dawn
> I trod your level lawn,

Oft woo'd the gleam of Cynthia silver-bright
In cloisters dim, far from the haunts of Folly,
With Freedom by my Side, and soft-ey'd
Melancholy.

Ketton-Cremer suggests that the lines reflect Gray's life at Cambridge "remotely but unmistakably."

However, the "Elegy" works because of the exquisite beauty of its language and the psychic complicity of the minds of readers with that of Thomas Gray. Our guide has disappeared; however, that is not an idiosyncratic moment of desertion but a great release of the imagination. Nevertheless, the vitality we project to the farmers and the buried speaker, is, of course, our own. Moreover, the poem serves as Gray's self-wrought myth, where life's verve is celebrated, a descent into the earth is recorded, yet a resurrection is shown. In fact, the "Elegy" presents the reader with the "moment of awareness, the essential substance of myth" (Aldus). Therefore, readers return to the poem to take a journey underground while still in "this pleasing anxious being." However, the "Elegy"'s exchange for our energy is a delight which turns us back to the world as we depart the poem's mimetic twilight with our own "wonted fires."

Short Answer Type Questions with Answers

Q. 1. What is an elegy?

Ans. An elegy is a poem lamentation. It is a lament on a dead person or on the general misery of men.

Q. 2. What type of Elegy is Gray's elegy?

Ans. gray's *Elegy Written in a Country Church-yard* is a general lament on the sad condition of the poor people of the village.

Q. 3. What is the occasion of the lament of the poet in the poem?

Ans. The poet stands in the church-yard and thinks of the poor vellagers buried in the church-yard.

Q. 4. What is meant by curfew? To what the curfew is compared?

Ans. The curfew means the evening bell. Curfew is compared to the knell.

Q. 5 "The curfew tolls the knell of the parting day". - Explain the comparison suggested in the line.

Ans. The curfew (Evening bell) is compared to knell which is sounded in the church when a man is dead. The curfew rings to announce the parting day. Dying man is compared to the parting day.

Q. 6. What id meant by "Lowing herd"?

Ans. *Lowing herd* means a group of sheep crying (bleating) as they go.

Q. 7. "The lowing herd wind slowly over the lea". - What is the picture contain in line?

Ans. The group of sheep returning home in the evening through a zig-zag path in the meadow. As they move forward, they make deep sound (mooning) through their nostrils.

Q. 8. How does the ploughman return home in the evening?

Ans. The ploughman is weary and he walks slowly and heavily - A tired ploughman returns home in the evening after day's labour.

Q. 9. What is meant by 'weary way'?

Ans. 'Weary way' means weary man going slowly on the way. It is a case of transferred epithet.

Q. 10. "Now fades the glimmering landscape" - What landscape is suggested? What is meant by 'glimmering'?

Ans. The evening landscape is suggested. 'Glimmering' means faintly lighted.

Q. 11. What disturbs the silence of the evening?

Ans. The silence of the evening is broken by the beetle that hums as it flies and the tinkling of the bells attached to the sheep heard from the folds.

Q. 12. What are the insects and birds of the evening mentioned by the poet?

Ans. The poet mentions beetle humming and the owl moping (unhappy because of loneliness).

Q. 13. What does the owl complain to the moon?

Ans. The owl complains to the moon because the moonrays disturb her solitary place.

Q. 14. "The rude forefathers of the hamlet." - What is meant by 'rude' and 'forefathers'?

Ans. 'Rude' means simple. 'Forefathers' mean ancestors of the men of the small village.

Q. 15. Whom and what does the poet think when he stands in the church-yard in the evening?

Ans. The poet thinks of the ancestors of the poor villagers who are buried in the church-yard. He thinks how poverty checked all their possibilities and promises.

Q. 16. What roused the poor villagers from sleep when they were alive?

Ans. When the poor villagers were alive, they used to rise from beds by the fragrant breeze of the morning, by the twittering of the swallows, by the cock's crow and the hunter's blowing of horn.

Q. 17. Where are the graves of the poor forefathers of the village laid?

Ans. The graves of the poor forefathers of the village are hid under the elm and yew trees outside the church (in the church-yard).

Q. 18. What kind of monument is erected over their graves?

Ans. Heaps of turfs which are crumbling are raised over their graves. These serve as the memorials.

Q. 19. What is meant by 'narrow cell'?

Ans. 'Narrow cell' means small grave for the dead villagers.

Q. 20. "For them no more the blazing hearth shall burn." - What is meant by 'blazing hearth'?

Ans. Blazing hearth means burning fireplace in the evening which is cold.

Q. 21. How were the poor villagers received at home when they returned from work in the evening?

Ans. The fireplace burned for them, the busy housewives plied their householdwork and children ran to them to welcome them with indistinct words and to share the kisses of their fathers.

Q. 22. What is meant by 'lisp'? Who lisped and why?

Ans. 'Lisp' means speak indistinctly. Children lisped to welcome their father's return and express joy.

Q. 23. What is the work of the villagers?

Ans. The villagers produce harvest by tilling the lands; they drive the cattle across the fields joyfully and cut down trees with strong blows.

Q. 24. What is meant by 'stubborn glebe'?

Ans. 'Subborn glebe' means the field which is hard to till. *Glebe* means field.

Q. 25. What are the qualities of villagers indicated by the poet?

Ans. The vllgers are hardy, strong and laborious.

Q. 26. How do the villagers live their lives?

Ans. The villagers are simple, joyful. They do useful work but they live unknown by others.

Q. 27. What is meant by the short and simple annals of the poor?

Ans. The poet means the short and simple lives of the poor. They lived humble, unassuming lives in obscure corners of the village but they were happy.

Q. 28. Whom does the poet ask not to mock the simple life of the poor villagers?

Ans. The poet asks the ambitions and the luxurious not to mock the humble life of the poor villagers.

Q. 29. 'Awaits alike the inevitable hour." - What is the meaning of 'inevitable hour'? What is the nominative of the verb 'awaits'?

Ans. 'Inevitable hour' means death. 'Inevitable' hour is the nominative and 'awaits' is the verb. (Inevitable hour awaits...)

Q. 30. Whom does the inevitable hour await?

Ans. The evitable hour awaits those who are proud of ancestry, of beauty, of wealth and of the poor villagers alike.

Q. 31. What is meant by 'heraldry'?

Ans. *Heraldry* means long descent or a family with long and glorious history behind it.

Q. 32. What does the poet mean by 'And all that beauty, all that wealth ever gave'?

Ans. Beauty and wealth give man pride. The poet means pride of beauty and wealth.

Q. 33. What is the meaning of paths of glory?

Ans. Golrious carrers have to go along the paths leading to death.

Q. 34. What are the personifications used in the stanza 8 and9?

Ans. Ambition stands for ambitious men. Grandeour means luxurious men. The boast of heraldry, the pomp of power mean those who are proud of glorious ancestry and of power.

Q. 35. How does the poet contrast the graves of the rich and those of the poor?

Ans. The graves of the rich are inside the church and have rich memorials over their graves. The graves of the poor villagers are in the church-yard and they heap up turfs over graves to indicate the existence of graves. No hymns are sung in their praise.

Q. 36. How does the poet suggest the insignificance of grandeur, honour and pride?

Ans. All men, rich and poor are subject to death. Grand memorials, honour and flattery cannot bring back the dead to life.

Q. 37. What is the meaning of 'fleeting breath'?

Ans. *Fleeting breath* means dying man-breath that is flying away.

Q. 38. "If Memory O'er their tombs no trophies raise." -What is meant by Memory here? What is the meaning of trophies?

Ans. *Memory* means here descendents who would remember. *Trophies* mean memorials.

Q. 39. What is meant by 'aisle' and 'fretted vault'?

Ans. 'Long drawn aisle' means long corridor and 'fretted vault' means the carved and vaulted roof of the church.

Q. 40. How are 'Honour' and 'Flattery' used in the sentence?

Ans. 'Honour' and 'Flattery' are personified.

Q. 41. What is meant bt 'Silent dust' and 'dull cold ear of death'?

Ans. 'Silent dust' means dead man. The body of man is reduced to dust after death.

Dull cold ear of death- death is personified and is supposed to be indifferent to the words of flattery and honour.

Q. 42. 'Perhaps in this neglected spot' - Whhat is the neglected spot meant here?

Ans. *Neglected spot* means the church-yard where the graves of the poor villagers are laid.

Q. 43. "Some heart once pregnant with celestial fire" - What is meant by 'pregnant'? What does the poet mean by 'celestial fire'?

Ans. *Pregnant* means filled with. *Celestial fire* means divine inspiration.

Q. 44. What does the poet imagine the possibilities of the poor villagers buried in the church-yard?

Ans. The poet (Gray) imagines that the villagers might have been powerful emperors or inspired poets if circumstances favoured them. They may have the powers and possibilities.

Q. 45. "Rich with the spoils of time" - What is the image suggested in the phrase 'spoils of time'?

Ans. *Spoils of Time* suggests the image of time as plunderer. A pliunderer plunders things and becomes rich by plundered things. As time passes, it acquires new knowledge and knowledge is enriched.

Q. 46. "Her ample page" --Whose page is suggested? Why is it 'ample'?

Ans. The page of knowledge is suggested. The page of knowledge is ample (abundant) because knowledge has increased with the passage of time and it is contained in the pages of books.

Q. 47. What is meant by chill Penury? How is the word used?

Ans. Chill penury means poverty which has cold effect. Penury is personified.

Q. 48. "Froze the genial current of soul." - To which the word 'froze' is connected? What does the line mean here?

Ans. *Froze* is connected with the phrase 'chill penury'. Like cold winter, poverty checks the natural movemênts and spontaneous urges of the soul. *Genial current* means natural movements. 'Noble rage' means inspiration.

Q. 49. How are villagers with some potentials are compared?

Ans. Villagers with some potentials and innate powers are compared to pure, bright gems lying unnoticed in the depths of the ocean and to fragrant flowers that bloom in some obscure corners unseen and unadmired by others.

Q. 50. Who was Hampden? In what connection is his name mentioned in the poem?

Ans. John Hampden was a member of Parliament who refused to pay the illegal tax called ship money which Charles I levied without the aproval of the Parliament. The poet (Gray) means that among the villages there might have been a courageous rebel like Hampden.

Q. 51. Who was Cromwell? Why his name is referred to? Why is it said guilty of his country's blood?

Ans. Cromwell was the leader of the Parliament that fought against the unjust and tyrannical rule of Charles I. He was guilty of shedding the blood of his countrymen because there was a long civil war in England. Gray means there might have been a rebel and ruler like Cromwell among the dead villagers.

Q. 52. Why is Milton referred to in the poem?

Ans. Milton was a great English poet (1609-1674). Gray means that there might been great poets lke Milton.

Q. 53. What prevented the villagers from fulfilling their possibilities and potentialities, according to Gray?

Ans. According to the poet Gray, among the dead villagers there might have been men with the potentialities of a rebel, a rebel, a leader and a poet. But these potentialities were checked by their poverty.

Q. 54. "Their lot forbade." - Whose lot is referred to? What is the meaning of forbade?

Ans. The lot of the poor villagers is referred to. 'Forbade' means prevented.

Q. 55. What is suggested by 'mute inglorious Milton'?

Ans. 'Mute inglorious Milton' means poets who are silent and inglorious because they could not develop their talents due to poverty.

Q. 56. What did their lot forbid?

Ans. The lot of the villagers prevented them from getting the praise of Senators, from defying threats of pain and ruin and from scattering plenty over a smiling land. It means that they could not become great men like members of the Parliament or rebels or good rulers because of their poverty.

Q. 57. How are the crimes of the villagers controlled?

Ans. Poverty limited the scope of virtues and crimes. Crimes were limited because they were humble and unambitious. They did not commit murders to gain a throne or showed unkindness to others and flattered the rich to gain favours.

Q. 58. "The struggling pangs of conscious truth to hide." - What is suggested in the line?

Ans. The poet suggests that the ambitious men often hide truth consciously and thus suffer the pain and shame. But the poor men had no ambition and so they did not have to suffer pain and shame of hiding truth.

Q. 59. What is meant by 'Sober wishes'?

Ans. 'Sover wishes' mean honest and simple wishes.

Q. 60. What is the kind of life that the villagers led?

Ans. The villagers lived calm, solitary, noiseless and honest life.

Q. 61. How are their memorials? Why are memorials necessary?

Ans. There are frail memorials erected near the graves their graves. Memorials are necessary to protect the dead bodies from desecration.

Q. 62. What is meant by unlettered Muse?

Ans. 'Unlettered muse' means uneducated village poet.

Q. 63. What are written on the memorials of the dead vilagers?

Ans. There are written on their memorials some clumsy verse, some shapeless decorations, the place, name, years of dead men wrongly spelt. Some holy texts are scattered over them.

Q. 64. What purpose do memorials serve?

Ans. Memorials serve the purpose of being remembered after death.

Q. 65. What does the poet say about man's desire for love of life?

Ans. Gray says that man loves life and wants to be remembered after deat. Even when a man des, he casts a long longing look behind.

Q. 66. What is meant by 'pleasing anxious being'?

Ans. 'Pleasing anxious being' means life made of pleasure and anxieties.

Q. 67. How does the poet describe man's longing for life?

Ans. A dying man wants a loving breast to rely on. He longs for affectionate drops of tears. This natural desire for life and love persists even after death. Man wants to be remembered after death.

Q. 68. "The voice of Nature cries." -What is meant by voice of nature? What does the word 'cries' nean?

Ans. Voice of nature means natural desire of man. 'Cries' means demands, insists.

Q. 69. "In our ashes live their wonted fire."- What is meant by 'wonted fire'?

Ans. *Wonted fire* means natural urgent desire. This desire persists even after death.

Q. 70. "For thee..." - Whom does the poet mean?

Ans. The poet means himself. He is the village poet who has thought of the unhonoured dead villagers.

Q. 71. "Some kindred spirit." - What is meant by kindred spirit? What will he do?

Ans. Some man of similar spirit and temperature is indicated. he would enquire about the poet who has related the simple tale of the humble villagers. A sensitive spirit like the poet is indicated.

Q. 72. What is meant by 'hoary-headed swain'?

Ans. Hoary-headed swain means old villager with grey hairs.

Q. 73. Where was the village poet found in the morning?

Ans. The village poet was found at dawn walking hastily to the upland lawn from where he saw the Sunrise.

Q. 74. Where was the village poet fouund at noon?

Ans. At noon, the village poet was found stretching out his idle body at the foot of the beech tree and observing the murmuring brook.

Q. 75. In what moods the village poet was seen?

Ans. The village poet was seen sometimes scornful, sometimes dejected, pale, sorrowful like a lonely man. He would mutter random fancies as he walked.

Q. 76. What happened to the village poet?

Ans. The village poet died and his dead body was carried in a procession.

Q. 77. What is the meaning of epitaph?

Ans. *Epitaph* means words written on the memorial about a dead person.

Q. 78. What was written on the epitaph of the tomb of the village poet?

Ans. The village poet was neither fortunate nor famous. He was humble and so did not have the advantage of education. he was melancholy, generous and kind.

Q. 79. What did the village poet get as recompense for his kindness to others?

Ans. The village poet gained a friend as reward for his kndness to the miserable people. He got the friendship of God.

Expalanation

Q. 1. ***The curfew tolls the knell ..to darkness and to me.*** **(Lines 1-4)**

Ans. These are the opening lines of the first stanza of gray's famou *Elegy Written in a Country Churchyard.* The poet builds up an atmosphere of evening here as he watches the evening scene of the surrounding landscape when he is standing in the country churchyard at Stock-poges. He gives a gloomy atmosphere prevailing in the church. The place is hushed up in silence. The evening bell is ringing, thus making the end of the day.The evening church bells serve as a funeral bell for the dying day. The sheep are walking back to the village over the pasture land. The ploughman who is completely exhausted after the day's work is also walking heavily homewards at the day's end. All the surrounding country is plunged into darkness. It is the poet alone, who is left contemplating on the lot of man.

Comment: The poet describes the desolate place and atmosphere of the country churchyard. Darkness pleasing to the poet is suggested here. The cufew is here regarded as a death bell for the day. Here we also trace an autobiographical touch. The poet laments the death of his aunt alone in the churchyard. Melancholy characterizes the thme.

Q. 2. ***Now fades the glimmering landscape..the distant folds.*** **(Lines 5-8)**

Ans. These lines occur in Gray's famous *Elegy Written in a Country Churchyard.* The poet notices the evening scene of the surrounding landscape around the country churchyard and describes the gloomy and silent atmosphere prevailing there. He notices the twiling deepening into darkness and scene becoming dim and indistinct to the view. The atmosphere looks faintly dim in the twilight. Silence and an air of solemnity mark this hour. A deep silence fiils the whole atmosphere. No sounds of vulgar mirth are heard and the silence is broken only by the dull, humming sound of thebeetle in its circular flight and by the twinkling of bells round thenecks of sheep returning from distant valleys. These sounds seem to lull the whole landscape to sleep.

Comment: Silence prevails in and around the churchyard.It is a silent evening.A beautiful romantic evening scene is depicted by the poet.

Q. 3. ***For them no more the blazing...envied kis to share.*** **(Lines 21-24)**

Ans. These lines form the sixth stanza of Gray's famous *Elegy Written in a Country Churchyard.* The poet says that the dead villages have gone to the eternal sleep in their graves. Such sounds as the twittering of swallows or crowing of the cock cannot break their sleep. Their death has cut them off from domestic happiness. These dead poor villagers have been with drawn for ever from all attachments of life. Their wives will no more light a comfortable fire to greet them in the evening when they returned home at the end of day's work. They will no more have the supper ready at their husband's arrival. No children will run to them either to greet them back home or to received paternal kisses. They are dead and buried and never again will they enjoy those simple domestic pleasures of life.

Comment: This stanza is sufficed with deep pathos. The poet grows philosophical to say that man loses everything with his death. Secondly the poet is a minute observer of life of the poor villagers. Death is cruel.

Q.4. ***Let Ambition not mock...annals of the poor.*** **(Lines 29-32)**

Ans. These lines form the eighth stanza of Thomas Gray's famous *Elegy Written in a Country Curchyard*. The poet mourns the death of the siimple, poor villagers and describes their happy domestic lives and their simple occupations. During their life-time men performed useful labours, enjoyed simple and ordinary pleasures and lived unknown, inconspicuous lives. Amibitious persons would perhaps think it a poor record. They would be amused by this unimpressive performance. The poet reminds them that the labour of the villagers is beneficial to mankind. He further asks the so-called civilized people who are proud of pomp and glory, not to mock ironically, while listening to the the humble and plain tales of the lives of the poor peasants. Great and high-born people should not listen to the history of these peasants' lives with feelings of contempt towards the humble folks who lies buried in that churchyard.

Comment: The poor stresses that the poor peasants who are dead and buried in the churchyard should be honoured. mankind reaps benefit from what they had done in their life time. The poet has personified "Ambition" and "Grandeur". The poet advises the proud and ambitious men not to ridicule the simple and unpoilshed peasures, low obscure social position and agricultural labour of these peasants.

Q. 5. ***The boast of heraldry...lead but to the grave.*** **(Line 33-36)**

Ans. These lines form the ninth stanza of Thomas Gray's *Elegy Written in a Country Churchyard.* The poet is a champion of the poor. He is critical of those who mockk the poor. He is also a great interpreter of life and death. Here he speaks of the inevitability of death. The pride and pretension of a glorious ancestry is vain. Neither beauty nor wealth can stand against death. All human glories and objects of pride are meaningless before death. Death is all-powerful and all-conquering. Death is a great leveller. All peoplr -great and small, rich and poor, beautiful and ugly-become one in death. It is the natural end of all human beings. Even a carrer of victory and conquest ultimately ends in death. A man may win glory in his life by his warlike deeds or spectacular exploits, but he must at last be ovewrtaken by death. All one's record of struggle and achievement becomes meaningless in the face of death.

Comment: A well-known, universal truth that death conquers all is expressed in these lines. The poet describes the vanity of human wishes and fultility of human ambition. Death is no respecter of high birth or high position.

Q.6. ***But knowledge to their eyes ...current of the soul.*** **(Lines 49-52)**

Ans. These lines form the thirteenth stanza of Thomas Gray's famous poem *Elegy Written in a Country Churchyard.* Here the poet reflects on the humble lot of the villagers who lie buried in the churchyard.They did not get any opportunity for education. Their dire poverty stood in the way of their development of their dormant powers and possibilities. The vast accumulated knowledge of centuries remained a closed book to them and they were consequently compelled to lead obscure lives. They did not attain fame and prosperity. Poverty had a benumbing effect upon their noble instincts and the same poverty dries up their religious enthusiasm on their spiritual ardour.

Comment: Poverty prevented the rustics from getting the benefits of a broad and liberal education. It checked the freeflow of their thought- their healthy and joyous feelings-their energies of mind. Poverty is abr to human progress and prosperity.

Q. 7. ***Far from the madding crowd's ....tenor of their way.*** **(Lines 73-76)**

Ans. These lines form the nineteenth stanza of Thomas Gray's famous poem *Elegy Written in a Country Churchyard.* The poor rustics were always chased by poverty. It crushed their spirits and prevented their intellectual development; they were the victims of poverty. The poet here describes their real nature and admires their quiet and humble life. They are now dead and buried in the churchyard. They lived far away from the cities where people indulge in futile struggle for gaining wealth, power and fame. They were detached from the cities where the noise is almost maddening and where sin and evil dominate human life. The poor rustics who are now dead and buried had no wild, soaring ambitions. The ynever strayed from the path of virtue and nobility. They never followed evil courses and their desires were humble and ordinary. They lived a simple and quiet life in the village. Their life passed as gently as a gentle stream flows through a valley.

Comment: The poet has condemned city life as being evil and sinful. Cities have corrupting influence on human life. As these poor rustics stayed away from the city life, they were able to lead a peaceful path of life. They preferred peace to materialistic possessions.

Q. 8. ***On some fond breast...live there wonted fires.*** **(Lines 89-92)**

Ans. These lines form the twenty third stanza of Thomas Gray's famous poem *Elegy Written in a Country Churchyard.* The poet here says that it is the instinctive desire of human beings to be remembered after death. When a man is on the verge of death, he seeks comfort and consolation from some loving friend or relative, for none likes to leave this happy life without casting towards it a painful and lingering look of separation. The presence of a loving friend by the bed-side provides a great comfort to the dying man. He feels relieved to find by his side someone shedding tears of grief. Even when one is deadand buried, the same natural desire for loving remembrance is felt by the departed soul/ When all is dust and ashes, the keen desire for remembrance that lived in the body still lives on. Gray means to say that the unfulfilled yearning of a man continues to make themselves felt either in the shape of inscription on the tombstones or in the form of grass, plats and flowers that grow on the graves.

Comment : The poet describes the emotional psychological crisis at the time of death. Nobody wants to depart from the world though he is aware of the inevitability of death. Everyone yearns for some kindly, lovingremembrance while a spark of life remains n him. Even death cannot put an end to his desire for affection, sympathy and remembrance. The poet believes in the immortality of soul.

Q. 9. *Here rests his head...for her own.* (Lines 127-130)

Ans. These lines form part of the epitaph of gray's famous poem *Elegy Written in a Country Churchyard.* As the elegy comes to a colse, the poet writes aninscription to bw engraved or written on his own grave. He writes that in this grave lies buried a youg man who attained neither name nor any political success. Good luck or fame never favoured him. But knowledge did not neglect him on the ground that he was born poor. In spite of his humble birth, science and scholarship favoured him.He was temeperamentally a melancholy or thoughtful person. Melancholy was his constant companion.

Comment: Gray was happy with his knowledge and scholarship, and this was consolation amidst his poverty. His melancholy mood is reflected here. He was a man of a naturally morose disposition.

Short Essay Type Questions with Answers

Q. 1. Comment on the Role of Memory in *Elegy Written in A Country Churchyard.*

Ans. One of the central ideas in the poem is related to the role of memory and remembrance. Gray was the fifth of twelve children in his family but he was the only child who survived past childhood. Therefore the idea of preserving the memory of those who cannot speak for themselves might have been especially valuable for the poet. The unnamed speaker is intent on preserving the memory of the humble villagers whose narratives will otherwise be dropped from the annals of history: "...who to dumb Forgetfulness a prey," (85). Memory is the only way for ordinary mortals to achieve immortality and defeat the obscurity effected by time and death:

On some fond breast the parting soul relies,
Some pious drops the closing eye requires;
Ev'n from the tomb the voice of nature cries,
Ev'n in our ashes live their wonted fires. (89-92)

The desire to be remembered is common to all humans. This commemoration is achieved through the act of writing. Poetry is the most long lasting relic of remembrance and it enables the speaker to preserve the memory of the villagers. Its effect is better than that of any urn or bust or grave. Memory and memorials (such as the epitaph and "Elegy"), unlike wealth and power, can defeat death. As Howard D. Weinbrot puts it, 'the "Elegy" is not concerned with a choice of life and death, but a choice of eternity.' (538) But Gray doesn't stop at saving the villagers from oblivion, he wants the same for himself. His desire is that his name too be preserved in the memory of others, specifically- the inhabitants of the village as well as the travelers passing by in the future. The speaker in the poem is not just a disinterested observer after all. Hence, through the "Elegy" Gray achieves dual commemoration: the speaker immortalizes the villagers and the 'hoary-headed swain' reciprocates the gesture for the speaker.

Commemoration is crucial to the poem's structure, particularly given that the poem ends with an epitaph. However, his desire to be remembered is of a special kind. He wants also to be remembered as a poet. Thus, in a way remembrance is not evoked only for the humans but for the poem itself. Gray's use of meta-poetic elements in the "Elegy"- such as in the lines "Dost in these lines their artless tale relate" (85) - should be considered in this regard. This self reflexive exercise is a testimony of Gray's poetic skill, but it also belies the anxiety of a poet uncertain about the reception and survival of his poems, and the difficulty of finding ideological kinship with readers in an increasingly commercialized literary market. The multiple points of focus create a tension with the poem which is belied by its tone of melancholic preponderance.

Q. 2. Comment on the Portrayal of the villagers in *Elegy Written in A Country Churchyard.*

Ans. The speaker identifies himself with the rustics. The poet's claim that he can/does empathize with the modest villagers is what gives his speech legitimacy. He presents himself as an outsider to the world of fame and fortune, the city. In the eighteenth century London had become the centre of all literary, scientific and intellectual activity. There was an unprecedented migration towards cities which were rapidly developing as centers of commerce. The distancing of the speaker from the city is an important stance. It is a move as much physical as it is ideological. Sensibility in "Elegy" affords the speaker and those like him an alternative world order where 'ambition' and 'glory' do not reign supreme. The poet's sympathy aligns him with the lot of the villagers and bolsters his critique of the city life and its ethos. For the readers of the "Elegy", especially contemporary readers, their ability to sympathize with the marginalized made them feel distinct from and superior to, others around them. This sense of a shared bond of finer/nobler emotions between poets and the readers of the literature of Sensibility was important. Therefore, although the idea of Sensibility is based upon an inclusive ideal of communal living it could also at times become exclusive and exclusionary. However the speaker's identification with the villagers is by no means absolute. On a closer look one realizes that his attitude towards the villagers is ambivalent.

In the "Elegy", the villagers are the subject of the poetic gaze. The speaker is like an elevated observer. When the poem begins the poet's panoramic eye is seen assessing the landscape as well as its inhabitants. This objectification of the villagers is problematic. He identifies himself with the villagers but it is obvious that he acts as the spokesperson for them. The villagers have no agency, the only villager who has speech in the poem is meant to ultimately talk about the poetic persona. The use of words like 'mute', 'rude', 'unlettered' and 'noiseless' in association with the villagers points towards the fact that he after all has the greater knowledge and poetic authority. The speaker articulates his concern for the impoverished state and thwarted potential of the villagers but it never quite reaches its logical end – the critique of power relations in society. Poetic sympathy is not bolstered by condemnation of the power relations which results in the unequal distribution of wealth in society. Questions have always been raised about the authenticity of the sympathetic impulse driving the cult of sensibility. Does this sympathy translate into concrete action for the emancipation of the downtrodden? Keith's observation sums up the objections to this aspect of the sensibility 'Part of what has been seen to corrupt the literature of sensibility is the way it directs the reader to gaze upon, and therefore objectify, the sufferer. Robert Markley describes this phenomenon as the "theatrics of virtue," where readers, characters, speakers, or audiences gaze on scenes of another's suffering, participating in a submerged sadism' ("Poetry, Sentiment and sensibility" 127). Also the relation between the villagers and the speaker in "Elegy" is not as straightforward as it might seem on the surface. The speaker's sympathy is tempered by the suggestion that the innocence and goodness of the villagers is intact because they are untouched by the lure of lucre. Rather than any sense of inherent morality their virtue is a result of ignorance. The poem is, as if, a double edged sword. Moments such as these force us to see "Elegy" as more than a poem about softer emotions of sympathy and sensibility. It prevents us from settling too comfortably in any certainty about the meaning of the poem.

Q. 3. Discuss *Elegy Written in a Country Curchyard* as a meditation on Death.

Ans. Gray's "Elegy" is one of the best-known poems about death in all of European literature. The poem presents the reflections of an observer who, passing by a churchyard that is out in the country, stops for a moment to think about the significance of the strangers buried there. Scholars of medieval times sometimes kept human skulls on their desktops, to keep themselves conscious of the fact that someday they, like the skulls' former occupants, would die: from this practice we get the phrase memento mori, which we say to this day to describe any token one uses to keep one's mortality in mind. In this poem, the graveyard acts as a memento mori, reminding the narrator to not place too much value on this life because someday he too will be dead and buried. The speaker of the poem is surrounded by the idea of death, and throughout the first seven stanzas there are numerous images pointing out the contrast between death and life. After mentioning the churchyard in the title, which establishes the theme of mortality, the poem itself begins with images of gloom and finality. The darkness at the end of the day, the forlorn moan of lowing cattle, the stillness of the air (highlighted by the beetle's stilted motion) and the owl's nocturnal hooting all serve to set a background for this serious meditation. However, it is not until the fourth stanza that the poem actually begins to deal with the cemetery, mentioned as the place where the village forefathers "sleep." In the following stanzas, the speaker tries to imagine what the lives of these simple men might have been like, touching upon their relations with their wives, children, and the soil that they worked. They are not defined by their possessions, because they had few, and instead are defined by their actions, which serves to contrast their lives with their quiet existence in the graveyard. This "Elegy" presents the dead in the best light: their families adored them and they were cheerful in their work, as they "hummed the woods beneath their steady stroke." The speaker openly admits that they are spoken of so well precisely because they are dead, because death is such a terrible thing that its victims deserve the respect of the living. In line 90, the poet explains, "Some pious drops the closing eye requires," explaining that the living should show their respect for death with their sorrow.

Novel	# FANTOMINA; or Love in a Maze - Eliza Haywood

❖ An Introduction to Eliza Heywood :

Very few details are known with certainty about Eliza Haywood's early life. She was born Eliza Fowler, likely either in Shropshire or London. In 1714, she is recorded working as an actress in Dublin under the name of Eliza Haywood. She would later go on to describe herself as a widow, but the husband whose surname she adopted has never been identified. Haywood did have two children, whose paternity is also debatable. Some contemporary sources suggest that these children resulted from a marriage that ended when her husband abandoned her. Others, including the poet Alexander Pope, accused Haywood of being the mother of illegitimate children. If the latter is true, the likely fathers of her children are Richard Savage, a well-known writer, and William Hatchett, a playwright and translator, since Haywood was rumored to have been romantically linked to both.

Haywood began her career as an actress, which at the time was considered a disreputable occupation for a woman, and may explain why her personal life was dogged by rumors of scandal. Her first novel, Love in Excess, was published in 1719 and served as the start of a long and varied literary career. While continuing to work as a stage actress, she wrote a number of novels and novellas (including Fantomina) during the 1720s. She also began writing plays and working as a translator, which shaped her own literary style due to the French fiction she was exposed to. In 1724, her first play was staged, and at about the same time she began writing essays to be published in periodicals and journals. Alongside becoming a notable public literary figure, Haywood actively entered into the political debates of the day, producing pamphlets, essays, and other writings to circulate her political opinions.

By the 1730s, Haywood was at the peak of her acting success. The final play she wrote was staged to great success in 1733. Shortly thereafter she began writing dramatic criticism, and continued to do so for the rest of her life. She also ventured into editing a successful periodical, The Female Spectator. She continued to write and publish up until her death on February 25, 1756.

❖ An Introduction to *Fantomina*

Fantomina is a novel written by Eliza Haywood in 1725. The book mainly revolves around an unnamed character who becomes intrigued by the men she sees in a playhouse in London. She then pretends to be a prostitute and enjoys talking to a man called Beauplaisir. He believes her to actually be a prostitute and rapes her despite her protests. She (the unnamed main character) is worried about her reputation and so tells Beauplaisir that her name is Fantomina. Beauplaisir tires of her and leaves for Bath, but she follows him. She disguises as herself as a maid at the inn Beauplaisir is staying at and manages to sleep with him again after he is interested in her. After Beauplaisir leaves Bath, he meets the unnamed main character again on his journey home, but now she is disguised as a widow. Beauplaisir ravishes her again and she becomes pregnant. The unnamed character's mother finds out, and she is sent to live in a French monastery.

Haywood wrote the book to illustrate how one woman's initial mistake could become her passion as a result of love, which is unguided in this storyline. Furthermore, the she wanted to portray a story of a 'persecuted maiden' and display how women were treated during the 18th century.

The book was received very well by critics and fans. Indeed, Eliza Haywood was one of the four bestselling authors of the first half of the 18th century. She has received widespread recognition for Fantomina since the rise of feminist literary criticism, and Fantomina has appeared in many anthologies since the 1980s

❖ Historical Background of *Fantomina* :

Some consider Eliza Haywood one of the more controversial writers to publish in eighteenth century England, and her work has been viewed accordingly as political, polarizing, and even subversive. "Fantomina" is one such work which has been both criticized and praised for reasons ranging from its promotion of reckless female activity to its empowerment of female sexuality, but it can be difficult to grasp the true narrative themes of this or any other of Haywood's pieces without a fundamental contextual understanding of her writing. While it may be more difficult today to read "Fantomina" in its original intended context, this interpretation is imperative to gaining a deeper and more accurate understanding of Haywood's purpose and motivation when crafting the novel.

Though certainly a fascinating and entertaining work on its own, the premise of "Fantomina" operates primarily as a commentary on female sexuality during the early 1700s. Karen Harvey published an article in 2002 examining a shift in the dynamic of eighteenth century gender relations, partially caused by perceived differences between the male and female body. She asserts that these changes began during the late seventeenth and early eighteenth century, the same era in which Haywood was writing, and that they helped create narratives which taught about female passivity and domesticity. Harvey contends that a primary cause for this discernment of increased differentiation of the sexes was due to new findings published in the medical field following the scientific revolution. Women were now seen to have very few similarities to men in terms of base physical sexuality, leading them to be "increasingly reimagined as belonging to another order of being: loving but without sexual needs" (Harvey 903).

The extensive measures the heroine in "Fantomina" takes in order to obtain Beauplaisir's affections seem far less dramatized and in some ways even more plausible when situated against the backdrop of the increasingly confined boundaries for high society women to express themselves as sexual beings. The first line of the text acknowledges that she is of "distinguished birth, beauty, wit and spirit," indicating that the heroine is herself high society and therefore meant to represent those women being sexually repressed (Haywood 2796). The actions of her mother provide a broader, more general perspective of society's views regarding female sexuality. Upon discovering her daughter's behavior she places all responsibility on the heroine, stating "The blame is wholly hers, and I have nothing to request further of you, than that you will not divulge the distracted folly she has been guilty of" (Haywood 2813). It may seem unrealistically cruel that a woman's own mother would react this way, but in the context of the "new, middle class image of the respectable, asexual female" which the heroine represents, it seems altogether natural, though perhaps still tragic, that this type of rampant sexual escapade would elicit such a response (Harvey 903).

The heroine's elaborate means of soliciting Beauplaisir may appear absurd or amusing, but the general idea behind them and particularly their specificity are of great importance. During Harvey's discussion of confined sexual activity, she cites Randolph Trumbach's idea that "women in this period could express sexual passion only as prostitutes, seduced servants, remarrying widows, and adulterous wives" (Harvey 907). It is of little coincidence that the heroine of "Fantomina" disguises herself as all but one of these identities when pursuing Beauplaisir. The essential absence of sexual agency in her own life requires her to take on the personas of those who do possess it so that she may attempt erotic exploration.

Historians have struggled to fully uncover Haywood's own background, but the pieces they have collected serve to additionally contextualize "Fantomina" and many of her other works. In 2000 Kirsten Saxton published a collection of essays about Haywood's life and work, and her presentation of the writer's personal life provides insight as to why she would write pieces so obstinately defiant of eighteenth century cultural norms. Through a compilation of letters written near the time "Fantomina" was published in the early 1720s, Saxton determines that Haywood likely had already experienced two failed marriages by the time she was thirty, leaving her single with two children. Additionally, the author speculates that these children were "almost certainly born outside of marriage" and that both were conceived with friends of Haywood's, one a writer and the other a bookseller (Saxton 6).Given this information regarding Haywood's own sexual and marital independence, it hardly seems surprising that she would feel indignant towards the continued domestication and desexualizing of women, particularly those who were married.

Haywood's personal distaste for this cultural shift directly influenced "Fantomina" and her other works in ways that, as Saxton describes, "create a space for active, if dangerous, female appetite, rather than assuming women should have no sexual desires" (Saxton 4). The heroine's seemingly drastic actions are certainly dangerous and perhaps even reckless, but Haywood purposefully employs this heightened drama to show just how far women had to go to free themselves from societal constraints on sexuality. Her critique lies not in the "appetite" of women itself, but is instead aimed towards the "lack of awareness of how to negotiate this desire" during such a period, a feeling she no doubt experienced herself when attempting to navigate her way through repressive marriages and birthing two children out of wedlock (Saxton 4).

The over-the-top occurrences and severe repercussions which take place in "Fantomina" should not be critiqued without an in-depth contextualization of female sexuality during the eighteenth century, a period which not placed sharp limitations on women of nearly any status, but also deeply affected the life of Eliza Haywood in a very personal way.

❖ The Story of *Fantmina* :

Fantomina is a high quality mistress in the eighteenth century and because of her social position she has many restrictions placed upon her. She is not allowed to carry out a conversation of any type with a person of the opposite sex, nor is she allowed to pursue them. These behaviors were unacceptable in Fantomina's society; therefore, women were supposed to have chaperones who were to protect them from men and also to make sure women behaved appropriately. Fantomina's recognition of a familiar face down below the balcony where she is sitting at reawakens her interest for Beauplasir whom she she has before seen, but because of society she has been unable to pursue him. However, because men were different from women and had the freedom to do anything they wanted to, Beauplasir is allowed to leave the balcony and pursue women. Fantomina "is fascinated by the dalliance between 'respectable' gentlemen and loose women of the town." "This excited a curiosity in her to know in what manner these creatures were addressed." . Although, Fantominas's actions seem intentional her new identity originates all from curiosity in her pursuit to sustain Beauplasir's interest.

Fed up with her restrictions, Fantomina decides to change her clothes to hide her real identity. It is here where Haywood reveals the restrictions on women of high social standing and the decisions of who belongs to what social position. In this case, clothing puts Fantomina in a lower social standing, even more, her new identity is that of a prostitute. Now as a prostitute, Fantomina is able to pursue Beauplasir without any restrictions as he is unable to recognize her new identity. In preparation to her encounter with Beauplasir, Fontamina puts on her new identity and while with Beauplasir she resists him at first because she is worried about her reputation. At this point, Fantomina is concerned about her moral actions, but her desires can do more now because that is what she has been looking for. This of course, confuses Beauplasir because that's what prostitutes are expected to do and in the end a prostitute gets paid in return. Fantomina's first disguise as a prostitute is all out of curiosity, but her imagination was so much talented that she had the power to change her appearance as she pleased. "As Fantomina changes character, she modifies her behaviors to align with his expectations.". The quote describes Fantomina's admirable skills in manipulating the situation for her own benefit. As expected, Beauplasir grows tired of Fantomina and this is where she takes on her new identity to continue to follow him.

Now as Celia, a low class woman she becomes Beauplasir's maid, a new identity that becomes a bit more important than the one before because of social status .As her seduction continues she feels that she has become attached to Beauplasir and she can't let go of him she spends much of her time coming up with new ideas to seduce him. Her actions become a little emotional, but at the same time she intelligent as she is willing to go even further to maintain her sexual relationship with Beauplasir. It seems that what had started from curiosity has now turned into a passion that reflects her deepest emotions. "Her consistent ability to perform means that she repeatedly creates a space in which she may express her emotions.". In a sense, Fantomina feels that she belongs to Beauplasir since he has taken her virginity and she attaches this to the fact that she now struggles to maintain her honor from being publicly exposed.

Fantomina's now passion for Beauplasir leads her to go even further in her seduction attempt. This time, as the widow Bloomer she becomes a little more vulnerable and portrays herself as weak. At one point, the widow fakes a sudden faint and allows Beauplasir to carry her off to bed. This proves that Fantomina is very calculating and her actions are being consistent with the character she assumes to be. In doing so, Fantomina believes her different roles are a source of power and freedom, but also her ability to succeed in her new role taking. Although, the role that she takes on for the most part is powerless because she gains nothing from it, she has quite effectively succeeded in making Beauplasir believe that he has been sleeping with different personas.

In her last disguise as Incognita, the significant thing they have in common is class and as the encounters continue, it seems that Fantomina's actions are driven by pure lust. Incognita its Fantomina's last attempt to seduce Beauplasir and it ultimately fails just as her other disguises. Despie Beuaplasir being desperately curious to know who she really is he never shows real interest in maintaining a relationship with Incognita because in the end he has nothing to gain from a woman who demands that her identity never be revealed. This culminates with Fantomina's realization that Beauplasir's real interest for her has been to satisfy his own sexual needs as he never remained faithful to her for the simple fact that he slept with the same person thinking he had been with four different women. Croskery describes that, "the heroine of Fantomina experiences one of her deepest moment of internalization at the precise moment when she becomes conscious of herself as an object of someone else's desire." (Croskery 2007). Through Beauplasir, the reader realizes that women are nothing but trophies and toys that are to be played with.

Ultimately, Fantomina's various identities accomplish nothing; they do serve to reveal how lustful Beauplasir is as well as Fantomina whether she acted on curiosity her real intentions remain ambiguous. Unfortunately, Fantomina's creative disguises only satisfy her sexual desires, but never create a long- lasting relationship with Beauplasir which results in her own betrayal. Fantomina's pregnancy becomes her true story in which she has lost everything including her reputation

❖ A Detailed Summary of *Fantmina* :

Part 1: The First Disguise

Summary :

The novel opens in a London playhouse during a performance. The novel's unnamed protagonist, a beautiful and intelligent young woman from a good family, is there to see the play. She has only recently arrived in London, having grown up in the country, and enjoys an uncommon amount of independence and autonomy.

As she gazes around at the other people attending the theatre, she notices that one woman in particular is receiving a lot of male attention. This woman is readily identifiable as a prostitute. The protagonist is surprised that men, some of whom she knows and considers to be intelligent, are still so willing to associate with her; however, when she expresses this idea to the well-bred ladies sitting near her, they dismiss her as sheltered and naïve. The more she thinks about it, the more the protagonist becomes intrigued with knowing how the experiences of a prostitute are different from her own.

Spurred by her ability to follow her own unchecked impulses, the very next night she returns to the playhouse in disguise. Hiding her identity by veiling her face, she sits in a different section of the theatre and imitates the behavior of the prostitute she had observed the night before. Men are immediately attracted to her, and begin flirting with her very openly. She enjoys the attention, and is particularly excited when a man named Beauplaisir approaches her.

The protagonist has interacted with Beauplaisir before and has always felt an attraction to him, but those interactions have always taken place under circumstances where her behavior was strictly controlled by a sense of what was socially appropriate. Now she is much more free in her interactions, and he takes a new interest in her. Beauplaisir does not recognize her; while he does detect a resemblance between the woman he assumes to be a prostitute and the well-bred lady of his acquaintance, he assumes it must be a coincidence. He is impressed to find that this mysterious new woman is much more intelligent and articulate than most of the prostitutes with whom he has interacted, and the two spend hours flirting and talking.

Analysis

The setting of the novel's opening scene in a playhouse highlights several key themes, such as acting, disguise, and deception. The protagonist will function much like an actress throughout the story, using devices such as costumes and adopting an accent to disguise her true identity. It seems probable that the setting in which she first encounters the prostitute plays a subconscious role in her audacious decision to dress up and pretend to be one. The setting of the theatre would have also immediately hinted to Haywood's readers that the novel might be concerned with a scandalous subject matter. There had long been debates about the morality of acting, and controversy about theatre had reached its peak in England when it was outlawed in the mid-seventeenth century during the English Civil War. By the time Haywood wrote, theatrical culture was thriving, but it remained linked to transgressive behavior. Acting essentially involved pretending to be something you were not, and this was perceived as dangerously close to sinful behavior like lying and deceiving.

Another reason why theatre were controversial is that playhouses were mixed social spaces; in an era where class position often rigidly defined one's experiences, especially for a woman, the theatre was a rare place where both aristocrats and working class individuals could find themselves in the same room. The protagonist's fascination with the prostitutes she observes suggests that she has never seen one before. Her reaction actually encapsulates the common fear around more relaxed social interactions: people feared that if sheltered young women learned about the behavior of prostitutes, they might be tempted to try it themselves.

A number of unique factors come together to make it feasible for the protagonist to conceive of her plan. Her wealth and high social position make her accustomed to getting what she wants. She has grown up outside of the city and is therefore more naïve and less aware of how strict social and moral codes can be. She is also unsupervised, without the usual parental or patriarchal figures to closely monitor her behavior and reputation. This gives her far more agency than an upper-class young woman would typically have, but it also leaves her vulnerable to making bad decisions as a result of following her whims. The narrator clearly positions the root of the protagonist's behavior as an impulsive but ultimately innocent curiosity, and this creates sympathy for a character that might quickly get in over her head by pursuing this plan.

The success of the protagonist's disguise reveals several things about class and gender dynamics. Firstly, external markers such as clothing, jewelry, speech patterns, vocabulary, etc. signify and define one's place in the world. Simply by modifying these markers, she can move into a completely different position and radically change the dynamic of how other individuals interact with her. Her status as an upper-class woman both protects and stifles her: it ensures that she is protected from sexually aggressive behavior from men, but it also means that they do not interact with any freedom and playfulness. As soon as she presents herself as a woman who is of a lower class position and sexually available, men treat her completely differently. The idea of masquerade and disguise appears frequently in eighteenth-century literature for precisely this reason: by obscuring one's identity, it can also be liberating. As Terry Castle explains in her study of masquerades, "The masquerade symbolized a realm of women unmarked by patriarchy, unmarked by the signs of exchange and domination, and independent of the prevailing sexual economy of the eighteenth century"

The appearance of Beauplaisir (whose name combines "handsome" and "pleasure") is the moment when the protagonist's careful plan starts to slide out of her control. She has already nursed an attraction to him when they have interacted in more formal circumstances, and she finds it intoxicating that he is now paying attention to her—and that she can openly flirt back. Because of her newly liberated sexual status, the protagonist can speak her mind more openly. As Juliette Merritt explains, "Here, Haywood makes the conventional link between women's speech and their sexuality. Sexual and verbal looseness are linked because the body and access to discourse are the two main sites of women's oppression" (p. 54).

The protagonist and Beauplaisir's interaction also suggests that she has not completely transitioned into the disguise she has taken on: Beauplaisir notes with interest that she is more educated and refined than he would expect. This heightens his attraction to her, and suggests that rigid social distinctions benefit neither men nor women. Like most aristocratic men of the time, Beauplaisir likely has to rely on one category of women for sexual satisfaction, and another for emotional or intellectual engagement. His pleasure in seeing these two attributes come together suggests that allowing young women more freedom in how they interact with men might lead to more organic and satisfying romantic connections.

Part 2: The First Disguise

Summary :

When the play comes to an end, the protagonist suddenly finds herself in an awkward situation. Because he believes she is a prostitute, Beauplaisir is eager to have sex with her, and proposes that they go either to his home or to her residence. She considers telling him her true identity but comes up with another solution, which has the advantage of giving her the opportunity to see him again: she tells Beauplaisir that she already has an appointment with another client that night. Beauplaisir accepts this story, and persuades her to agree to return to the theatre the following night so that they may meet again. She agrees, and the two part ways.

The protagonist returns to her home in a flurry of emotions. She knows she is taking a risk by continuing the charade; however, she is intoxicated by the freedom it gives her, and she believes she will be strong enough to resist sexual temptation. She is also obsessed with the idea of continuing her interactions with Beauplaisir. The next day, before she goes to the theatre, she rents rooms in a nearby house. This gives her a space to which she and Beauplaisir can go, one where she hopes she will feel a sense of agency and control.

That evening, she meets Beauplaisir at the theatre again. He is determined that she will go home with him after the play ends, and happily accompanies her back to the rooms she has rented. Once there, he tries to make arrangements to have food delivered to them, but she has a lavish meal provided at her own expense. This makes Beauplaisir believe that she must be a very high-ranking courtesan; he becomes concerned that her services will be very expensive, but he decides that she will be worth the expenditure.

After they eat, Beauplaisir becomes very assertive in his attempts to seduce her. The protagonist begins to panic and almost reveals her true identity, but she realizes that she has already violated social convention and that revealing her true identity will only damage her reputation. She tells him that she is a virgin and that she only pretended to be a prostitute in order to get close to him, but this does not dissuade Beauplaisir. The two have sex.

In contrast to the first part of the novella, this section shows the protagonist's plan quickly spiraling out of control and putting her into vulnerable situations. At first she sees only the pleasures associated with the new identity she has taken on: she can enjoy herself and openly talk and flirt with Beauplaisir. This freedom, however, comes with a price: he expects she will have sex with him, something he would never demand or suggest of an aristocratic woman. The protagonist's innocence and lack of foresight is revealed when she is astonished by this expectation and is unsure how to handle it. The protagonist is clever, but not sophisticated; therefore, she never has as much control over her plans as she believes she does.

Another weakness of the protagonist's becomes apparent in this section: her feelings for Beauplaisir and her desire to keep seeing him. Even after realizing that he has clear sexual expectations and that it will be risky to continue to see him, she cannot simply resign herself to the experience having been a one-time occurrence. She agrees to meet him again. The elaborate plans she puts into motion to secure a space for them to be alone in speak either to deep naivety or deep denial. She is either convinced or trying to be convinced that she can fend off his sexual advances, even if they are alone in a private space together.

The desire to retain control of the situation and to be able to make decisions about how far the relationship goes manifests interestingly in the protagonist's behavior. She wants to be in control of the space where they go, and she also retains financial control by not allowing him to pay for the late-night supper they eat. In a surprisingly modern twist, the protagonist attempts to use her financial agency to assert her power within the relationship, worrying that by allowing Beauplaisir to purchase things for her, he will get the impression that he can also purchase access to her body.

Ultimately, however, all of the protagonist's careful plans are unsuccessful. Beauplaisir has interpreted all of her previous behavior as sexual encouragement and believes he is entitled to sexual gratification. The question of consent is ambiguous in the pair's first sexual encounter. She is clearly attracted to him, but also unprepared to stand her ground, and taken aback at how far things have gone. He undoubtedly ignores her protests and insists on the two having sex. While the narrator suggests that the protagonist experiences pleasure, the description is also marked by loss and a sense that this is a negative turning point for the protagonist. The sexual encounter seems to mark a moment where her plans have failed her by actually leaving her more vulnerable and unprotected.

Part 3, The First Disguise

Summary :

Afterwards the sexual encounter, the protagonist is very distressed; Beauplaisir is very confused as to why she had pursued him if she did not intend to have sex with him. He thinks she might be afraid that he is unwilling to pay her, and offers her a generous amount of money. The protagonist reacts angrily to him giving her money, saying it cannot compensate her for what she has lost. She tells Beauplaisir that the only adequate compensation for her loss of virtue will is his love and fidelity.

Beauplaisir vows to be true to her. No longer believing she is a prostitute, he asks her who she is. The protagonist is still unwilling to reveal her true identity and risk losing her reputation, so she tells him her name is Fantomina. and that she is the daughter of a country gentleman. Beauplaisir thinks to himself that she will undoubtedly eventually end up as a prostitute, but does not say anything to this effect.

Beauplaisir does not leave until very late, and Fantomina makes him promise to return to her the following day. In the morning, she bribes a servant of the house to back up her story if she is ever questioned. She also explains that she will only be at the house while visiting Beauplaisir, but, should he come looking for her, he is to be told that she has just gone out. With these arrangements made to keep her secret safe and conceal her identity, she returns to her actual residence and tells her aunt that she had taken a short trip and been left unable to return the night before.

As she reflects on what has happened, Fantomina feels secure that she has protected herself: even if Beauplaisir proves untrue, she will never have to worry about being publicly shamed. As time passes, she does indeed seem to be successfully executing her plan. She regularly meets Beauplaisir, but tells no one about the affair. She conceals her identity so effectively that when she meets her lover while presenting herself as a well-born lady, he has no idea that she is the same woman he knows as Fantomina. He notices a strong physical resemblance, but this similarity only makes the affair more arousing to him.

The protagonist's initial reaction after the two have sex suggests that she feels deceived, manipulated, and used. It also shows the limits of the disguise she has adopted. She enjoyed being perceived as a prostitute when it gave her freedom and required her only to flirt, but she is offended at actually taking money in exchange for sex. Her demands of Beauplaisir reflect the resurfacing of a more traditional model of feminine behavior in the text. She feels that the two of them engaging in a loving and monogamous relationship is the only thing that will legitimize her sexual transgression, allowing it become an expression of love rather than a tawdry exchange.

Despite her hopes that the two of them will cultivate a genuinely loving relationship, the protagonist is unwilling to be fully honest with Beauplaisir. She does admit that her presentation as a prostitute was a ruse, but she replaces this lie with a different one rather than telling the truth. Even though she does love him, she doesn't trust him and takes care to make sure her identity will remain concealed. This strategic choice suggests that the protagonist has quickly become more worldly and cynical. Having seen how quickly a seemingly innocent plan came to have real consequences, she takes steps to protect her future by ensuring her identity remains concealed.

The protagonist also seems to quickly bounce back from having been placed in an unanticipated situation, and reshapes her relationship with Beauplaisir into something over which she has control. She is quick-thinking, persuasive, and discreet, and all of these characteristics allow her to set up a framework in which she can pursue the relationship with very little fear of detection. By doing so, she adopts a position traditionally occupied solely by men: she can pursue a pleasurable relationship with the partner of her choice and not suffer any negative social consequences as a result. In this way, the power balance between her and Beauplaisir seems to shift: he is the naïve and blissfully ignorant one, while she calculates and makes decisions that best serve her interest. What mihgt have begun as a relationship in which she was vulnerable quickly becomes one in which she arguably has the upper hand. Margaret Case Croskery points out that, at this point in the novel, "she remains remarkably safe from the loss of honor, financial ruin, and emotional harm which traditionally plague the maiden raped by a man who does not intend to marry her"..

The novel's central plot of deception certainly stretches credibility: it seems outlandish that Beauplaisir could regularly be having sex with a woman and then fail to recognize her under other circumstances. The idea of characters being tricked into having sex without recognizing someone's identity has roots at least as far back as Shakespeare, often in a theatrical tradition that Haywood would have been familiar with. The narrator does also point out that he recognizes a similarity between his mistress and the protagonist, but uses this as an opportunity to illustrate how much social norms determine perception. It would seem impossible to Beauplaisir that an aristocratic woman would freely seek out sexual pleasure in the way he has observed his mistress doing, and so he simply discounts the resemblance as coincidence. He does. however. find the fantasy of combining a reserved, off-limit object of desire with an open-minded and sexually available woman to be particularly arousing.

Part 4: The Second and Third Disguises

Summary :

In time, Beauplaisir eventually begins to grow bored with her. It is time for him to go to Bath for the summer, and when Fantomina offers to go with him, he makes excuses about why she should not. Fantomina is hurt by this but conceals her feelings and sends him off, all the while laying plans to follow him. She desperately wants Beauplaisir to be infatuated with her again. As soon as he leaves, she tells her aunt that she is going to visit another relative and sets off, accompanied by two servants whom she quickly dismisses.

Before arriving in Bath, the protagonist assumes her second disguise, adopting a country accent and unfashionable clothes. She goes to the house where she knows Beauplaisir is lodging and offers to work as servant; the landlady hires her to attend to the male guests by bringing them their breakfasts and making their beds every morning. This role brings the disguised Fantomina, now going by the name of Celia, into close proximity with Beauplaisir, who is immediately attracted to her. The second morning that she comes into his room, he seduces her; after she feigns some shyness so as to maintain he disguise, the two have sex. Afterwards he gives her money, which she takes in order to avoid alerting his suspicions.

Beauplaisir plans to stay in Bath for a month; at first the two enjoy the affair, but he eventually becomes tired of Celia as well. Knowing this, the protagonist prepares a third plot. She quits her job and moves to a different house in the town in order to assume her new disguise. This time she poses as a widow, and when she knows Beauplaisir is on his way back to London, she arranges to be at an inn just outside of the town. When his carriage is passing by, she stops it and calls out to him, asking for help.

Beauplaisir is surprised by this request, since the widow appears prosperous, but he is eager to help. The disguised protagonist explains her story: she is a widow from Bristol and is trying to get to London so that she can claim her inheritance before the brother of her deceased husband squanders her. However, she has not been able to secure a coach and is now stranded; she asks if Beauplaisir would be willing to let her travel in his carriage. He readily agrees, but is disappointed to find that, once she enters the carriage, she weeps, laments, and will only talk about her dead husband. Hoping to distract her, he brings up the subject of love, and is surprised and pleased to notice how passionately she talks about love.

Beauplaisir now hopes to seduce the attractive widow, but he takes a much less direct tactic. He gradually indicates his interest, and when the two stop to spend the night at an inn, he makes bolder overtures. In order to maintain her disguise, the protagonist pretends to faint. He takes her to lie down, and when she has recovered, the two have sex.

The protagonist is so skilled at disguising herself that Beauplaisir does not see any connection between her and his previous lovers. They return to London together and promise to continue seeing each other. Beauplaisir gives her an address at which to contact him, and the protagonist promises to provide her details as soon as she has determined where she will be staying.

This section reveals that the protagonist has been right to doubt the sincerity and fidelity of Beauplaisir. In the traditional trope of the rake, he cannot remain interested in a woman for very long, and as soon as he loses interest, he tries to find a way out of the relationship. What makes Haywood's narrative innovative and unexpected is how her protagonist responds to him losing interest. She is very self-aware and notices that he is no longer attracted to her. Rather than being frustrated or angry, she reacts coolly, immediately starting to calculate how best to win him back. She is not critical of Beauplaisir for his lack of fidelity, and in fact seems to view it as the natural result. At the same time, however, she is committed to continuing the relationship rather than also moving on and finding another lover. Patricia Comitini connects this unexpected devotion to a central debate at the heart of the text: "knowing Beauplaisir is a rake whose interest in women is transitory does not stop the Lady from pursuing him over and over again. The conundrum of the novella is that knowledge does not always lead to rational action".

The protagonist's second disguise is even bolder than her first. It involves a more dramatic shift of class position and requires her to be very shrewd about understanding how to completely change her self-presentation in order to adopt a position at the opposite end of the social scale. Beauplaisir's response also reveals how class positions intersected with sexuality in this time period. In her first disguise, he assumed he was free to have sex with the protagonist because she earned money from sex. A maidservant earns wages in a different way, but he also assumes that she will not say no to a wealthy and powerful man. Again, he offers money to the protagonist after they have sex; this time, she accepts it because she assumes that is what the woman as whom she is disguised would accept it. This shows how much less idealistic she has become: she is now willing to do whatever it takes to maintain secrecy and hold onto Beauplaisir's interest.

Beauplaisir's identity as a rake is further confirmed when he loses interest in Celia just as he lost interest in Fantomina. The protagonist simply concocts another plan, displaying her willingness to try different types of disguises to see what else might appeal to him. Her various disguises play into the different stereotypes of women: from an innocent and coy maidservant, she then adopts the guise of a wealthy widow. Predictably, Beauplaisir finds this new opportunity for seduction an appealing challenge. His wide-ranging appetite suggests that he is largely fueled by a constant search for novelty: almost any woman can be appealing to him if she represents the new and unexpected.

Beauplaisir's strategy for seducing the widow is also telling. With both Fantomina and Celia, he was very direct and assertive, assuming that their class positions made them unlikely to say no. With the widow, he takes a much more subtle and gradual approach, assuming that a woman of a higher social position will be more wary. In an ironic twist, while he is performing the kind of seduction that he thinks will be most effective, the protagonist is also performing the kind of reaction she thinks he will expect, including pretending to faint in shock and horror. These deceptions and counter-deceptions reveal that social conventions prevent both men and women from acting naturally and being honest with one another.

Part 5: The Fourth Disguise

Summary :

Once the protagonist and Beauplaisir part ways in London, she rents rooms under the name of Widow Bloomer and sends word for him via letter to come and visit her there. Then she goes back to the rooms she rented as Fantomina and instructs the servants to make sure that if Beauplaisir comes looking for her, he is not told that she has been away from London. Disguising her handwriting, she sends him a letter lamenting that he has not come to see her, and attributes it to Fantomina.

Beauplaisir promptly responds to both letters, vowing his affection and fidelity to both women. The protagonist is outraged at his lies, but is relieved that she has protected herself, and decides to keep enjoying the sexual aspect of the relationship. Beauplaisir visits her both when she is the Widow and when she is Fantomina, and she notices that he strongly prefers the former, because that relationship is newer. However, within a fairly short time, Beauplaisir has also tired of the widow.

Fantomina now has a new scheme, and this one requires help. She finds two men and offers to pay them to render her some service. They happily agree and she arranges to meet them the following day. Then she goes to rent a large and splendid house. When she meets the two men she has hired, she presents them with uniforms resembling those worn by the servants of the wealthy. She tells one of them to deliver a letter to Beauplaisir. This letter has been written in a handwriting that is different from that of her other letters. It purports to be from an anonymous woman (signed Incognita) who is in love with him and wants him to come and visit her. She promises to do anything he wants, but insists that she will not reveal her name or face. The messenger has been instructed to refuse to give any details if Beauplaisir tries to find out her identity.

When the letter is delivered, Beauplaisir does indeed try to find out who Incognita is, but he is not given any information. With his curiosity inflamed, he writes back expressing his eagerness to meet this mysterious woman. The two meet at the house the protagonist rented, and she appears with a mask. They have sex, and then Beauplaisir begins to try to persuade her to show him her face. She refuses, and when he realizes she is not going to change her mind, he asks if he can spend the night at her house. The protagonist agrees, but is suspicious of what his motives are. She is right to be suspicious, as Beauplaisir plans to unmask her while she is sleeping. The protagonist ensures that she joins him in bed in a very dark room, and even when it grows light outside, the windows are so tightly sealed that no light penetrates the room. As soon as they awake, she hurries out of the room without his having seen her face. Frustrated, Beauplaisir expresses his unhappiness that she will not show him her face. However, the protagonist holds firm, and he leaves the house determined not to see her again.

Beauplaisir has already demonstrated his lack of constancy, but this section highlights his tendency towards outright deception. Rather than simply ending his relationships, he continues to deceive and string along whom he believes to be multiple women. This realization seems to validate the protagonist's suspicions and makes her happy that she has taken precautions to protect herself. However, knowing that Beauplaisir is willing to blatantly lie and be unfaithful to her does not make her want to sever contact with him. She hopes to continue to enjoy the sexual aspect of their relationship while being pragmatic about his failings. This decision on her part can be read as either empowered, or self-delusional. In one reading, she does not need his fidelity or even affection: she can assess the relative merits of the relationship, and so long as he continues to gratify her sexually, she can make a clear-eyed decision to keep him around. Alternatively, it can be argued that she is so infatuated with Beauplaisir that she simply continues to find excuses to pursue the relationship even though it offers her little benefit and no security.

Tricking and manipulating Beauplaisir also appears to have become something of an obsession for the heroine. It may enhance her sexual pleasure to know that she secretly has the upper hand, and that she can also set the terms of their encounters. Her disguise as Incognita is the most explicit form of trickery yet, in that here it is clear to Beauplaisir that information is being withheld from him and that he does not actually know the woman with whom he is interacting. This final disguise also generates a more explicit reversal of power. While the protagonist has of course stage-managed her previous encounters with Beauplaisir, to him they appeared as simple coincidences. Here, it is very obvious that the mysterious woman has summoned him for her own sexual gratification and is controlling the situation. It is also noted that here, for the first time, the protagonist does not even try to pretend to fend off his sexual overtures. In the disguise of Incognita, she can finally portray a woman who takes full ownership of her sexuality and dictates the terms of her encounters.

Beauplaisir's reaction to actually knowing he is being manipulated and deceived shows why the protagonist was right to pursue secrecy. He has no interest in respecting the boundaries Incognita sets, and immediately starts plotting to find a way to reveal her true identity. He ignores the fact that she has said she does not want to show him her face, just as he previously ignored Fantomina saying she did not want to have sex with him. When he realizes he has been outwitted, and that by making sure the room will remain totally dark, Incognita has ensured he will be unable to see her face, he reacts with frustration and anger. Ironically, considering the number of women with whom he thinks he is being dishonest, he expects total transparency from her, and is angry that she will not simply give in to his demands of revealing her identity.

Part 6: The Unmasking

Summary :

Over the next several weeks, the protagonist continues to see Beauplaisir in the guise of both Fantomina and the Widow Bloomer, but she is bored by the now unenthusiastic encounters. This pattern is interrupted by two surprising events. First, the protagonist's mother arrives in the city, having heard rumors of her daughter's reckless behavior. She has no idea of the extent of what the protagonist has done, but is sufficiently concerned so as to begin to limit her daughter's freedoms. More importantly, the protagonist discovers that she is pregnant. It is difficult for her to hide this condition from her mother, but she manages to do so for a time. Since her mother plans to send her back to the country anyways, her plan is to wait until she leaves the city, then slip away and discreetly give birth in secret.

Unfortunately for the protagonist, she goes into labor during a court ball. She is clearly in pain, but everyone at the ball assumes she has been abruptly taken ill, including her mother. She is rushed back home, where her mother summons a doctor. The doctor quickly informs the protagonist's mother what the situation actually is; the mother is horrified and outraged. She demands that the protagonist reveal the father of her child, which is something the protagonist tries to avoid doing. The mother, however, insists that she will not call a midwife to help the protagonist unless she first reveals her lover. Afraid and in pain, she names Beauplaisir as the father.

The mother immediately sends for a midwife and also sends a message for Beauplaisir to come and see her. He promptly arrives, confused as to why this aristocratic woman has summoned him. When she accuses him of having impregnated her daughter, he denies it, insisting that he has had only brief interactions with her during formal social occasions. The mother is more infuriated than ever, and drags Beauplaisir into the room where the protagonist is resting, having just given birth to a baby girl. Humiliated and horrified, the protagonist reveals the whole story of how she deceived and tricked Beauplaisir repeatedly, so that, while he is indeed the father of her child, he is innocent of any deliberate intent to dishonor a respectable lady.

After listening in astonishment, the mother admits that she can no longer demand that Beauplaisir marry her daughter, which is what she had initially planned to insist on. She asks only that he not publicly reveal the scandal to others. He agrees to keep the secret and also offers to raise his daughter, but both the protagonist and her mother reject this offer. Beauplaisir leaves the house in a state of deep confusion and shock. For a time, he continues to visit to check in on the protagonist's health, but when her mother becomes concerned that these visits will lead to the two renewing their affair, she puts a stop to them. As soon as the protagonist has recovered, she is sent to a convent in France.

In the novel's final section, the protagonist's ruse is interrupted by two reassertions of authority, one social and the other biological. The abrupt appearance of her mother signals the return to a more socially conventional dynamic in which the protagonist's behavior would be closely scrutinized and monitored by parental authority figures so as to maintain her reputation and value on the marriage market. From the very beginning, the protagonist's ability to do whatever she wants and pursue her desires has been linked to the lack of parental supervision; when her mother appears, this freedom and autonomy quickly disappears. While her mother clearly does not know the extent of the liberties the protagonist has taken, she already has some suspicions. This suggests that the protagonist might not have been quite as discreet as she believes.

Pregnancy is the second and more serious consequence to the freedoms the protagonist has enjoyed. In an era where medical knowledge of effective contraception was very limited, and where young women would have been sheltered from even the most basic biological knowledge, unintentional pregnancy would have been a common consequence of sexual activity. While the protagonist's careful planning and foresight has helped her to avoid many of the social consequences of illicit sexual activity, she has not been able to avoid the biological one, and in a sense it seems that her body finally triumphs over her mind. As Charles Hinnant explains, "the deceptions expose an insoluble conflict between the dual imperatives of pleasure and procreation. Fantomina seems blissfully (and most implausibly) unaware of the obvious risk to which her successive disguises and liaisons with Beauplaisir expose her" (p. 406), that risk being pregnancy. At first, however, she seems confident in her ability to solve this problem just as she has resolved many others. Having the child in secret and presumably arranging to have it adopted would have been the most common strategy for aristocratic women trying to hide illegitimate pregnancies. With her intelligence and wealth, it seems possible that the protagonist might be able to successfully execute this plan.

Pregnancy, especially before modern medicine, makes her physically vulnerable, and ultimately undermines the agency she has exerted throughout the novel. When she goes into labor, she is in too much pain to be able to conceal it. For the first time, her ability to disguise herself fails her. When her mother realizes that she is in labor and becomes determined to find out the identity of the father, the physical pain of childbirth also finally breaks the protagonist's secrecy. The mother coldly and ruthlessly exploits this suffering to her own end, but is also behaving shrewdly: she hopes that by confronting the father, she can shame him into marrying her daughter, thereby concealing the affair and legitimizing the child. It seems probable that the protagonist may have inherited her quick-thinking and adaptability from her mother.

The mother's success at obtaining Beauplaisir's identity results in the novel's climax, at which the protagonist is finally forced to reveal her deception. She has to endure the shame of admitting her scandalous behavior, and of surrendering control. Beauplaisir's reaction is far more measured than might be expected, given how much he has been deceived. He does not lash out, and he offers to provide for his newborn daughter. More strikingly still, he continues to visit regularly and inquire about the protagonist. This gesture suggests a sincere and ongoing affection for her in spite of all the lies. Indeed, it may indicate that Beauplaisir finds the possibility of one woman possessing a multi-faceted identity, a vivid sexuality, and keen intelligence to be attractive.

However, the forces of social normativity and a return to patriarchal culture exemplified in the protagonist's mother serve to punish her for her transgressions. For Haywood's primarily English, Protestant readership, the prospect of being sent to a convent in France would have been very grim. Catholic cultures were perceived as more repressive and focused on strictly curtailing a woman's freedoms; thus, the protagonist can be assumed to be being sent off to live out her days in isolation, with no freedom or further sexual adventures in store. Moreover, she will not even be able to redeem herself by a legitimate marriage and family. While not clearly explained, it seems likely that the protagonist will also be estranged from her infant daughter.

Thus, for the three generations of women assembled at the end of the story, little seems to have changed. The protagonist has boldly challenged the status quo, and highlighted the ways in which a woman might occupy a complex identity. She is ultimately not successful in maintaining this position, and ends up ironically with far fewer freedoms than she would have possessed as a respectably married woman in England. Whether the ending should be read as a punishment for her transgressions or as an indictment of how society conspires to repress women is ambiguous. What is clear is that the protagonist's innocent curiosity costs her a high price.

❖ *Fantomina*-এর সারাংশের বঙ্গানুবাদ :

কাহিনীর সূচনা হয়েছে লন্ডনের একটি নাট্যশালায় যেখানে কাহিনীর নামহীণ মহিলা কেন্দ্রীয় চরিত্রটি, একটি বেশ্যার প্রতি নাট্যশালায় উপস্থিত সমস্ত পুরুষের আগ্রহ ও ঔৎসুক্য দেখে নিজে একজন বেশ্যার ছদ্মবেশ ধরার সিদ্ধান্ত নেয়। ছদ্মবেশ ধরা অবস্থায়, সে বিউপ্লাউসির নামক এক যুবকের সাথে কথোপকথন বিশেষভাবে উপভোগ করতে থাকে। এই যুবকটির সাথে তার আগেও কথাবার্তা হয়েছিল যদিও তখন সেই কথাবার্তায় তার নিজের সামাজিক বিধিনিষেধের সীমাবদ্ধতার বাঁধন ছিল।যুবকটি, তাকে চিনতে না পারায়, আর তাকে বেশ্যা বলে মনে করায়, তাকে একান্তে দেখা করার প্রস্তাব দেয়। সে দ্বিধাবোধ করে আর তাকে পরের দিন সন্ধ্যা অবধি বিলম্বিত করে।

প্রস্তুতি স্বরূপ সে একটি ঘর ভাড়া নেয় এবং পরেরদিন রাতে যুবকটির সাথে নাট্যশালায় দেখা করে। তারা দুইজনে সেই ভাড়াবাড়িটিতে যায় আর নৈশভোজ সারে। ইতিমধ্যে এই নারীটি বঝতে পারে যে বিউপ্লাউসির তার সাথে যৌনসঙ্গম করতে চায় আর সে তাকে এই বলে বাধা দিতে চায় যে সে আসলে কুমারী ও সতী। তাসত্ত্বেও, যুবকটি কামনায় এতটাই ব্যাকুল হয়ে পড়েছিল যে সে মেয়েটির কোনও কথায় কান দেয়না ও তাকে ধর্ষন করে।

এরপরে মেয়েটি মনমরা হয়ে পড়ে ও যুবকটির দেওয়া টাকা নিতে অস্বীকার করে যা যুবকটিকে হতভম্ব করে দেয়, যেহেতু সে মেয়েটির পূর্বকার বাধাপ্রদানকে গুরুত্বপূর্ণ মনে করেনি। নিজের সম্মানের বিষয়ে আশঙ্কিত হয়ে মেয়েটি নিজের নাম বলে 'ফ্যান্টমিনা'।

যাইহোক, শীঘ্রই বিউপ্লাউসির মেয়েটির প্রতি আগ্রহ হারায় আর বাথ-এর উদ্দেশ্যে যাত্রা করে। যদিও মেয়েটি গোটা উপন্যাস ধরে 'ফ্যান্টমিনা'-র আড়ালে নিজেকে ঢেকে রাখে, তবুও কিছু সময়ের জন্য সে নিজের এই নকল পরিচয় ত্যাগ করে যখন সে সেই যুবকটির পিছু নিয়ে বাথ-এ পৌঁছোয়। এক গ্রাম্য দাসীর ছদ্মবেশে, সে সেই অতিথিশালায় কাজ নেয় যেখানে সেই যুবকটি বসবাস করছিল। সে এখানে নিজেকে সিলিয়া বলে পরিচয় দিল। যখন বিউপ্লাউসির তাকে দেখল, যুবকটি তাকে একজন নতুন চাকরানী বলে মনে করল, আর তার সাথে প্রেমসুলভ আচরণ করা শুরু করল। মেয়েটি এবারে দুইজনের যৌন সঙ্গমটি যত্নের সাথে পরিকল্পনা করল আর বিউপ্লাউসির-এর প্রতিটি প্রতিক্রিয়া মেয়েটির ছলনাকারী আচরনের প্রতিক্রিয়ায় বেরিয়ে এল, কিন্তু প্রেমিক যুবকটি মনে করল যে সে মেয়েটিকে তার অমতে ধর্ষণ করেছে। ক্ষতিপূরণ স্বরুপ যুবকটি মেয়েটিকে কিছু টাকা দিল।

সিরিয়ার প্রতি আগ্রহ হারিয়ে একমাস পরে যুবকটি বাথ থেকে চলে গেল। বাড়ি ফেরার পথে, যুবকটির সাথে মিসেস ব্লুমার বলে এক মহিলার দেখা হল, যে ছিল আসলে বিধবার ছদ্মবেশ ধরা সেই মেয়েটিই, আর যুবকটি তাকে নিজের গাড়িতে যাত্রা করার প্রস্তাব দিল। মেয়েটির কল্পিত বেদনার কাহিনী শীঘ্রই মেয়েটিকে সান্ত্বনা দেওয়ার সুযোগ করে দিল যুবকটিকে, যার ফলশ্রুতি স্বরূপ পথের ধারের এক সরাইখানায় তারা যৌন সঙ্গমে লিপ্ত হল।

যখন এই পরিচয়টিও বিউপ্লাউসির-এর আগ্রহ ধরে রাখতে ব্যর্থ হল, তখন গল্পের নায়িকাটি বিউপ্লাউসিরকে নিজের অমর ভালোবাসা ও আবেগের কথা জানিয়ে চিঠি লিখল "ইনকগনিটা" নাম ধরে। সে জানাল যে সে তাকে কোনও কিছুই দিতে অস্বীকার করবে না, কেবল সে তাকে নিজের মুখ দেখাবে না। তারা দেখা করল আর নায়িকাটি, একটি মুখোশ পড়া অবস্থায়, যুবকটির সাথে অন্ধকারে শয্যাসঙ্গী হতে রাজী হল। বিউপ্লাউসির প্রতিটি শারীরিক মিলনে অংশগ্রহন করল কিন্তু বুঝতে পারল না যে এরা সকলেই একই মেয়ে ছিল।

নায়িকাটি অন্তঃসত্ত্বা হয়ে পড়ল আর যখন যে সন্তান প্রসব করল তখন তার মা তাকে সন্তানের পিতার নাম বলার জন্য জোর করতে লাগলেন। যখন বিউপ্লাউসির উপস্থিত হল, সে বুঝতে পারল না মেয়েটি আসলে কে যতক্ষণ না মেয়েটির পুরো কাহিনীটি তাকে জানান হল। শেষে, মেয়েটির মা তাকে বসবাসের জন্য ফ্রান্সের একটি সন্ন্যাসিনীদের মঠে প্রেরণ করলেন।

❖ A Critical Analysis of *Fantomina* :

In spite of the immense popularity of her novels which, at the time of their publication, were legitimate sales rival to works by such writers as Pope and Swift, traditional scholarship has attached little importance to the name of Eliza Haywood. Such scholarship, however, is misguided; as one of the founders of popular literature, and especially the popular novel, Haywood is a key figure in Eighteenth Century Literature whose influence remains with us to this day. Moreover, Haywood's works were, and still remain, revolutionary in theme as they focus largely upon the role of the female within patriarchal society, the possibilities of female empowerment, and even the taboo subject of female sexual freedom. In Fantomina: Or Love in a Maze, Haywood's revolutionary views on society come to the fore in relation to the topic of female identity. Ultimately, this short novel offers the troubling thesis that the very notion of female identity is displaced by patriarchy, which forces women into restrictive, powerless roles.

Fantomina is fittingly labelled "A Masquerade Novel" (786). Indeed, the central plot of the work revolves around masquerade as the protagonist constructs for herself several different personas in an attempt to win and to keep the object of her desire, Beauplaisir. However, the implications of the term 'masquerade' seem to go deeper than this. Haywood introduces her main character as "A young Lady of distinguished Birth, Beauty, Wit, and Spirit" (786); other than this somewhat generic description, which could fit any number of upper-class Eighteenth Century "young ladies," Haywood's characterization of her protagonist is virtually nonexistent. In fact, this young lady is not even provided a name. In short, she is not so much a three-dimensional character as she is a typical persona, a recognizable female role rather than a specific individual. While on the surface this may seem to be an indication of inferior writing skills, the lengths to which Haywood goes in the maintaining her protagonist's lack of individuality and identity, such as having her referred to as "Lady Such-a-one" (787), suggest that a specific motif is being consciously developed. Haywood seems to be indicating that, before her protagonist has begun to scheme, before the very outset of the novel even, the masquerade has already begun. Within the world presented by Haywood, the woman's role always involves the wearing of a mask.

It is for this reason that the transformation of Haywood's protagonist from a "fine Lady to a prostitute takes place with such ease. Her disguise does not involve the covering of her true identity with a false one; rather, it is achieved through the mere shedding of one persona for another. Haywood's Protagonist is, in essence, a tabula rasa of sorts; her only identity is the one that she constructs. Thus, when Beauplaisir encounters her playing the role of Fantomina, a prostitute, he does fancy "that she very much resemble[s] the Lady whom she really [is]; but the vast Disparity there appear[s] between their Characters, prevent[s] him from entertaining even the most distant Thought that they could be the same" (787). This theme is played out throughout the novel as Beauplaisir repeatedly fails to recognize the protagonist as being anything other than that which she professes to be, in spite of his having intimate relations with each of her several personas. As readers we may be tempted to view Beauplaisir as being overly gullible in this respect; it must be noted, however, that in many ways Fantomina (along with the personas that follow) does, indeed, come to life as a far more real, mire believable, character than the protagonist she starts out as. In fact, the persona of Fantomina is actually chosen by Haywood as the character after whom the novel is entitled.

Certainly, the several personas of Fantomina are most fascinating in their ultimate success in becoming believable to the protagonist herself as she changes not only her appearance, but also, as it would seem, her very character. In taking on the identity of the prostitute, Fantomina's actions soon come to match her appearance as she allows Beauplaisir sexual privileges to which the "fine lady" described at the beginning of the novel would, most assuredly, not have consented. Further, she is offered "a purse of Gold" (789) as reward for her consent; although she does not accept it, Beauplaisir's offer nevertheless forces us to realize that Fantomina's sexuality has, indeed, become commodified. This pattern continues as she takes on the role of Celia, a country girls, and offers "herself to Service in the House where Beauplaisir [is] lodged" (792). In doing so, she not only gives up her upper-class status to the "Amorous Violence" (792) of the man she has been hired to serve. While she considers herself fortunate that Beauplaisir, whom she desires, is the only man at the house who is able to take such liberties, she never makes her desires known but, rather, gives in to his. As the Widow Bloomer, she retains this air of vulnerability and, "not thinking it Decent, for the Character she [has] assumed, to yield so suddenly [...], she counterfeit[s] a fainting" (795) and allows him to carry her off to bed. Simply put, her concern is not that her actions remain consistent with any notion of selfhood that she may have, but that they remain consistent with the persona of "the character she has assumed." In short, Haywood's protagonist does not simply take on several false appearances; she actually takes on, actually becomes, several different roles.

Ironically, this role playing is seen by Haywood's protagonist as a source of power and freedom. Although the roles that she takes on are for the most part powerless, she believes herself to be in control of her situation; it is herself, after all, who decides which role she will step into. Certainly, Fantomina does manipulate Beauplaisir quite effectively in leading him to believe that he is being unfaithful when, in reality, he is having several affairs with the same woman. Of this manipulation she triumphantly declares, "while he thinks the fool of me, [Beauplaisir] is himself the only beguiled person" (796). Nonetheless, we see in Haywood's protagonist a character who is trying desperately to retain a relationship with a man who has no desire to so the same. Thus, it is she who is forced to jump through hoops and take on roles while he is free to do as he wishes and remain true to his own identity, as contemptible as that identity may seem.

Nonetheless, it is difficult to argue with Fantomina's reasoning that as long as Beauplaisir is kept from "discovering her true Name and Quality [...] he should not have it in his Power to touch her Character" (790). This passage, however, seems to imply that it is not so much the taking on of new roles that empowers Haywood's protagonist as it is the shedding of her old role. Haywood seems to be suggesting that the only way in which women can achieve true power within patriarchal society is to resist being confined to any role whatever. This hypothesis is made most explicit in the persona (or lack thereof) of Incognita. It is only as Incognita that Haywood's protagonist gains any true control over Beauplaisir. As a woman without any identity or reputation Incogniat is, for the first time, able to make advances on "the All-conquering Beauplaisir" (798). By shedding all roles and refusing to take up a new one, Haywood's protagonist is finally able to enter a relationship with Beauplaisir in which she is not limited by any preconceived expectations of behaviour and is, thus, free to conquer him, rather than allowing for herself to be conquered by him. In fact, Beausplaisir seems well aware of his defeat and is "so much out of Humour [...] at the Disappointment of his Curiosity, that he resolve[s] never to make a second Visit" (801).

Unfortunately, this development, coupled with "the Arrival of her Mother" (801), finally forces Haywood's protagonist back into her original role. However, by now it has become obvious that this role is nothing more than another of her many personas. In order to fit the expectations placed upon her as "A Young Lady of distinguished Birth" (786), she is forced to conceal the fact that "[s]he is with child" (801). Of course, she is ultimately found out when she goes into labour, thereby changing roles once again from the "fine lady" to the "fallen woman." Perhaps the most troubling aspect of Haywood's novel is the reaction of the protagonist's own mother to her daughter's plight as "[a]ll the Pity and Tenderness she had been for some Moment before possessed of, now [vanish], and [are] succeeded by an adequate Shame and Indignation" (802). In short, even the feelings that the protagonist's mother displays are, like those of Beauplaisir, based upon what rather than who she perceives her daughter to be.

In the final analysis, Haywood's novel, Fantomina, presents a critique of patriarchal society in which female identity is virtually non-existent. Instead, the person is displaced and overshadowed by the personas that women are forced to put on. Hence, Haywood's works are of prime importance as they provide not only a bridge between elitist and popular literature, but also offer some valuable insights concerning the role of the female within Eighteenth Century society, as well as our own.

The actions the young lady in Eliza Haywoods Fantomina in her desire to find a sexually and emotionally stimulating relationship demonstrates the difficulty of relationships between men and woman in the eighteen century. My lady such- a-one, as she is referred to by Haywood takes the roles of many different women to repeatedly seduce a man named Beauplasir. For the most part of her new identities, Fantomina's creative ideas resemble her increased desire for Beauplasir and her initial curiosity becomes reflected upon her need to change her identity in order to recapture Beauplasir's attention. Fantomina enjoys the fact that her disguises allow her do anything that she wishes, although, she seems to not think of the idea that a relationship between an upper class man and a low class woman is not very lasting and that her actions will eventually make herself the author of her own story.

Fantomina is a high quality mistress in the eighteenth century and because of her social position she has many restrictions placed upon her. She is not allowed to carry out a conversation of any type with a person of the opposite sex, nor is she allowed to pursue them. These behaviors were unacceptable in Fantomina's society; therefore, women were supposed to have chaperones who were to protect them from men and also to make sure women behaved appropriately. Fantomina's recognition of a familiar face down below the balcony where she is sitting at reawakens her interest for Beauplasir whom she she has before seen, but because of society she has been unable to pursue him. However, because men were different from women and had the freedom to do anything they wanted to, Beauplasir is allowed to leave the balcony and pursue women. Fantomina "is fascinated by the dalliance between 'respectable' gentlemen and loose women of the town." "This excited a curiosity in her to know in what manner these creatures were addressed." (Haywood, 2739- 2740). Although, Fantominas's actions seem intentional her new identity originates all from curiosity in her pursuit to sustain Beauplasir's interest.

Fed up with her restrictions, Fantomina decides to change her clothes to hide her real identity. It is here where Haywood reveals the restrictions on women of high social standing and the decisions of who belongs to what social position. In this case, clothing puts Fantomina in a lower social standing, even more, her new identity is that of a prostitute. Now as a prostitute, Fantomina is able to pursue Beauplasir without any restrictions as he is unable to recognize her new identity. In preparation to her encounter with Beauplasir, Fontamina puts on her new identity and while with Beauplasir she resists him at first because she is worried about her reputation. At this point, Fantomina is concerned about her moral actions, but her desires can do more now because that is what she has been looking for. This of course, confuses Beauplasir because that's what prostitutes are expected to do and in the end a prostitute gets paid in return. Fantomina's first disguise as a prostitute is all out of curiosity, but her imagination was so much talented that she had the power to change her appearance as she pleased. "As Fantomina changes character, she modifies her behaviors to align with his expectations." (Anderson 2005). The quote describes Fantomina's admirable skills in manipulating the situation for her own benefit. As expected, Beauplasir grows tired of

Fantomina and this is where she takes on her new identity to continue to follow him.

Now as Celia, a low class woman she becomes Beauplasir's maid, a new identity that becomes a bit more important than the one before because of social status .As her seduction continues she feels that she has become attached to Beauplasir and she can't let go of him she spends much of her time coming up with new ideas to seduce him. Her actions become a little emotional, but at the same time she intelligent as she is willing to go even further to maintain her sexual relationship with Beauplasir. It seems that what had started from curiosity has now turned into a passion that reflects her deepest emotions. "Her consistent ability to perform means that she repeatedly creates a space in which she may express her emotions." (Anderson 2005). In a sense, Fantomina feels that she belongs to Beauplasir since he has taken her virginity and she attaches this to the fact that she now struggles to maintain her honor from being publicly exposed.

Fantomina's now passion for Beauplasir leads her to go even further in her seduction attempt. This time, as the widow bloomer she becomes a little more vulnerable and portrays herself as weak. At one point, the widow fakes a sudden faint and allows Beauplasir to carry her off to bed. This proves that Fantomina is very calculating and her actions are being consistent with the character she assumes to be. In doing so, Fantomina believes her different roles are a source of power and freedom, but also her ability to succeed in her new role taking. Although, the role that she takes on for the most part is powerless because she gains nothing from it, she has quite effectively succeeded in making Beauplasir believe that he has been sleeping with different personas.

In her last disguise as Incognita, the significant thing they have in common is class and as the encounters continue, it seems that Fantomina's actions are driven by pure lust. Incognita its Fantomina's last attempt to seduce Beauplasir and it ultimately fails just as her other disguises. Despie Beuaplasir being desperately curious to know who she really is he never shows real interest in maintaining a relationship with Incognita because in the end he has nothing to gain from a woman who demands that her identity never be revealed. This culminates with Fantomina's realization that Beauplasir's real interest for her has been to satisfy his own sexual needs as he never remained faithful to her for the simple fact that he slept with the same person thinking he had been with four different women. Croskery describes that, "the heroine of Fantomina experiences one of her deepest moment of internalization at the precise moment when she becomes conscious of herself as an object of someone else's desire." (Croskery 2007). Through Beauplasir, the reader realizes that women are nothing but trophies and toys that are to be played with.

Ultimately, Fantomina's various identities accomplish nothing; they do serve to reveal how lustful Beauplasir is as well as Fantomina whether she acted on curiosity her real intentions remain ambiguous. Unfortunately, Fantomina's creative disguises only satisfy her sexual desires, but never create a long- lasting relationship with Beauplasir which results in her own betrayal. Fantomina's pregnancy becomes her true story in which she has lost everything including her reputation.

Short Questions with Answers

Q. 1. What is the alternative title of the novel *Fantomina*?

Ans. The allternative title of the novel *Fantomina* by Eliza Haywood is "LOVE in a Maze. Being ASecret History of An Amour between Two Persons of Condition".

Q. 2. When was *Fantomina* first published?

Ans. 'Fantomina' was first published in 1725, in *Secret Histories, Novels, and Poems,* by Eliza Haywood, Vol. 3, pp. 257-91 [Second Edition].

Q. 3. Who is Fantomina?

Ans. Fantomina is the first identity the novel's unnamed protagonist takes on. Fantomina is a playhouse prostitute. This is opposite of who the protagonist really is, because the protagonist comes from a distinguished family. She assumes this identity out of curiosity about how freely the prostitutes can speak to men without being judged. Thinking that she is an actual prostitute, Beauplasir rapes her and then he leaves for Bath when he gets tired of Fantomina.

Q. 4. Who is Celia in the novel *Fantomina*?

Ans. Celia is the identity the protagonist embodies after Beauplasir moves to Bath. The protagonist follows him and assumes the role of Celia, a country girl working as a maid. She seduces Beauplasir (even though he doesn't realize he's being seduced). Beauplasir quickly grows tired of Celia and departs again.

Q. 5. Who is Mrs. Bloomer in the novel *Fantomina*?

Ans. This is the third disguise the protagonist uses. Mrs. Bloomer is a traveling widow. Beauplasir uses her "grief" to his advantage and "seduces" her (quotes around seduces because he technically is not the one doing the seducing: it was the protagonist's plan all along). They have sex many times (including when they stop for a while at an inn).

Q. 6. Who is Incognita in the novel *Fantomina*?

Ans. The final disguise the protagonist assumes. Incognita is a masked lady. Her ambiguity/mystery signifies a very high-class woman, and in his encounters with her, Beauplaisir is aware that he is being deceived.

Q. 7. Who is Beauplaisir in the novel *Fantomina*?

Ans. Beauplaisir is a wealthy, handsome, aristocratic man. He is a rake who is accustomed to pursuing sexual pleasure and then discarding women when he tires of them. However, he cannot read between the lines, and therefore gets seduced multiple times by the same woman without realizing it. The woman gets away with seducing him by wearing a series of disguises. He eventually gets her pregnant before she is forced to live in a monastery.

Q. 8. Give a brief intorduction to The protagonist's mother in the novel *Fantomina.*

Ans. The mother of the protagonist abruptly appears late in the novel when she learns that her daughter is misbehaving. She is very shrewd and observant, which makes it difficult for the protagonist to conceal her pregnancy. She is also interested in preserving norms and social conventions, and hopes that she can conceal the illegitimate pregnancy by quickly arranging a marriage between her daughter and Beauplaisir.

Q. 9. Give a brief intorduction to The protagonist's aunt in the novel *Fantomina.*

Ans. At the beginning of the novel, the protagonist is being supervised by her aunt. However, the aunt is easily fooled and does not place any constraints on her behavior, which leaves the protagonist free to pursue her own desires.

Q. 10. Where do the part -1 of the novel open? What was the unnamed woman protagonist doing when the novel opens? How is she described by the novelist?

Ans. The novel opens in a London playhouse during a performance.

The novel's unnamed protagonist, a beautiful and intelligent young woman from a good family, is there to see the play. She has only recently arrived in London, having grown up in the country, and enjoys an uncommon amount of independence and autonomy.

Q. 11. What does the woman protagonist notice in the play house in the first part of the novel *Fantomiona*?

Ans. As unnamed woman protagonist gazes around at the other people attending the theatre, she notices that one woman in particular is receiving a lot of male attention. This woman is readily identifiable as a prostitute.

Q. 12. What was the reaction of the woman protagonist in novel *Fantamonia* on seeing men paying attraction to a prostitute woman?

Ans. The protagonist is surprised that men, some of whom she knows and considers to be intelligent, are still so willing to associate with her; however, when she expresses this idea to the well-bred ladies sitting near her, they dismiss her as sheltered and naïve. The more she thinks about it, the more the protagonist becomes intrigued with knowing how the experiences of a prostitute are different from her own.

Q. 13. What does the woman protagonist do to know the expperience of a prostitute in the paly house?

Ans. Spurred by her ability to follow her own unchecked impulses, the very next night she returns to the playhouse in disguise. Hiding her identity by veiling her face, she sits in a different section of the theatre and imitates the behavior of the prostitute she had observed the night before. Men are immediately attracted to her, and begin flirting with her very openly. She enjoys the attention, and is particularly excited when a man named

Beauplaisir approaches her.

Q. 14. Who was the man whose company the woman protagonist enjoyed the most under her disguise of a prostitute? What was her previous experience with him?

Ans. The unnamed woman protagonist enjoyed the company of the man named Beauplaisir.

The protagonist has interacted with Beauplaisir before and has always felt an attraction to him, but those interactions have always taken place under circumstances where her behaviour was strictly controlled by a sense of what was socially appropriate.

Q. 15. How does the woamn protagonist enjoy the company of Beauplaisir under her disguise as a prostitute? What was the reaction of Beauplaisir in the same occasion?

Ans. The unnamed woman protagonist is now more free in her interactions, and Beauplaisir.takes a new interest in her.

Beauplaisir does not recognize her; while he does detect a resemblance between the woman he assumes to be a prostitute and the well-bred lady of his acquaintance, he assumes it must be a coincidence. He is impressed to find that this mysterious new woman is much more intelligent and articulate than most of the prostitutes with whom he has interacted, and the two spend hours flirting and talking.

Q. 16. Why does the woman protagonist finds herself in a awkward situation in the theatre in company of Beauplaisir, when the play ends?

Or, What does Beauplaisir propose the protagonist thinking her to be a prostitute? What was the reaction of the protagonist?

Ans. When the play comes to an end, the protagonist suddenly finds herself in an awkward situation. Because he believes she is a prostitute, Beauplaisir is eager to have sex with her, and proposes that they go either to his home or to her residence.

Q. 17. How does 'Fantomina', the protagonist put aside the proposal of Beauplaisir for having sex in the first occasion?

Ans. She considers telling him her true identity but comes up with another solution, which has the advantage of giving her the opportunity to see him again: she tells Beauplaisir that she already has an appointment with another client that night. Beauplaisir accepts this story, and persuades her to agree to return to the theatre the following night so that they may meet again. She agrees, and the two part ways.

Q. 18. What was going in the mind of the woman progonist after returning home from the theatre putting aside the proposal of Beauplaisir?

Ans. The protagonist returns to her home in a flurry of emotions. She knows she is taking a risk by continuing the charade; however, she is intoxicated by the freedom it gives her, and she believes she will be strong enough to resist sexual temptation.

Q. 19. What prompted the woman progonist to continue her relationship with Beauplaisir?

Ans. She knows she is taking a risk by continuing the charade; however, she is intoxicated by the freedom it gives her, and she believes she will be strong enough to resist sexual temptation. She is also obsessed with the idea of continuing her interactions with Beauplaisir.

Q. 20. What does the woman progonist do before meeting Beauplaisir the next night in the theatre?

Ans. The next day, before she goes to the theatre, she rents rooms in a nearby house. This gives her a space to which she and Beauplaisir can go, one where she hopes she will feel a sense of agency and control.

Q. 21. What was the reaction of Beauplaisir after experiencing the arrangements in the rented room by the woman protagonist?

Ans. Beauplaisir was determined that she would go home with him after the play ended, and happily accompanied her back to the rooms she had rented. Once there, he tried to make arrangements to have food delivered to them, but she had a lavish meal provided at her own expense. This made Beauplaisir believe that she must be a very high-ranking courtesan; he became concerned that her services would be very expensive, but he decided that she would be worth the expenditure.

Q. 22. How did the night end in the room rented by the woman protagonist?

Or, How did the protagonist try to dissuade Beauplaisir from having sex with her? What did Beauplaisir do?

Ans. After they eat, Beauplaisir becomes very assertive in his attempts to seduce her. The protagonist begins to panic and almost reveals her true identity, but she realizes that she has already violated social convention and that revealing her true identity will only damage her reputation. She tells him that she is a virgin and that she only pretended to be a prostitute in order to get close to him, but this does not dissuade Beauplaisir. The two have sex.

Q. 23. What happened when Beauplaisir tried to pay the protagonist for having sex with her?

Ans. After the sexual encounter, the protagonist became very distressed; Beauplaisir thought she might be afraid that he was unwilling to pay her, and offered her a generous amount of money. The protagonist reacted angrily to him for giving her money, saying it could not compensate her for what she had lost. She told Beauplaisir that the only adequate compensation for her loss of virtue would be his love and fidelity.

Q. 24. How did Beauplaisir react in reply to the protagonist's demand of love and fidelity from him after the first sexual encounter between them? What name does the protagonist give to herself? Why?

Ans. Beauplaisir vows to be true to her. No longer believing she is a prostitute, he asks her who she is. The protagonist is still unwilling to reveal her true identity and risk losing her reputation, so she tells him her name is Fantomina, and that she is the daughter of a country gentleman. Beauplaisir thinks to himself that she will undoubtedly eventually end up as a prostitute, but does not say anything to this effect.

Q. 25. How does the woman protagonist make necessary arrangement to keep her identity secret to Beauplaisir and others after her first sexual encounter with Beauplaisir?

Ans. In the morning, she bribes a servant of the house to back up her story if she is ever questioned. She also explains that she will only be at the house while visiting Beauplaisir, but, should he come looking for her, he is to be told that she has just gone out.

Q. 26. What reason does the woman protagonist give for her absence at home at night to her aunt after her first sexual encounter with Beauplaisir?

Ans. After the arrangements made to keep her secret safe and conceal her identity, she returns to her actual residence and tells her aunt that she had taken a short trip and been left unable to return the night before.

Q. 27. Why does Fantomina want to follow Beauplaisir to Bath?

Ans. In time, Beauplaisir eventually begins to grow bored with her. It is time for him to go to Bath for the summer, and when Fantomina offers to go with him, he makes excuses about why she should not. Fantomina is hurt by this but conceals her feelings and sends him off, all the while laying plans to follow him. She desperately wants Beauplaisir to be infatuated with her again.

Q. 28. With whom does Fantomina set out for Bath?

Ans. As soon as Beauplaisir leaves, she tells her aunt that she is going to visit another relative and sets off, accompanied by two servants whom she quickly dismisses.

Q. 29. What disguise does Fantomina take before reaching Bath? What name does she take here?

Ans. Before arriving in Bath, the protagonist assumes her second disguise, adopting a country accent and unfashionable clothes. She takes the name Celia.

Q. 30. What does Fantomina do to come in contact with Beauplaisir in Bath? take before reaching Bath? What name does she take here?

Ans. Before arriving in Bath, the protagonist assumes her second disguise, adopting a country accent and unfashionable clothes. She takes the name Celia. She goes to the house where she knows Beauplaisir is lodging and offers to work as servant; the landlady hires her to attend to the male guests by bringing them their breakfasts and making their beds every morning. This role brings the disguised Fantomina, now going by the name of Celia, into close proximity with Beauplaisir, who is immediately attracted to her.

Q. 31. Describe the second sexual encounter between Beauplaisir and Fantomina.

Ans. Fantomina takes the job of maid servant in the house where Beauplaisir is lodging. This role brings the disguised Fantomina, now going by the name of Celia, into close proximity with Beauplaisir, who is immediately attracted to her. The second morning that she comes into his room, he seduces her; after she feigns some shyness so as to maintain he disguise, the two have sex. Afterwards he gives her money, which she takes in order to avoid alerting his suspicions.

Q. 32. What does Fantomina do when Beauplaisir loses interest in 'Celia' ?

Ans. Beauplaisir plans to stay in Bath for a month; at first the two enjoy the affair, but he eventually becomes tired of Celia as well. Knowing this, the protagonist prepares a third plot. She quits her job and moves to a different house in the town in order to assume her new disguise. This time she poses as a widow, and when she knows Beauplaisir is on his way back to London, she arranges to be at an inn just outside of the town. When his carriage is passing by, she stops it and calls out to him, asking for help.

Q. 33. What new story does Fantomina tell Beauplaisir about her disguise of a widow?

Ans. The disguised protagonist explains her story: she is a widow from Bristol and is trying to get to London so that she can claim her inheritance before the brother of her deceased husband squanders her. However, she has not been able to secure a coach and is now stranded; she asks if Beauplaisir would be willing to let her travel in his carriage.

Q. 33. How does Beauplaisir console the bereaved widow in his carriage while returning from Bath?

Ans. The widow in his carriage was Famtomina, ailas Celia inguise. She wants his help to reach to London. Beauplaisir readily agrees, but is disappointed to find that, once she enters the carriage, she weeps, laments, and will only talk about her dead husband. Hoping to distract her, he brings up the subject of love, and is surprised and pleased to notice how passionately she talks about love.

Q. 34. Describe the third sexual encounter between Beauplaisir and Fantomina.

Ans. The third sexual encounter between Fantimina and Beauplaisir takes place in an inn beside the way from Bath to London. Beauplaisir now hopes to seduce the attractive widow who is actually Fantomina in disguise, but he takes a much less direct tactic. He gradually indicates his interest, and when the two stop to spend the night at an inn, he makes bolder overtures. In order to maintain her disguise, the protagonist pretends to faint. He takes her to lie down, and when she has recovered, the two have sex.

Q. 35. How does Fantomina befool Beauplaisir in their third sexual encounter?

Ans. The protagonist is so skilled at disguising herself that Beauplaisir does not see any connection between her and his previous lovers. They return to London together and promise to continue seeing each other. Beauplaisir gives her an address at which to contact him, and the protagonist promises to provide her details as soon as she has determined where she will be staying.

Q. 36. How does the woman protagonist contact Beauplaisir in London both as Mrs. Bloomer and Fantomina?

Ans. Once the protagonist and Beauplaisir part ways in London, she rents rooms under the name of Widow Bloomer and sends word for him via letter to come and visit her there. Then she goes back to the rooms she rented as Fantomina and instructs the servants to make sure that if Beauplaisir comes looking for her, he is not told that she has been away from London. Disguising her handwriting, she sends him a letter lamenting that he has not come to see her, and attributes it to Fantomina. Beauplaisir promptly responds to both letters, vowing his affection and fidelity to both women.

Q. 37. How does the woman protagonist enjoy relationship with Beauplaisir in London both as Mrs. Bloomer and Fantomina simultaneously?

Ans. The woman protagonist sends letters to Beauplaisir to meet her both as Mrs Bloomer and as Fantomina. Beauplaisir promptly responds to both letters, vowing his affection and fidelity to both women. The protagonist is outraged at his lies, but is relieved that she has protected herself, and decides to keep enjoying the sexual aspect of the relationship. Beauplaisir visits her both when she is the Widow and when she is Fantomina, and she notices that he strongly prefers the former, because that relationship is newer.

Q. 38. What does the protagonist do when Beauplaisir loses interest in Widow Bloomer?

Ans. Within a fairly short time, after meeting the Widow Bloomer, Beauplaisir becomes tired of her. She hires two woman as her maid and sends Beauplaisir a letter through one of them. This letter has been written in a handwriting that is different from that of her other letters. It purports to be from an anonymous woman (signed Incognita) who is in love with him and wants him to come and visit her. She promises to do anything he wants, but insists that she will not reveal her name or face. The messenger has been instructed to refuse to give any details if Beauplaisir tries to find out her identity.

Q. 39. Under which name does the protagonist send Beauplaisir the letter after he loses interest in Mrs. Bloomer?

Ans. The protagonist sends a letter to Beauplaisir. This letter has been written in a handwriting that is different from that of her other letters. It purports to be from an anonymous woman (signed Incognita) who is in love with him and wants him to come and visit her. She promises to do anything he wants, but insists that she will not reveal her name or face.

Q. 40. What condition does Incognita give to Beauplaisir in her letter?

Ans. Incognita promises to do anything he wants, but insists that she will not reveal her name or face. The messenger has been instructed to refuse to give any details if Beauplaisir tries to find out her identity.

Q. 41. How does Beauplaisir accept the letter of Incognita ?

Ans. The messenger has been instructed by Incognita alia Fantomina to refuse to give any details if Beauplaisir tries to find out her identity.When the letter is delivered, Beauplaisir does indeed try to find out who Incognita is, but he is not given any information. With his curiosity inflamed, he writes back expressing his eagerness to meet this mysterious woman.

Q. 42. Where does Beauplaisir meet Incognita? How does Beauplaisir try to know her true identity? How does Incognita delude him? What his reaction?

Ans. The two meet at the house the protagonist rented, and she appears with a mask. They have sex, and then Beauplaisir begins to try to persuade her to show him her face. She refuses.

When he realizes she is not going to change her mind, he asks if he can spend the night at her house. The protagonist agrees, but is suspicious of what his motives are. She is right to be suspicious, as Beauplaisir plans to unmask her while she is sleeping.

The protagonist ensures that she joins him in bed in a very dark room, and even when it grows light outside, the windows are so tightly sealed that no light penetrates the room. As soon as they awake, she hurries out of the room without his having seen her face.

Frustrated, Beauplaisir expresses his unhappiness that she will not show him her face. However, the protagonist holds firm, and he leaves the house determined not to see her again.

Q. 43. Why does Fantomina's mother come to city ?

Ans. Fantomina's mother arrives in the city, having heard rumors of her daughter's reckless behaviour. She has no idea of the extent of what the protagonist has done, but is sufficiently concerned so as to begin to limit her daughter's freedoms.

Q. 44. How does Fantomina try to hide the news of her pregnancy from her mother?

Ans. It is difficult for her to hide this condition from her mother, but she manages to do so for a time. Since her mother plans to send her back to the country anyways, her plan is to wait until she leaves the city, then slip away and discreetly give birth in secret.

Q. 45. How is Fantomina's pregnancy revealed?

Ans. Unfortunately for the protagonist, she goes into labor during a court ball. She is clearly in pain, but everyone at the ball assumes she has been abruptly taken ill, including her mother. She is rushed back home, where her mother summons a doctor. The doctor quickly informs the protagonist's mother what the situation actually is; the mother is horrified and outraged.

Q. 46. How is Beauplaisir's name revealed as the father of Fantomina's child?

Ans. Fantomina's mother is horrified and outraged when Fantomina gives birth to her child. She demands that the protagonist reveal the father of her child, which is something the protagonist tries to avoid doing. The mother, however, insists that she will not call a midwife to help the protagonist unless she first reveals her lover. Afraid and in pain, she names Beauplaisir as the father.

Q. 47. What is Beauplaisir's reaction when Fantomina's mother accuses him of having impregnated her daughter?

Ans. The mother immediately sends for a midwife and also sends a message for Beauplaisir to come and see her. He promptly arrives, confused as to why this aristocratic woman has summoned him. When she accuses him of having impregnated her daughter, he denies it, insisting that he has had only brief interactions with her during formal social occasions.

Q. 48. How does Beauplaisir come to know that he is really the father of Fantomina's child?

Ans. When Beauplaisir denies that he had impregnated her daughter, the mother of Fantomina is more infuriated than ever, and drags Beauplaisir into the room where the protagonist is resting, having just given birth to a baby girl. Humiliated and horrified, the protagonist reveals the whole story of how she deceived and tricked Beauplaisir repeatedly, so that, while he is indeed the father of her child, he is innocent of any deliberate intent to dishonor a respectable lady.

Q. 49. How does Fantomina's mother become convinced that Beauplaisir has not intentionally impregnated Fantomina? What does she request Beauplaisir?

Ans. Humiliated and horrified, the protagonist reveals the whole story of how she deceived and tricked Beauplaisir repeatedly, so that, while he is indeed the father of her child, he is innocent of any deliberate intent to dishonor a respectable lady. After listening in astonishment, the mother admits that she can no longer demand that Beauplaisir marry her daughter, which is what she had initially planned to insist on. She asks only that he not publicly reveal the scandal to others.

Q. 50. How does Beauplaisir try to recompensate his deed of having impregnated Fantomina?

Ans. Beauplaisir agrees to keep the news of Fantomina's pregnancy a secret and also offers to raise his daughter, but both the protagonist and her mother reject this offer. Beauplaisir leaves the house in a state of deep confusion and shock.

***Q. 51.* What happens to Fantomina at the end of the story?**

Ans. For a time, Beauplaisir continues to visit to check in on Fantomina's health, but when her mother becomes concerned that these visits will lead to the two renewing their affair, she puts a stop to them. As soon as Fantomina has recovered, she is sent to a convent in France.

Explanation

Q. 1. ***She depended on the strength of her virtue, to bear her safe thro trials more dangerous than she apprehended this to be, and never having been addressed by him as a lady — was resolved to receive his devoirs as a town-mistress, imagining a world of satisfaction to herself in engaging him in the character of such a one, and in observing the surprise he would be in to find himself refused by a woman who he supposed granted her favors without exception.***

Ans. This quotation discusses the protagonist's initial intentions and frame of mind when she first initiates her plan of disguise. Importantly, she has no intention of engaging in sexual activity with Beauplaisir. Making it clear that the protagonist begins as a woman who conforms to social norms of protecting her chastity and virtue makes the protagonist potentially more sympathetic to contemporary readers, who would be inclined to judge a woman who deliberately set out in pursuit of sexual gratification. Instead, the novella becomes a story of how even a woman who expects to be able to maintain self-control can be seduced by the prospects of pleasure and freedom. The language of danger and trials in the quote creates a mood of foreshadowing, and implies that the protagonist is naïve and misguided in her beliefs. While in some ways the quote serves to align the protagonist with a more conventional model of feminine behavior by highlighting her commitment to her chastity, it also reveals her desire to occupy a position of power. She takes pleasure in the idea of undermining Beauplaisir's sense of control and dominance by turning him down after leading him to expect that she will have sex with him.

Q. 2. ***In the present burning eagerness of desire, 'tis probable, that had he been acquainted both with who and what she really was, the knowledge of her birth would not have influenced him with respect sufficient to have curbed the wild exuberance of his luxurious wishes, or made him in that longing, — that impatient moment, change the form of his addresses. In fine, she was undone; and he gained a victory so highly rapturous that had he known over whom, scarce could he have triumphed more.***

Ans. This quotation reveals Beauplaisir's state of mind the first time he and the protagonist have sex, and reveals the ambiguity around power and consent in this moment. The narrator notes that by this point Beauplaisir is so determined to have sex with the protagonist that even if he had known that she was a aristocratic woman, he would likely not have stopped. It remains unclear whether the forceful, vigorous language such as "eagerness" and "impatience" is meant to signal strenuous persuasion or outright force, but it is very clear that Beauplaisir does not take no for an answer, and persists in pressuring the protagonist to have sex even when she clearly indicates she does not want to. Other words also signal that even though the protagonist has displayed agency in masterminding the plan to get to this point, she ends up losing power and being placed in a vulnerable position. "Undone" suggests the potential consequences of this sexual act for the protagonist, while the description of Beauplaisir's "victory" implies that he has defeated or conquered her in some way, not that this was an act they mutually chose to engage in.

Q. 3. ***He had no reason to distrust the truth of this story and was therefore satisfied with it; but did not doubt by beginning of her conduct but that in the end she would be in reality the thing she so artfully had counterfeited; and had good Nature enough to pity the misfortunes he imagined would be her lot. But to tell her so, or offer his advice in that point was not his business, at least, as yet.***

Ans. This quotation reveals Beauplaisir's mindset when, after they have sex, the protagonist tells him part of the truth by admitting that she is not actually a prostitute and only dressed up as one in order to get close to him. He assumes that now that she has lost her chastity, she will end up in engaging in further sexual improprieties and will eventually end up actually being a prostitute. There are two reasons he might believe this. The first is the possibility that now that she has had a taste of sexual gratification, she will not be able to return to self-restraint. The second is that now that she is no longer a virgin, she will be unable to find a husband and will end up eventually relying on being a mistress for hire as a way of providing for herself. In either case, the quotation reveals Beauplaisir's cynical, worldly nature: he is very aware of how grave the consequences of sexual impropriety can be for a woman. At the same time, he feels no guilt about having seduced the protagonist, even if her life will be ruined as a result.

Q. 4. ***Thus did the lady's vivacity and wit assist her in all but where it was most needful. She had discernment to foresee, and avoid all the ills which might attend the loss of her reputation, but was wholly blind to those of the ruin of her virtue; and having managed her affairs so as to secure the one, grew perfectly easy with the remembrance she had forfeited the other.***

Ans. This quotation reveals one of the major juxtapositions in the character of the protagonist: she is remarkably intelligent and calculating, and yet at the same time she can be very naïve. She readily comes up with a lie that ensures no one will know she has spent the night with Beauplaisir and is able to devise a plan enabling her to continue seeing him in secret. At the same time, as the narrator points out, she remains blind to what the consequences of her liaison might be on a personal level. In fact, because the protagonist is so confident that she can successfully have an affair while escaping social consequences, she seems to very quickly recover from any guilt or distress she might have felt when she first had sex with Beauplaisir. This quotation marks a moment where the protagonist experiences a renewed sense of power and control over her personal life, but fails to realize that by exercising sexual agency, she is actually endangering her future.

Q. 5. ***[she] wisely considering that complaints, tears, swoonings and all the extravagancies which women make use of in such cases have little prevailance over a heart inclined to rove and only serve to render those who practice them more contemptible by robbing them of that beauty which alone can bring back the furtive lover.***

Ans. This quotation describes how the protagonist responds to the knowledge that Beauplaisir has grown tired of her and wants to go to Bath alone. It demonstrates both her control of her emotions, and her shrewd, pragmatic attitude. She immediately understands that her lover will not be moved by emotional displays. As the narrator notes, such displays are not only ineffective, they are actually counter-productive because a woman is less beautiful when she is weeping or scolding, and therefore her lover will be even less motivated to experience renewed interest in her. This quotation reveals the way in which the novella often takes a somewhat cold and cynical perspective on romantic affairs, as it suggests that men are primarily motivated by admiration of physical beauty, and are not likely to feel empathy for emotional suffering. The protagonist does not seem disturbed or upset by Beauplaisir's fickle nature, and accepts that it is her job to keep him interested, not his job to remain loyal to her.

Q.6. ***can only say that besides the alteration which the change of dress made in her, she was so admirably skilled in the art of feigning, that she had the power of putting on almost what face she pleased, and knew so exactly how to form her behavior to the character she represented that all the comedians at both playhouses are infinitely short of her performances.***

Ans. This quotation attempts to explain how the protagonist is successfully able to disguise her identity, even while pursuing intimate relationships with Beauplaisir. It implies that she has strong acting skills and that she also understands how factors such as education and social position can manifest in someone's speech and mannerisms. Part of what is so disruptive about the protagonist's trickery is that she moves between different social classes. This cannot be achieved simply by altering one's physical appearance: it also requires a finely nuanced understanding of how an aristocratic woman behaves differently from a maidservant. By being able to switch between these roles, the protagonist reveals both her own skill and cleverness, as well as the unsettling possibility that women from different social ranks might not be so different from each other after all.

Q. 7. ***Had he been faithful to me, (said she, to herself) either as Fantomina, or Celia, or the Widow Bloomer, the most violent passion if it does not change its object, in time will wither: Possession naturally abates the vigour of desire, and I should have had at best but a cold, insipid, husband-like Lover in my arms; but by these arts of passing on him as a new mistress whenever the ardour which alone makes love a blessing, begins to diminish, for the former one, I have him always raving, wild, impatient, longing, dying.***

Ans. In this passage, the protagonist rationalizes why it is actually to her advantage to be constantly deceiving Beauplaisir about her identity. She presents the cynical perspective that sexual passion is short-lived and that relationships are only exciting in their initial stages. Thus, Beauplaisir constantly reenacting what he perceives to be the start of a new relationship leads him to be a more enthusiastic lover than if he were to remain faithful to her. The quote makes clear what is implicit throughout the novel: that the protagonist, and by extension women in general, value sexual gratification as an important part of a romantic relationship. By contrasting the ardor of a man with whom she pursues an illicit relationship to a faithful but less sexually energetic husband, the quote subverts stereotypes of what women hope to obtain in their relationships.

Q. 8. ***She, covering herself with the cloaths, and ready to die a second time with the inward agitations of her soul, shriek'd out, Oh, I am undone! —I cannot live and bear this shame!***

Ans. This quote is located at the point when the protagonist's mother drags Beauplaisir into the room where the protagonist has just given birth. She realizes that she will have to reveal all of her actions, and reacts with horror and shame. Her attempt to hide herself under the bed cloths ("cloaths") mirrors her various disguises throughout the novel, but now in a pathetic way: her trickery has failed. Interestingly, the phrase she uses to describe the situation (being "undone") is the same word that the narrator used in a previous climatic moment, to describe the protagonist losing her virginity to Beauplaisir (see Quote 2). This repetition of language could be interpreted in a number of ways. On one hand, it could suggest that the protagonist's sexual activity was always going to be her downfall, and that she was doomed from the time she first had sex with Beauplaisir. On the other hand, it could reveal how the protagonist does not view her sexual behavior as transgressive, and is not ashamed of what she has done, but only that she failed to fully conceal it.

Q. 9. ***A thousand times has he stood amazed at the prodigious likeness between his little mistress and this court beauty; but was still as far from imagining they were the same, as he was the first hour he accosted her in the play-***

house though it is not impossible but that her resemblance to this celebrated lady, might keep his inclination alive something longer than otherwise they would have been; and that it was to the thoughts of this (as he supposed) unenjoy'd charmer, she owed in great measure the vigour of his latter caresses.

Ans. This quotation describes Beauplaisir's thoughts and feelings during the time in which he is pursuing an affair with protagonist disguised as Fantomina. The quotation adds a touch of realism to the novella in that it acknowledges that he does notice a physical resemblance between the protagonist and her disguised self. It also shows why the protagonist is able to successfully maintain the illusion: it is so inconceivable to Beauplaisir that a well-born woman could engage in the kind of behavior that his mistress does that he never even considers the possibility. He does, however, achieve greater erotic satisfaction due to the resemblance, which also suggests part of the power that the protagonist wields by disguising herself. She can take advantage of the fantasy of having multiple women at the same time and also the possibility of combining traits from what are assumed to be totally separate social spheres. In her guise of Fantomina, the protagonist combines the elegance and education of a lady with the frank sexuality of a prostitute, and Beauplaisir finds the combination intoxicating.

Q. 10. ***With her sex's modesty, she had not also thrown off another virtue equally valuable, tho' generally unfortunate, constancy: She loved Beauplaisir; it was only he whose solicitations could give her pleasure; and had she seen the whole species despairing, dying for her sake, it might, perhaps have been a satisfaction to her pride, but none to her more tender inclinations.***

Ans. This quotation suggests one of the ways in which the protagonist's character offers a complex and ambivalent perspective on femininity. She is often presented as being unlike other women due to her assertiveness, intelligence, and open sexuality. However, here the narrator suggests that she does embody a stereotypical characteristic in that she is very faithful to Beauplaisir and not interested in pursuing any other lovers. Although it often seems that the protagonist has a great deal of agency and independence in the relationship, this attachment to only being with one man makes her vulnerable because it prevents her from simply abandoning the relationship when he grows tired of her.

Short Essay Type Questions with Answers

Q. 1. Comment on the symbol of Female Body in *Fantomina.*

Ans. The moment that Fantomina decides to impersonate a prostitute is also the moment that her body becomes symbolic of merely physical features; posing as a prostitute reduces her to just a body, without status or class. Her body therefore acts as a symbol of the injustices surrounding the female gender, and their sexuality. First of all, the few men within the novel—setting aside Beauplaisir for the moment—are not judged by their appearances. They attempt to woo Fantomina with their words, and this is deemed enough. However, a woman's value is judged wholly on her looks, and she can only demand freedom with men when she is a prostitute, and allows them free reign with her body. Secondly, the female body is symbolic of Beauplaisir's attitude (and perhaps male attitude generally) towards female sexuality. Despite treasuring the female body before intercourse, the female body during sex is merely a vessel to fulfill male desire, and there is no need to have a personality attached to the limbs. Thus the female body is affected with the stigma of expectation: the woman must be ready to please a man, but she is restricted in pleasure she is allowed to enjoy herself.

Q. 2. Comment on the symbol of Theatre in *Fantomina.*

Ans. Haywood's novella is a story of disguise and deception, and the story opens in a theatre. Haywood perhaps chose this setting as particularly poignant in suggesting a 'show' that not only occurs on the stage. In fact, Fantomina neither names nor even hints that she is watching the play, and instead studies the people down below in the 'Pit'. First of all, the structure of the theatre is symbolic of social class, as the prostitutes are at the bottom of the hierarchy, socially and physically. Fantomina is clearly a woman of noble birth, as she is separate and higher, in a Box, where she can observe but does not have to engage in the lower classes. Additionally, the theatre setting suggests a continuation of the show beyond the stage to the people watching it: in eighteenth-century society, there is always an audience, watching and judging every action.

Q.3. Comment on the symbol of Incognita's mask in *Fantomina.*

Ans. The plot of Haywood's novella is only possible through disguise, a theme that materializes in the symbolic mask that the protagonist wears as part of Incognita's disguise. This is an especially important symbol for two reasons: it completely resonates and represents the major theme of how aesthetics and identity are linked, and it bears connotations that a eighteenth-century audience would have recognized. Firstly, the mask is almost ironic in its representation of of Fantomina's 'Frolick'. She has previously donned disguises to fool Beauplaisir, yet this is the first time she has actually worn a mask. This is ironic, as up to this point, she has needed no mask to fool Beauplaisir, so it becomes also a symbol of her talents, and a mockery of his intuition. Secondly, in the eighteenth century, the mask worn by a woman was a sign that she was a prostitute. This connotation mocks both Fantomina, for acting as a prostitute and tragically being raped, and Beauplaisir, who assumes she is a prostitute from appearance alone. While this symbol could appear to be merely a device to cement the already obvious theme of disguise, Haywood seems to use it with a different awareness: it suggests there is a difference between what the audience would assume the mask means, what it means to Beauplaisir, and how Fantomina uses it to invoke a particular meaning.

Q. 4. Comment on the symbol of Letters in *Fantomina.*

Ans. In the eighteenth century, when Haywood was writing Fantomina: Or, Love in a Maze, writing in the epistolary format was popular. Novels such as Samuel Richardson's Pamela and Frances Burney's Evelina both include, or use as the entire structure, letters in the novel. Haywood's use of the epistolary is minimal, yet important. It allows the reader to see the culmination of all Fantomina's lies, and the hand that she writes each in is a symbol of the character itself that she has constructed each time. It is also a further symbol of Fantomina's mockery of Beauplaisir: she sends the letters from "different women" at the same time, demonstrating her capabilities and the extend to which she will maintain this 'frolick'. The letters therefore demonstrate how intricately Fantomina has woven a web of lies, and acts as the first outward symbol of her beginning to lose control.

Q. 5. Comment on the symbol of the male gaze in *Fantomina.*

*Ans.*The male gaze as a symbol is especially recognizable in the opening scenes of the novel, at the theatre. The original motive behind Fantomina's frolic is a curiosity based on how men react to prostitutes, and how these women can partially control the male gaze. Within Fantomina, the male gaze can be read as a motif because it is a constant stimulus that the protagonist seeks, and that occurs over and over. It is especially important, as Beauplaisir's male gaze not only has complete control over Fantomina, but is also controlled by her. She seems to understand the psychology behind what pleases this particular man, and assumes different disguises that all attract his gaze. Therefore, while the motif of the 'male gaze' in other novels presents a patriarchal dominance where women are objects, Haywood inverts this standard. Instead, Fantomina encourages the gaze, yet simultaneously is able to manipulate it to see what she wants it to see.

Q. 6. Comment on the metaphor in the line "the present burning eagerness of desire" in *Fantomina.*

Ans. Here the metaphor of burning is used to reveal the intensity of the desire Beauplaisir feels for the protagonist. While the metaphor signals that he is very passionate, it also subtly foreshadows the ways in which their sexual relationship will be damaging to the protagonist. Burning implies destruction, and the affair she has with Beauplaisir has the potential to destroy her reputation and chances of future happiness with another partner. Also, something that burns can also be extinguished, and the period of burning often tends to be quite short-lived. Thus, this metaphor already hints at how Beauplaisir will eventually tire of his lover even as he seems to be at his most passionate.

Q. 7. Comment on the metaphor in the line "the influence of her ill stars prevented it" in *Fantomina.*

Ans. The metaphor of stars is here used to describe how the protagonist is doomed, even though she believes she is exerting agency and control over her life. The idea that the alignment of the constellations at the time of one's birth predicted one's future (an early version of astrology) was fairly popular and gives rise to the metaphor of "ill stars" describing her bad luck. The metaphor reveals the novel's interest in the extent to which anyone, but especially a woman, can be said to be in control of her life. The protagonist seems able to exert immense control over her life by seamlessly changing identities, but she cannot control either her desire for Beauplaisir or her biology, the combination of which leads to her pregnancy and discovery.

Q. 8. Comment on the metaphor in the line "devoured her lips, her breasts with greedy kisses" in *Fantomina.*

Ans. This metaphor is used to describe the way in which Beauplaisir acts as he seduces the protagonist while she is in disguise as the maidservant Celia. The metaphor of "devouring" suggests the forceful, physical way in which he presents his desire and reveals his lustful nature. The metaphor also shows that he does not take Celia seriously. Because of the differences in their social class, he has far more power than she does and can therefore treat her like an object to be consumed for his own gratification.

Q. 9. Comment on the metaphor in the line "the rack of nature growing more fierce" in *Fantomina.*

Ans. This metaphor compares the labor pains the protagonist is experiencing to the experience of being tortured (the "rack" was device used to torture individuals by gradually dislocating their joints). The metaphor communicates the physical intensity of the pain of childbirth, but it also suggests a punitive element to what she is experiencing. Torture would usually be applied to a criminal, so this metaphor suggests that her pregnancy and labor might be seen as a kind of punishment for her sexual transgressions. Torture could also be used as a way to exact information or confessions, and this is exactly how her mother uses it. By refusing to provide the protagonist with medical assistance until she names the father of her child, labor becomes the one thing strong enough to break the protagonist's resolve and finally lead her to reveal her secret.

Q. 10. Comment on the metaphor in the line "Men would be caught in their own snare" in *Fantomina.*

Ans. This metaphor is used to describe the possibilities of how gendered power dynamics could be reversed if women employed the kinds of cunning and deceit that the protagonist utilizes. Men are figured as hunters who create snares or traps by doing things like lying, flattering, and deceiving women. In this metaphor, women are presented as vulnerable victims, but also as animalistic and therefore less intelligent and rational. However, by suggesting that this pattern could potentially be reversed, the metaphor suggests that women are just as capable of using schemes and lies to their own advantage.

Q. 11. Comment on the irony on the subject of "Dressing as a prostitute, but maintaining the expectations of a lady" in *Fantomina* as a situational irony.

Ans. In Haywood's novella, the protagonist Fantomina is a lady who dresses as a prostitute to experience freedom. She is therefore aware of her higher status, despite her lower-class dress. Others, such as Beauplaisir, see only her outward dress, and not her true status as upper-class. It is ironic that Fantomina dresses as a prostitute yet expects her virginity to be treated with respect when she and Beauplaisir spend the night together. This highlights the difference between female and male expectation of desire. For Fantomina, a woman should be treated in accordance to their social status, whereas Beauplaisir assumes her as lower-class due to her clothing. Ironically, Fantomina expects treatment in accordance with the very status she wants to keep secret.

Q. 12. Comment on the irony on the subject of "The irony of accusing Beauplaisir of treachery" in *Fantomina* as a situational irony.

Ans. After Fantomina has played out her roles as Widow Bloomer, Celia, and Fantomina, she returns to London and writes letters to Beauplaisir under her different personas. When Beauplaisir refuses Fantomina, but agrees to see the Widow the next day, Fantomina accuses him of treachery and betrayal. There is an undeniable sense of irony here: she brands Beauplaisir as a typical, lying male, when she has fooled him no fewer than three times already by dressing as different women. However, the motive behind her deception almost makes this irony acceptable. Becoming three different women at once was the only way in which Fantomina could prove that Beauplaisir is a rake, promising affection to many women simultaneously. This irony does not, then, mock Fantomina, but is rather a result of what she must do in order to prove the unreliability of the male gender.

Q. 13. Comment on the irony on the subject of "The irony of claiming

control over female sexuality" in *Fantomina* as a Dramatic irony.

Ans. The motivation behind Fantomina's actions throughout the entirety of Haywood's novellas is freedom from the constraints that accompany her role in society as a lady. Most importantly, this is inclusive of sexual freedom: without her usual upper-class dress, she can now interact with men without any judgement. Fantomina thereby possesses control over expression of her female sexuality, and refuses to conform to the constraints of a society that expects women to only become sexually active as a man's wife. It is therefore ironic that at the end of the story, despite her greatest efforts, Fantomina goes in to labor and is finally a slave to the bodily functions that only occur to the female sex. Fantomina has fought for the entire novella to dictate her own secret desires, only to be forced to submit and admit to the societal bonds that her status as a female impose on her.

Q. 14. What does the protagonist do when Beauplaisir loses interest in Widow Bloomer?

Ans. Within a fairly short time, after meeting the Widow Bloomer, Beauplaisir becomes tired of her.

Fantomina now has a new scheme, and this one requires help. She finds two men and offers to pay them to render her some service. They happily agree and she arranges to meet them the following day. Then she goes to rent a large and splendid house. When she meets the two men she has hired, she presents them with uniforms resembling those worn by the servants of the wealthy. She tells one of them to deliver a letter to Beauplaisir. This letter has been written in a handwriting that is different from that of her other letters. It purports to be from an anonymous woman (signed Incognita) who is in love with him and wants him to come and visit her. She promises to do anything he wants, but insists that she will not reveal her name or face. The messenger has been instructed to refuse to give any details if Beauplaisir tries to find out her identity.

Q. 15. Comment on the irony on the subject of "The irony of the protagonist loving Beauplaisir, yet approaching him as a prostitute" in *Fantomina* as a Dramatic irony.

Ans. Upon meeting Beauplaisir for the first time, Fantomina mentions that she has seen him before and taken a shine to him. While the only way she can approach him is dressed as a lower-class prostitute, this comment confirms that she seeks him out specifically, suggesting there is more to her interest in him than just lust. It is therefore heavily ironic that Fantomina perhaps seeks something similar to love by approaching Beauplaisir dressed as a prostitute: by tricking Beaulaisir into thinking she is a prostitute, Fantomina effectively prevents him from falling in love with the person who she truly is.

Q. 16. Comment on the imagery of The Play House in *Fantomina*.

Ans. Haywood wrote in an era that tended to focus less on prose description, so much of her imagery is subtle. Simply by setting the first scene of the novella in a playhouse, she conjures up imagery of wealthy individuals wearing their most fashionable clothes, and of a hot, crowded atmosphere in which bodies were crammed close together. The space of the theatre was always sexually charged and involved potential voyeurism, both because of the opportunity to watch bodies on stage and also the opportunity to observe individuals from different social classes gathered in the audience together.

Q. 17. Comment on the imagery implied in *The contrast between Fantomina in disguise and the protagonist in formal attire* in *Fantomina.*

Ans. In order to explain how Beauplaisir fails to see the similarity between his mistress and the woman he frequently observes in social situations, the narrator uses imagery to describe the contrast between them. When he sees the protagonist in disguise as Fantomina, she is wearing loose, flowing, and revealing clothing, all of which communicate intimacy and accessibility. The imagery of what she wears in formal situations is the exact opposite, with tight, impenetrable clothing and many jewels to signal her wealth and status. The imagery subtly conveys the difference in class position between the two women, and this is why Beauplaisir perceives them so differently.

Q. 18. Comment on the imagery implied in *The dawn of morning when Beauplaisir spends the night with Incognita* in *Fantomina.*

Ans. After having sex with the protagonist in her disguise as Incognita, Beauplaisir persuades her to let him spend the night in hopes that he can see her face. He is very impatient for the day to dawn so that the room will be light enough for him to see. Imagery, particularly auditory imagery, is used to convey that it is morning; he can hear the sounds of the city coming to life outside of the house. The imagery is important because the room remains totally dark and he has to rely on the sounds to know what time it is. This darkness prevents him from glimpsing the face of the woman with whom he has spent the night; it also symbolizes the ignorance and blindness of Beauplaisir throughout the novel.

Q. 19. Comment on the imagery implied in *The description of the protagonist going into labor.*

Ans. When the protagonist goes into labor, she is attending a court ball and tries to hide what is happening. She is in too much pain to disguise her suffering, and imagery is used to dramatically convey this. To other individuals, such as her mother, it seems like she must be extremely ill. This imagery conveys the physical pain and danger that the protagonist is in, and also suggests the way in which her pregnancy might be perceived as a punishment for her sexual transgressions.

Q. 20. Comment on the Theme of Gender in *Fantomina.*

Ans. Discussions of gender are central to this eighteenth-century novel, as it is based primarily on the behavior of a male and a female. Fantomina manipulates what is expected of a woman: instead of exhibiting mildness and virtue, she instead exhibits an entertaining wit and ability to outsmart others. Beauplaisir, on the other hand, can be described as a 'rake', a typical eighteenth century 'stock' character that represents the vulgar and predictable nature of male behavior. Beauplaisir is accentuated as a fool through the different scenarios that Fantomina places him in, as we see especially well towards the climatic ending as she writes to him as Fantomina, Widow Bloomer, and Incognita all at once. Yet, at the end of the novella, Beauplaisir escapes unscathed, with the same lack of responsibility he has held throughout the story. This presents a complex picture: that men are promiscuous and easy to predict, yet they are still accepted as the superior gender in eighteenth-century society.

Q. 21. Comment on the Theme of Desire in *Fantomina*.

Ans. Female and male desire are completely different ideologies in the eighteenth century, and Haywood expects this to be common knowledge for her readers. Even when acting as a prostitute, belonging to a profession that centers on desire, Fantomina must still act with modesty. When in the disguise of Celia, her body is 'half-reluctant, half-yielding', displaying the struggle that women faced in the expression of their desires. In public, they must adopt a modest and mild exterior, yet they are still expected to please men in private. In the world of prostitution and casual intercourse, these spheres are confused. However, as a man, Beauplaisir can be both public and extremely forward with his desire. He is 'rapacious' in seeking the affections of all four characters Fantomina plays, and barely waits for her consent before he seeks satisfaction.

Q. 22. Comment on the Theme of Class in *Fantomina*.

Ans. Within this novel, class hierarchies are not described from a privileged and content perspective, but rather from the perspective of one who is restricted by her class. Despite their sordid careers, prostitutes are highlighted due to the social freedom they hold in talking to men, whether or not they are of appropriate class or demeanor. Therefore, the theme of class centers on movement between the classes, and not interaction within a class. Fantomina's actions are restricted by her reputation as a higher class Lady, as her public relations are constantly monitored and her eligibility to marry based upon virginity as well as status. Her act of relocating herself to a lower class is thus portrayed as positive, as it allows Fantomina the freedom she seeks. It remains interesting that she only poses as the lower class, and thus has the option at any point to return to the privileges of a richer life.

Q. 23. Comment on the subject of Sexual Segmentation in *Fantomina*.

Ans. There are clearly different sexual domains in the novella: the rules and practices involved in being a mistress are different to that of being a whore are, in turn, different to being that of a wife. Like Defoe's Moll Flanders, Haywood begins to probe the segmentation of sexual culture that this implies.

Not least, whilst men such as Beauplaisir can apparently move across this segmented erotic experience freely (basically, the 'sexual double-standard'), women usually can't. However, Fantomina does: in fact, as pointed out in Thursday's seminar, she out-seduces the supposed seducer. In fact, she seemingly adopts mutually incompatible roles: outraged by Beauplaisir's falsity even as she engages him in a seduction based entirely on her own disguise.

There's some neat little ironies here, observed by students, which could be profitably chased down in essays. For example, the novella plays cleverly with ideas of a 'universal' women's experience - e.g. Beauplaisir's predictably inconstant desire, which rapidly wanes once the woman is possessed, is supposedly what all women must cope with. Yet, in a sense, the many masquerades of Fantomina could be read as a kind of parody of the view that women have no/ fluid character, which is a mainstay of anti-woman satire (as explored last week). Or, consider the fact that the most superficially deceptive and unknowable of Fantomina's personae - Incognita - is, paradoxically, perhaps the closest to the 'real' Fantomina: in Incognita, Beauplaisir is confronted by a literal masquerade - a disguise which announces itself unambiguously - whereas he has previously fallen for disguises he didn't realise were disguises.

Drama

THE WAY OF THE WORLD

-William Congreve

❖ An Introduction to William Congreve:

William Congreve, 1670-1729, was born in Yorkshire, England. As his father was an officer in the army and the commander of a garrison near Cork in Ireland, Congreve was educated at Kilkenny and then at Trinity College, Dublin, where he was a slightly younger college-mate of Jonathan Swift. In 1691, he was admitted to the Middle Temple in London to study law. It is likely that, like Young Witwoud in The Way of the World, his interest in law was only a means to take him to London, the center of all excitement.

By 1692, Congreve was already a recognized member of the literary world. His first play, The Old Bachelor, was first acted in January 1693, before he was twenty-three years old, and was triumphantly successful. His other plays, The Double-Dealer, Love for Love, The Mourning Bride, and The Way of the World, all followed at short intervals. The last of them was presented in March 1700.

For the rest of his life, Congreve wrote no plays. The Way of the World was not successful on the stage, and this disappointment may have had something to do with his decision. He engaged in controversy with Jeremy Collier on the morality of the stage, a frustrating experience. He suffered from gout and bad sight. He became an elder statesman of letters at the age of thirty, honored by the nobility, highly respected by younger writers.

In his later years, Congreve conducted an ambiguous romance with Henrietta, Duchess of Marlborough. When he died, she erected a tablet to his memory in Westminster Abbey. She also ordered a life-size figure of him and had it seated in his regular place at her table. The feet were swathed in bandages and a doctor "treated" Congreve for gout daily. This rather surprising memento casts its own odd light on the Duchess, perhaps on Congreve, and certainly on the status of the medical profession at the time.

❖ An Introduction to *The Way of the World*:

The Way of the World premiered in 1700 at London's theatre in Lincoln's Inn Field, performed by Majesty's Servants, an acting company of the time. Though it is now regarded as one of the best Restoration comedies in existence, it was not well received by audiences at the time, who felt it was too vulgar.

❖ Historical Background of *The Way of the World*:

Congreve's play was written and performed during the end of what scholars call the Restoration, the period in which Charles II was restored to the throne in 1660 (Charles II's father, Charles I, was beheaded on charges of treason on January 30, 1649 after a lengthy civil war and England briefly became a commonwealth with Oliver Cromwell as its leader.) In 1700, the nation was still struggling to define succession. King William III, a Dutch prince was brought over from Hanover in 1688, to rule the Protestant nation alongside his wife/cousin, Queen Mary, an event known as the Glorious Revolution. The pair essentially took the throne from the then-reigning Catholic King James II, Mary's father, who fled to France. They promised to rule the nation well by upholding its Protestant tradition, something many citizens felt James II wasn't doing. Congreve weaves much of this political detail into his poem through its preoccupation with marriage, capital, and laws.

❖ The Story of *The Way of the World* :

Before the action of the play initiates, some events are supposed to have taken place. Mirabell, a typical young Restoration man, but not a man of great wealth, has had an affair with Mrs. Fainall, the widowed daughter of Lady Wishfort. Mirabell has arranged a marriage between Mr. Fainall and the Mrs. Fainall to protect her from scandal in the event of pregnancy.

Fainall married the young widow because he wanted her fortune to support his courtship with Mrs. Marwood. In time, Mirabell found himself in love with Millamant, the niece and ward of Lady Wishfort, and the cousin of his former mistress. He is strongly in the pursuit of gaining her for love and also for the wealth she possesses. 6000 pounds of Millamant's fortune were under her own control, but the other half, 6,000 pounds, was controlled by Lady Wishfort. She put a condition if she marries a suitor approved by her then only she could get her fortune.Sadly, Mirabell had earlier hurt Lady Wishfort; she had misinterpreted his flattery as love.

Mirabell made a plan in which he has arranged a fake uncle (Waitwell) to make Lady Wishfort fall in love with him. Waitwell is married to Foible, the maid of Lady Wishfort. He then plans to reveal the real identity of Waitwell and pretends to save her from this mismatch. He thinks that he would gain lady Wishfort's favor and permission to marry Millamant. Millamant is aware of the plot, probably through Foible.

When the play opens, Mirabell is eagerly waiting to hear that Waitwell is married to Foible. Mirabell's card game with Mr. Fainall reveals their relationship is not good. Fainall has been twice tricked by Mirabell: Mrs. Fainall is Mirabell's former mistress, and Mrs. Marwood, Fainall's former mistress, is in love with Mirabell. Meanwhile, although Millamant secretly loves Mirabell, she enjoys teasing him in his state of uncertainty.

Unfortunately, Mrs. Marwood hears Mrs. Fainall and Foible discussing the scheme of Mirabell, along with Mirabell and Mrs. Fainall's earlier love affair. She also overhears insulting comments about herself, so, she is vengeful and immediately informs Fainall of the plot and the fact that his wife was once

Mirabell's mistress. The two conspirators now have both motive and means for revenge. In the same afternoon, Millamant accepts Mirabell's proposal and rejects Sir Wilfull Witwoud, Lady Wishfort's candidate for her hand.

Fainall, the conspirator, now leads the action. He reveals the truth of Waitwell, the false uncle, and starts blackmailing Lady Wishfort with the threat of her daughter's disgrace. He demands that the balance of Millamant's fortune should be turned over to his sole control. In addition, he wants to be sure that Lady Wishfort will not marry so that Mrs. Fainall is certain to be the heir.

This plot of Fainall's is now defied by Millamant. She says that she will marry Wilfull to save her own fortune. Fainall goes on insisting that he wants control of the rest of his wife's money and immediate management of Lady Wishfort's fortune. At the same time, Mirabell brings two servants to prove that Fainall and Mrs. Marwood were themselves guilty of adultery. Fainall ignores the blame and points out that he will still create a scandal which would blacken the name of Mrs. Fainall if he does not get the money.

At this point, Mirabell victoriously reveals his most successful trick. Before Mrs. Fainall married Fainall, she and Mirabell had suspected the man's character, so, she had appointed her lover trustee of her fortune. Fainall, now cannot claim the fortune because Mrs. Fainall does not control her own money. He and Mrs. Marwood leave in great anger. Lady Wishfort forgives the servants and gives consent to the match of Mirabell and Millamant.

❖ A Detailed Actwise Summary of *The Way of the World* :

Dedication

In this dedication, as in most others of the period, we may ignore the rather fulsome praise of the man to whom it was addressed; that praise is a convention of the time. Some of the comments made in the letter, however, are of interest. Congreve was obviously chagrined at the play's lukewarm reception and attributed it to the coarse taste of the audience. The playgoers were accustomed to plays where "the characters meant to be ridiculed" were "fools so gross" that "instead of moving our mirth, they ought very often to excite our compassion." Congreve's description of his own purpose when creating comic characters is revealing: "to design some characters which should appear ridiculous, not so much through a natural folly . . . as through an affected wit . . . which . . . is also false." This statement has often been considered the basic definition of characterization in the "Comedy of Manners," a genre where "affectation" is the great fault. Unfortunately, Congreve continues, many people could not distinguish between "a Witwoud and a Truewit."

Not all of the comic characters in The Way of the World are "affectations," for Congreve included some that were created as "humours." He is here making the point that he is avoiding the extremes of farce, what we might call slapstick, in this comedy.

Prologue

The Prologue was a conventional requirement for all plays. This one was delivered by the sixty-five-year-old Betterton, the grand old man of the Restoration stage. Congreve did not keep the promises he made in this prologue:

He swears he'll not resent one hissed-off scene,
Nor, like those peevish wits, his play maintain,
Who, to assert their sense, your taste arraign.

The dedicatory letter indicates that he did arraign the taste of his audience because it did not approve his play (although his scenes were not hissed).

His statement about what is in his play has more value: "some plot," "some new thought," "some humor too," but "no farce," the absence of which, he adds, ironically, would presumably be a fault. The fact that he describes his play as having no farce indicates that he planned the Wilfull-Witwoud scenes and the Lady Wishfort scenes as less broadly burlesqued than some of his contemporaries might have wished.

The statements that there is no satire because the town is so reformed and that there are surely no knaves or fools in his audience are, of course, ironic.

Act I

Summary :

The curtain rises as Mirabell is defeated by Fainall in a desultory card game at the chocolate-house. The conversation reveals that Mirabell is in love with Millamant but is intensely disliked by Millamant's guardian. Lady Wishfort's dislike seems to have some justification: Mirabell at one time pretended to court her in order to conceal his love for her niece. She is fifty-five years old, and her vanity was offended when she discovered that Mirabell did not love her.

When Fainall leaves for a moment, a servant enters and informs Mirabell that his valet married that day. Mirabell is pleased because his marriage is a necessary prelude to some secret scheme — which is not revealed. Witwoud and Petulant then enter, and we gain the additional information that Witwoud's elder brother is coming to town to court Millamant. Witwoud and Petulant are also both courting Millamant but only because she is the currently reigning belle. There is further talk of an uncle of Mirabell's who is coming to court Lady Wishfort. The men leave for a walk in the park.

Analysis

The summary of this act points up one of the difficulties in the structure of the play. The first act does not seem to move forward. It contains only partial exposition so that the reader has trouble following the play. The relations between Mirabell and Fainall are not made clear. It would be the actors' task to suggest the strain between them. The skilled and, we might say, suspicious reader may glean as much from the lines.

Fainall distrusts Mirabell, with good cause. He suspects the nature of the friendship between Mirabell and his wife before their marriage. He also suspects that his mistress, Mrs. Marwood, loves Mirabell. Mirabell is aware of Fainall's suspicions and, of course, suspects that Mrs. Marwood is Fainall's mistress. When Mirabell says that "for the discovery of this amour, I am indebted to your friend, or your wife's friend, Mrs. Marwood," the actor will put the emphasis on "or your wife's friend" so as to suggest that the innocent comment is barbed. Fainall pointedly replies, "What should provoke her to be your enemy unless she has made you advances which you have slighted? Women do not easily forgive omissions of that nature." The actor must read the lines properly on the stage, and so must the reader.

Other lines also demand careful reading. The talk about Lady Wishfort is not merely casual: She is very important in the subsequent action. The comments about Millamant's character are highly significant. Despite Mirabell's wit and irony, we must realize his sincerity. The speech beginning "I like her with all her faults" is a highly ironic yet thoroughly convincing admission of love. The rather mysterious concern with Waitwell's marriage seems strange until later developments.

Witwoud and Petulant are a pair of the fops and false wits that abounded in Restoration London, or at least in Restoration drama. They have no part in the action of The Way of the World; at most, they serve to suggest Millamant's train of suitors. Congreve's deftness of line is such that, over the years, critics have complained about the brilliance of some of Witwoud's speeches — for instance, "a letter as heavy as a panegyric in a funeral sermon" is not a bad line. But we can see that Witwoud lacks the style and the dignity that is so marked in Mirabell, the ideal Restoration gentleman, and he is so self-satisfied that he is unable to distinguish between legitimate raillery and the personal insults directed at him by both Mirabell and Fainall. As Mirabell ironically states: "He has indeed one good quality — he is not exceptious; . . . he will construe an affront into a jest, and call downright rudeness and ill language satire and fire."

Petulant is a clearer case. He comes closer to the kinds of characters one observes in Jonson. The foppishness of both characters can be reinforced by the arts of the costumers and the actor.

Act II

Summary

In St. James' Park, Mrs. Fainall and Mrs. Marwood discuss their favorite subjects, men and how to manipulate them. Beneath their apparent friendliness, they are wary of each other as they talk of Mirabell. Mrs. Fainall suspects, quite correctly, that Mrs. Marwood is in love with him.

After Fainall and Mirabell enter, Mirabell and Mrs. Fainall stroll off and leave Fainall and Mrs. Marwood alone on the stage. We now discover that Mrs. Marwood is Fainall's mistress and that he only married his wife for her fortune so as to finance his amour. However, their love includes neither faith nor trust. Fainall is sensitive to the fact that Mrs. Marwood's seeming enmity of Mirabell covers her attraction for him. The scene ends with mutual recrimination and a reconciliation as they leave the stage when Mirabell and Mrs. Fainall return.

The conversation of Mirabell and Mrs. Fainall supplies new revelations. Mirabell and Mrs. Fainall were lovers; she married Fainall as a cover for her affair with Mirabell. Mirabell, during their stroll, has told her of his scheme to trick Lady Wishfort and marry Millamant. As he does not trust Waitwell, he arranged for a marriage between Waitwell and Foible, Lady Wishfort's maid. (The news of this marriage arrived in the first act.) After all, having wooed and won Lady Wishfort, Waitwell might plan on actually marrying her.

Millamant now makes her first entrance, accompanied by Witwoud and her maid, Mincing. She is thoroughly aware of her own charm and her power over Mirabell, and toys with Mirabell's love at the same time that she returns it. She is apparently quite prepared to go along with Mirabell's plot, which Foible has revealed to her, a clear indication that in the end she intends to have Mirabell.

After her exit, Waitwell and Foible appear. Waitwell will woo Lady Wishfort in the guise of Sir Rowland, Mirabell's imaginary uncle. As Sir Rowland, he would be a fine match; in addition, the marriage would serve Lady Wishfort as a way to be revenged on Mirabell for his earlier slight, for presumably Mirabell would be disinherited when Sir Rowland married. All exit, with Waitwell making wry, typically Restoration comments.

In this act, the tensions between the characters are exposed. Just as Fainall and Mirabell, presumably friends, engaged in a verbal duel that hid a real one, so Mrs. Fainall and Mrs. Marwood now fence. There is good reason for Mrs. Fainall and Mrs. Marwood not to trust each other; it is true that Mrs. Marwood is the mistress of Mrs. Fainall's husband. By the same token, she is in love with Mirabell, Mrs. Fainall's former, and perhaps present, lover.

One can, from a modern point of view, question the nature of the love of Mirabell and Mrs. Fainall. After all, if he had loved her, why had he not married her? She was presumably young, beautiful, wealthy, and available. Interesting also is the affair between Fainall and Mrs. Marwood. Fainall seems to love Mrs. Marwood after his fashion. That love should include trust does not even occur to him. As he says, does she think that the lover will sleep, though the husband may nod?

The scenes between Mrs. Marwood and Mrs. Fainall and between Mrs. Marwood and Fainall present a real challenge to the actors. Before the audience is given the information that makes it possible to follow the play, the actors must convey the currents of feeling, essentially cynical and unpleasant, which underly the very polished manners and high style of the exchanges of wit.

The act includes important revelations of character. A clue to the character of Mirabell is presented when Mrs. Marwood accuses Mirabell of being proud. Mrs. Fainall reacts strongly: Pride, she says, is the one fault he does not have. We may have some difficulty interpreting the term "proud"; it would appear that he is gracious rather than arrogant.

Fainall describes himself as having "a heart of proof and something of the constitution to bustle through the ways of wedlock and this world." He is, we might translate, a man who can adjust to circumstance. Mirabell describes him as "a man lavish of his morals, an interested and professing friend, a false and designing lover, yet one whose wit and outward behavior have gained a reputation with the town, enough to make that woman stand excused who has suffered herself to be won by his addresses." These observations are ample preparation for Fainall's future actions. His suspicions of others are accurate because he recognizes his own faults in them.

Act III

Summary

At her home, Lady Wishfort is trying to hide the signs of age with cosmetics applied externally and brandy internally. Mrs. Marwood enters and tells her that Foible was talking to Mirabell in the park. While Mrs. Marwood hides in a closet, Lady Wishfort taxes Foible with disloyalty. However, Foible takes advantage of this opportunity to forward Mirabell's plot; she says he stopped her only to insult Lady Wishfort, who therefore determines to accept Sir Rowland, due to arrive that day.

Unfortunately, after Lady Wishfort leaves, Mrs. Fainall enters, and she and Foible discuss Mirabell's scheme; Mrs. Marwood, still hidden, overhears their conversation. They also mention that Mrs. Fainall was Mirabell's mistress at one time, and that Mrs. Marwood is in love with Mirabell, but he finds her unattractive. Mrs. Marwood's anger is reinforced in the next scene when Millamant also accuses her of loving Mirabell and makes biting remarks about her age.

When the guests arrive for dinner, Petulant and young Witwoud, and then Sir Wilfull Witwoud, the elder brother and Millamant's suitor, appear. In a scene that perhaps comes closer to farce than any other in this play, Sir Wilfull does not recognize his foppish brother, and young Witwoud refuses to recognize his country-bumpkin elder brother. Afterward, Mrs. Marwood, left alone with Fainall, describes Mirabell's plot. He is certain now that he has been a cuckold and wants revenge.

Mrs. Marwood then outlines a plan for Fainall. Since Lady Wishfort has control of Millamant's fortune, and since she is very fond of her daughter, Mrs. Fainall, he can insist that Millamant's money be made over to him on threat of making public his wife's transgressions.

Lady Wishfort is a stock character of Restoration drama; and, indeed, the older woman, eager to entrap a husband, has always been a figure of fun. But that is not to say she has no individuality. In the last three acts, Congreve devotes more attention to her character development and gives her more lines than any other character. She is eager to be wooed but would not seem to pursue. She would be forward but not too forward. She dare not smile or frown, for the paint might crack. She is concerned about appearances, but "what's integrity to an opportunity?" She is a sanctimonious hypocrite (as her description of her daughter's rearing in Act V makes clear); her private library, to which she directs Mrs. Marwood in the closet, is made up of devotional and anti-theatrical books. Quarles' Emblems are didactic poems, each with its moral attached; Prynne's Histrio-Mastix is a long attack on the immorality of the theater; Collier's Short View of the Immorality and Profaneness of the English Stage was published in 1698, two years before the production of The Way of the World. "Bunyan's Works" hardly need comment.

Lady Wishfort is in every way worth watching — obnoxious, laughable, vulgar, a little disgusting, and sometimes oddly pathetic. She craves friends, but with amazing consistency she invariably puts her trust in people who betray her.

Foible is different from the typical comedy lady's maid, represented, perhaps, by Mincing. She is an alive, mentally agile young woman and knows all the intrigues in the Wishfort household. She is aware of the passages between Marwood and Fainall, and the passages before that between Mrs. Fainall and Mirabell. She is indeed the key to all matters. Foible's comment that Mrs. Marwood "has a month's mind," with all its insulting connotations, is a key phrase in the development of the plot.

Mrs. Marwood's love for Mirabell now turns to hatred; she is the woman scorned. (It is Congreve's famous line in The Mourning Bride that hell has "no fury like a woman scorned.")

In the scene between young Witwoud and Sir Wilfull, some of the incidental values of the play are made clear. Witwoud's witticisms are, after all, clever and frequently apropos. Up to this scene, the fact that he has, as Mirabell says in Act I, "some few scraps of other folks' wit" has to be brought out by the actor in his portrayal of the character. However, his treatment of his brother is not that of the Restoration gentleman, who might deplore Sir Wilfull's crudeness but would never try to deny his brother. He does not display the polish that Mirabell would under the same circumstances. Although Sir Wilfull is a stock Restoration country bumpkin, he displays a common sense and a forthright honesty that make him appear far the worthier of the brothers.

The last scene between Marwood and Fainall indicates clearly the direction of the play for the two following acts. The counterplot, opposed to the plot of the hero, is now set up.

Millamant is a contrast to all others about her. She is surrounded by intrigue, and, together with her fortune, she is the object and the potential prize of much of it. However, she is not herself active in any intrigue. Her banter and wit are usually good-natured and direct. She does not have the cynical opinion of human nature which is so important a part of the attitude of everyone else in the play. She delights in teasing Mirabell, with the justification that she thinks of him as already her property. She is vain but amused at her own vanity. She can play the game of wit and make jokes about pinning up her hair with letters written in poetry — prose, of course, would be completely unacceptable. She is an ingénue of a type that could only have been presented on the Restoration stage, and she is without question the most successful of her kind.

The love story of Mirabell and Millamant differs from what might be expected. In most love plots, the male has to overcome the unwillingness, dislike, or simple reluctance of the other party. In The Way of the World, all the problems connected with the love affair are external. There is never any feeling that these two are not in love. Millamant postures, primps, and teases; it is fun to be desired and desirable. But these lovers have no internal conflicts.

Act IV

Summary

After Lady Wishfort is seen preparing for the visit of Sir Rowland, Millamant and Sir Wilfull are onstage together. Sir Wilfull, somewhat drunk but very shy, is too bashful actually to complete his proposal to Millamant. Overawed by the aloof lady, he is eager to get away and grateful when she dismisses him. It is obvious that he will not succeed, but he is likable in his embarrassment.

Immediately after occurs the scene between Millamant and Mirabell that is often called the proviso scene. They discuss the conditions under which he is prepared to marry her and under which she is prepared to accept him. At the end of the scene, when Mrs. Fainall enters, Millamant admits that she does love him violently. As Mirabell leaves, the company — Sir Wilfull, young Witwoud, and Petulant — come in from dinner. They are all drunk — Sir Wilfull the drunkest of the three. Now the spurious Sir Rowland arrives to woo Lady Wishfort, and his wooing bids fair to be successful when a letter is brought from Mrs. Marwood in which she tells Lady Wishfort of the plot. However, Waitwell and Foible between them manage to convince Lady Wishfort that the letter is actually sent by Mirabell and is designed as a plot against Sir Rowland. Apparently Lady Wishfort is convinced, at least for the moment.

Much of Act IV is devoted to variations on the theme of courtship in the Restoration manner. First the comic country squire is portrayed. At the end of the act, the obviously burlesqued Sir Rowland woos Lady Wishfort in a broadly comic manner. Between the two is the proviso scene.

The proviso scene in The Way of the World is generally considered the finest in Restoration comedy. The motif was first used by Dryden in Secret Love. The scene must be read carefully and, in a performance, must be developed by the actors with some finesse. Under the polished phrases and the verbal fencing, the happy couple are very much in love, as Millamant admits at the end of the scene. The careful student might reread the scene at this point to see what has led up to this admission.

This proviso scene is an emblem of the Restoration comic convention at its civilized best. At no time do the characters descend to any obvious display of emotion, let alone pathos. Even though in love, they conduct the scene with complete decorum. In the Restoration convention, in every exchange between a man and a woman, each is trying to build his or her own ego. All encounters are duels, and to be bested in the game of wits is to lose. The proviso scene is the reconciliation of these seeming irreconcilables. Mirabell will be a husband, Millamant will dwindle into a wife, but they have made a victory of their mutual surrender.

The gentlemen, drunk after dinner, who enter immediately afterward, are at once a comic interlude and a wry commentary. We have seen the Restoration ideal; we now see the gentleman as he actually exists.

The comic scene between Sir Rowland and Lady Wishfort is broad. Sir Rowland is a masquerade. He is the servant pretending to be a gentleman. Lady Wishfort plays the salacious widow to the hilt. Inevitably, the scene is a marked contrast to the love duel of the proviso scene.

The drunken comments are also nice counterpoint. Petulant's "if you can love me dear nymph, say it — and that's the conclusion. Pass on, or pass off — " and Sir Wilfull's "A match or no match, cousin with the hard name . . ." are a significant contrast with the mastery of style displayed in the preceding scene.

Act V

Summary

The scene, as before, is Lady Wishfort's house. Lady Wishfort has discovered Mirabell's plot. Foible tries unsuccessfully to make excuses for herself.

Fainall now makes his demands. As Millamant's fortune of 6,000 pounds was presumably forfeit when she refused to marry a suitor selected for her by Lady Wishfort, he wants the money as his price for not blackening his wife's reputation. He also wants the remainder of Mrs. Fainall's fortune turned over to his sole control. And he insists on Lady Wishfort's not marrying again so that he be sole heir. These terms are very harsh, and Lady Wishfort might not be prepared to go along with them except that Mrs. Marwood, standing by, goads her on by harping on the public disgrace of her daughter, Mrs. Fainall.

When the two maids now reveal that Fainall, in his turn, has been unfaithful to his wife, he refuses to be deterred; he is willing to be the subject of scandal himself, but he will still make public his wife's shame. When Millamant states that she is prepared to marry Sir Wilfull, thus meeting the wishes of her aunt and saving her 6,000 pounds, Fainall suspects a trick, but he can still demand control of the balance of his wife's estate, and now also the control of Lady Wishfort's. At this point, Mirabell presents the evidence which will protect Mrs. Fainall. At the time of her marriage, they had judged Fainall's character correctly, and Mrs. Fainall secretly signed over her fortune to Mirabell's control. There is, therefore, no money which Fainall can successfully obtain.

In great anger, Fainall and Mrs. Marwood leave the stage, vowing dire vengeance. Lady Wishfort, having discovered that Fainall was a villain and that Mrs. Marwood, her friend, was not a true friend, is now prepared to forgive Mirabell; Millamant can now marry him with her aunt's consent. It is on this happy but somewhat indeterminate note that the plays ends.

The fifth act is muddled; there is far too much plotting and action. Fainall comes in with his demands. Mirabell and Sir Wilfull Witwoud enter to frustrate part of them. Foible and Mincing disclose the information that Fainall and Mrs. Marwood have also been guilty of adultery. For the first time, we hear of the deed Mrs. Fainall signed. And, finally, Lady Wishfort forgives everyone.

If one looks at it structurally, it is possible to see that Mirabell's original scheme is here balanced by the counterplot of Fainall and Mrs. Marwood. They, in turn, are foiled by Foible and Mincing on the one hand, and by Millamant's presumed willingness to marry Sir Wilfull on the other. But these developments are then countered by Fainall's insistence on the balance of Mrs. Fainall's money. And this move is conclusively countered by Mirabell's producing the deed signed before Mrs. Fainall's marriage, presumably in anticipation of, and protection against, just such a situation.

Lady Wishfort, in this act, becomes almost a sympathetic character. Her faults and her vanities are many, but here we see her trying to protect her daughter, finding that the people whom she trusted have proven completely treacherous. Caught on the one hand by the desire to save those whom she loves, and trapped by the treachery of those she trusted, she is an odd figure in a very unusual situation in Restoration drama.

The ending of the play is not entirely satisfactory. For one thing, one is finally left with the question, "What of Mrs. Fainall?" She will retain her money, but her lover is lost to her, and it is not entirely clear that Fainall and Mrs. Marwood will not find some rather unpleasant revenge.

Epilogue

Spoken by Mrs. Bracegirdle, who played Millamant, the epilogue only makes conventional points: the essential inadequacy of critics who decry plays without knowledge, and the statement that the characters are fictitious, and no individual is represented; the satire is universal, for

So poets oft do in one piece expose
Whole belles assemblees of coquettes and beaux.

❖ *The Way of the World* -এর সারাংশের বঙ্গানুবাদ :

নাটকটির কর্মকান্ড শুরু হওয়ার আগেই কিছু ঘটনা ঘটে গেছে বলে বোঝা যায়। রেস্টোরেশান যুগের পক্ষে একেবারে আদর্শ , কিন্তু সে অর্থে বিত্তশালী নয় এমন যুবক মিরাবেলের সাথে লেডি উইসফোর্টের বিধবা কন্যা শ্রীমতী ফেইনলের সাথে প্রেমের সম্পর্ক ছিল। মিরাবেল মিস্টার ফেইনলের সাথে এই মিসেস ফেইনলের বিবাহ সম্বন্ধ স্থির করিয়েছিলেন মিসেস ফেইলের গর্ভবতী হয়ে পড়ার কেচ্ছাটিকে আড়াল করার জন্য।

ফেইনল এই যুবতী বিধবাটিকে বিয়ে করেছিল, কারণ মিসেস মারউডের সাথে নিজের অবৈধ প্রেমটি চালিয়ে যাওয়ার জন্য তার মিসে ফেইনলের অর্থের প্রয়োজন ছিল। সময়মত, মিরাবেল লেডি উইসফোর্টের ভাইঝি তথা তাঁর সম্পত্তির উত্তরাধিরারিণী তথা নিজের পূর্বতন প্রেমিকার বোন মিলামেন্টের প্রেমে পড়ে। মিরাবেল মেয়েটির ভালোবাসা ও তার প্রচুর সম্পত্তি লাভের জন্য ব্যাকুল হয়ে পড়ে। মিলামেন্ট তার সম্পত্তির ৬০০০ পাউন্ডের অধিকারিনী ছিলেন কিন্তু তার সম্পত্তির অপর ৬০০০ পাউন্ডের উপর নিয়ন্ত্রণ ছিল লেডি উইসফোর্টের। তিনি মিলামেন্টকে এই শর্ত দিয়েছিলেন যে যদি মিলামেন্ট তাঁর পছন্দ করা পাত্রকে বিয়ে করে, তবেই সে বাকি অর্থ লাভ করতে পারবে। দুর্ভাগ্যবশতঃ, মিরাবেল অতীতে লেডি উইসফোর্টকে মানসিকভাবে আঘাত দিয়েছিল। লেডি উইসফোর্ট মিরাবেলের তোষামোদকে তাঁর প্রতি মিরাবেলের প্রেম নিবেদন বলে ভুল করেছিলেন।

মিরাবেল একটি ষড়যন্ত্র করল যাতে সে এক নকল কাকাকে (ওয়েটওয়েলকে) যোগাড় করল যাতে লেডি উইসফোর্ট সেই কাকার প্রেমের ফাঁদে পড়ে। ওয়েটওয়েলের সাথে লেডি উইসফোর্টের চাকরানী ফোয়েবলের বিয়ে হয়েছিল। এরপর মিরাবেল পরিকল্পনা করে ওয়েটওয়েলের প্রকৃত পরিচয় উদ্ঘাটিত করার মাধ্যমে এমন ভান করবে যে সে লেডি উইসফোর্টকে প্রতারিত হওয়ার থেকে উদ্ধার করেছে যাতে লেডি উইসফোর্ট তার উপর প্রসন্ন হন আর তাকে অনুমতি দেন মিলামেন্টকে বিয়ে করার জন্য। মিলামেন্ট এই চক্রান্তের ব্যাপারে অবগত হয়েছিল, সম্ভবতঃ ফোয়েবলের মাধ্যমে।

যখন নাটকটি শুরু হল, তখন দেখা গেল যে মিরাবেল আকুলভাবে ওয়েটওয়েলের সাথে ফোয়েবলের বিয়ে সম্পন্ন হওয়ার খবরটি শোনার জন্য অপেক্ষা করছে। মিস্টার ফেইনলের সাথে মিরাবেলের তাস খেলার দৃশ্য থেকে জানা যায় যে তাদের মধ্যে সম্পর্কটি মধুর নয়। মিসেস ফেইনল ছিল মিরাবেলের প্রাক্তন প্রেমিকা, আর মিস্টার ফেইনলের প্রাক্তন প্রেমিকা মিসেস মারউডের সাথে বর্তমানে মিরাবেলের প্রেমের সম্পর্ক চলছে। ইতিমধ্যে, যদিও মিলামেন্ট গোপনে মিরাবেলকে ভালোবাসে, তবু সে মিরাবেলকে অনিশ্চয়তার শঙ্কা দেখিয়ে রাগানোর কাজটি বেশ উপভোগ করে।

দুর্ভাগ্যবশতঃ, মিসেস মারউড মিরাবেলের ষড়যন্ত্রের বিষয়ে ও তার সাথে সাথে মিরাবেল ও মিসেস ফেইনলের পূর্বতন প্রেমের সম্পর্কের বিষয়ে মিসেস ফেইনল ও ফোয়েবলকে আলোচনা করতে শোনে। সে নিজের বিষয়ে অপমানজনক মন্তব্যও শোনে, তাই সে প্রতিহিংসাপরায়ণ হয়ে ওঠে আর তৎক্ষণাৎ ফেইনলকে এই ষড়যন্ত্রের কথা আর এক সময় তার স্ত্রী যে মিরাবেলের প্রেমিকা ছিল সে কথা জানিয়ে দেয়। এই দুই ষড়যন্ত্রকারীরই উদ্দেশ্য ও পন্থা রয়েছে প্রতিশোধ নেওয়ার মত। সেই একই সন্ধ্যায়, মিলামেন্ট মিরাবেলের প্রস্ত্রব মেনে নেয় আর প্রত্যাখ্যান করে লেডি উইসফোর্টের মনোনীত পাত্র, স্যার উইলফুল উইটউডকে।

ষড়যন্ত্রকারী, ফেইনল, এবার ঘটনাক্রমের নিয়ন্ত্রণ করতে শুরু করে। সে নকল কাকা ওয়েটওয়েলের প্রকৃত পরিচয় প্রকাশ করে দেয়, আর মেয়ের অসম্মানের ভয় দেখিয়ে লেডি উইসফোর্টকে কালো হুমকি দিতে শুরু করে। সে দাবী করে যে মিলামেন্টের প্রাপ্য বাকি অর্ধেক অর্থ তাকে দিয়ে দিতে হবে। এর সাথে সাথে, সে এই প্রতিশ্রুতিও দাবী করে যে লেডি উইসফোর্ট কখনও বিয়ে করবেন না যাতে মিসেস ফেইনল তাঁর সমস্ত সম্পত্তির উত্তরাধিকারিনী হতে পারে।

ফেইনলের এই চক্রান্তটি বানচাল করে দেয় মিলামেন্ট। সে জানায় যে সে স্যার উইলফুলকে বিয়ে করতে রাজি আছে নিজের সম্পত্তিকে রক্ষা করার জন্য। ফেইনল জোর করতে থাকে যে তার স্ত্রীর সমস্ত প্রাপ্য অর্থ তথা লেডি উইসফোর্টের সমস্ত সম্পত্তির নিয়ন্ত্রণ অবিলম্বে তার হাতে সমর্পন করতে হবে। সেই মুহূর্তেই মিরাবেল দুইটি চাকরকে নিয়ে হাজির হয় এটা প্রমাণ করতে যে ফেইনল ও মিসেস মারউড নিজেরাই অবৈধ প্রণয়ে লিপ্ত থাকার অপরাধে অপরাধী। ফেইনল এই দোষারোপ অস্বীকার করে আর ইঙ্গিত করে যে সে এসব সত্ত্বেও একটা কেচ্ছা ছড়িয়ে দিতে পারে যা মিসেস ফেইনলের নামকে কলঙ্কিত করবে যদি সে তার দাবীমত অর্থ না পায়।

এই সময়, মিরাবেল বিজয়ীর মত উদ্ঘাটিত করে তার সবচেয়ে সফল কৌশলটি। মিসেস ফেইনলের সাথে ফেইনলের বিয়ে হওয়ার আগেই মিসেস ফেইনল ও মিরাবেল ফেইনল নামক লোকটির চরিত্র বিষয়ে

সন্দেহ প্রকাশ করেছিল আর তাই মিসেস ফেইনল তার প্রেমিক মিরাবেলকে তার সম্পত্তির জামিনদার নিয়োগ করেছিল। তাই এখন ফেইনল মিসেস ফেইনলের সম্পত্তি দাবী করতে পারবে না যেহেতু মিসেস ফেইনল তার নিজের সম্পত্তির নিয়ন্ত্রণকারিনী নয়। ফেইনল ও মিসেস মারউড অত্যন্ত ক্রুদ্ধভাবে সেখান থেকে চলে যায়। লেডি উইসফোর্ট দুই চাকরকে ক্ষমা করে দেন আর মিরাবেল ও মিরামেন্টের বিয়েতে সম্মতি জ্ঞাপন করেন।

❖ A Critical Analysis of *The Way of the World*:

The precise statement of the theme of a work of art is always a little unsatisfactory. The pithy sentence must omit a great deal; it always does violence to the whole work. Nevertheless, it is worth making the effort to determine a theme, or themes, in a play as a guide to study or analysis.

As a point of departure, it is valid to say that the theme of this play is given us by Congreve in the title, The Way of the World. All the events and characters of the play can be related to this central theme. The obvious criticism is that the same "theme" can be ascribed to unlimited numbers of other, and quite different, novels and plays. Further, Congreve does not, in this play, seem to take a consistent position. Sometimes he is direct, sometimes ironic; sometimes he deplores, sometimes he approves; at times he is amused; and most of the time his position is a compound of all of these attitudes.

To get a more satisfactory statement we might use a different approach that would give a better sense of the texture of the play. Most Restoration playwrights supplied their plays with alternate titles, or subtitles. Since Congreve did not, we might seek for the different subtitles that are appropriate. Each one would suggest a theme, although not the theme. These may put flesh on the bare bones the title gives us.

Love a la Mode

Certainly, the play can be seen as a dramatic presentation of varieties of love in the England of the year 1700. Central is the delicate handling of the love game as played by Mirabell and Millamant. They represent the ideal of the Restoration attitude, intense yet balanced, their love based on mutual esteem with no surrender of individuality. Contrasted with it are Mirabell's earlier and quite ambiguous love affair with Mrs. Fainall; the illicit love of Fainall and Mrs. Marwood, presumably passionate, but wholly without mutual trust; the spurious court young Witwoud pays to Millamant; the direct and somewhat coarse approach of Sir Wilfull; and, at the opposite extreme completely, the aging and undignified longings of Lady Wishfort, vain, unrealistic, over-eager, desperate, and a little pathetic.

Love and Money

Such an approach is closely related to that of love a la mode, although they are not identical. In the world whose way is presented here, love and money are values to be taken into account at all times. The sincerity of Mirabell's love does not make him lose sight of the importance of Millamant's fortune. Fainall marries for money to support an illicit love; apparently the thought of marrying Mrs. Marwood without adequate money (however "adequate" might be defined) is unthinkable. Money is Lady Wishfort's sole hold over her child and her ward. Even the marriage of the servants is built on a promise of a handsome sum of money. This is the world's way. Love without money is an impossible sentimental dream, although money often corrupts what love there is.

A Gallery of Portraits

Congreve's statements in the dedication, the prologue, and the epilogue suggest that this might be a valid subtitle. Since it is the way of the world to put a premium on youth, Mirabell and Millamant stand at the center, representing all that is to be commended. Mirabell is the beau ideal: polished, poised, rational and balanced, witty and perspicacious without being what we might today call over-intellectual. Millamant is the belle: feminine, beautiful, witty, not prudish, but with a sense of her own worth. She has avoided the messiness and humiliation of sexual intrigue. Opposed to Mirabell are would-be wits, worthy but graceless boors, and deep intriguers. Opposed to Millamant are women who engaged in adultery and an old dowager without decorum. Every character reveals himself in action, and together they produce a gallery of self-portraits.

Jungle of High Intrigue

This subtitle would focus attention on some of the values of London society. Everyone is engaged in intrigue: Mirabell intrigues to gain consent to his marriage from Lady Wishfort, and this involves intrigue within intrigue, for he does not trust Waitwell. Fainall intrigues in turn. Everyone is involved in one or the other of these schemes — Mrs. Fainall, Mrs. Marwood, and the servants. Even Lady Wishfort in her willingness to marry Sir Rowland has a devious purpose — revenge on Mirabell. When Mrs. Fainall married her husband, that was part of an intrigue, as was his marriage to her. And as we see in the play, victory goes to Mirabell, not because of his virtue, but simply because he is the most successful intriguer.

Certainly all these possible subtitles, rather than any one, add up to the ironic commentary on society that is in the title, The Way of the World.

Style, Wit, and Irony in The Way of the World

In the most common use of the word, style describes the author's use of language within the shorter rhetorical units, the sentence or at most the paragraph. It includes the choice of words and the rhythmic and musical quality of the sentences. Since it also includes a discussion of the relations of language to thought, fact, and reality, at some point it becomes identical with a discussion of wit and irony.

If irony is included in the discussion, then arbitrary limits must be set because from some points of view, irony pervades The Way of the World. The title is ironic; the action is ironic; the relationships of the characters to each other are ironic. This section, however, is concerned only with irony as a function of the speeches of characters, not as a function of plot or theme. It is concerned with that kind of irony that is closely related to style and wit.

Congreve avoids attempting any definition of wit, although, in the dedication, he distinguishes between true wit and false wit, the latter a product of affectation. Another comment of Congreve's on wit also casts some light on his practice. In "Concerning Humour in Comedy," he writes:

Every person in a comedy may be allowed to speak them [pleasant things]. From a witty man they are expected and even a fool may be permitted to stumble on 'em by chance. . . . I do not think that humourous characters exclude wit; no, but the manner of wit should be adapted to the humour . . . ; a character of a splenetic and peevish humour should have a satirical wit. A jolly and sanguine humour should have a facetious wit.

In practice, all of Congreve's characters speak "pleasant things." There is not a speech that does not have its biting edge of wit, satire, or irony.

Discussions of style and wit in a play are in some ways simple. Certain kinds of problems do not have to be discussed since they do not exist. Unlike novels, plays have no long passages of description which may or may not be well written; there are no elaborate expositions of motives. There is no reason to consider whether the author is inside his creatures' minds or external to them. The characters speak; what they say can be examined. To talk of style or wit in a play is to talk of the different styles and different kinds of wit of the characters.

Congreve wrote so that his characters were sharply differentiated by their speech patterns and their wit. As Congreve used style and wit as one of his ways of characterization, the material in this section may be considered additional data for study of the characters, collected here so that a rather technical subject can be treated in one place.

Mirabell

Mirabell's style is not an easy one. We do not feel that he is spontaneous, for his periods are carefully prepared. The sentences are long, flowing, and syntactically intricate. He indulges in no slang or canting expressions. While he can be acid in his judgment, there is no vituperation in his speech. The objects of his disapproval are so deftly lanced in his gracious phrases that they can scarcely feel the knife.

Mirabell's wit and irony are also intricate. His observations about others are shrewd, including a mixture of distaste, tolerance, and amusement. Considerable irony is also directed at himself. There is a strong element of self-criticism that makes him a most unusual hero.

Any number of speeches might serve to reveal these characteristics; this famous speech from the first act about his feelings toward Millamant will do:

I'll tell thee, Fainall, she once used me with that insolence, that in revenge I took her to pieces, sifted her and separated her failings: I studied 'em, and got 'em by rote. The catalogue was so large that I was not without hopes one day or other to hate her heartily: to which end I so used myself to think of 'em, that at length, contrary to my design and expectation, they gave me every hour less and less disturbance, till in a few days it became habitual to me to remember 'em without being displeased. They are now grown as familiar to me as my own frailties, and, in all probability, in a little time longer I shall like 'em as well.

The characteristics can be seen: the long smooth passages (one might read aloud from "to which end" to the end of the sentence), the real wit, the clear vision of the object of the speech, and the wry ability to laugh at himself.

Millamant

The ultimate proof of the individuality of Millamant's style is in this — that to read the passage aloud is immediately to sense the manner and mannerisms of the character. She is flippant, delightfully spoiled, spirited. When, in the fourth act, she reveals a depth that we might not have expected, that, too, is in the style. Her speech in her first appearance is abrupt; she moves not so much from one subject to another as from one feeling to another with an ability to turn anything into wit.

Mrs. Millamant: Oh, aye, letters: I had letters. I am persecuted with letters. I hate letters. Nobody knows how to write letters; and yet one has 'em, one does not know why. They serve one to pin up one's hair.

Witwoud: Pray, madam, do you pin up your hair with all your letters?

Mrs. Millamant: Only with those in verse, Mr. Witwoud; I never pin up my hair with prose. I think I tried once, Mincing.

Mincing: O mem, I shall never forget it.

After a series of short, flippant statements, there comes an inspired thought: "They serve one to pin up one's hair." She then pursues the train of thought that this conceit suggests: "Only with those in verse." It is incidentally pleasant that Mincing can pick up her cue and proceed further.

The passage "One makes lovers as fast as one pleases" is similar, as is "Now I think on't, I'm angry. No, now I think on't, I'm pleased; for I believe I gave you some pain!" The style and wit are the character of Millamant.

In the proviso scene, more serious in content, the pace changes. There is still a teasing element, but there is less skipping from point to point. Millamant is stating her conditions for marriage:

Trifles — as liberty to pay and receive visits to and from whom I please; to write and receive letters, without interrogatories or wry faces on your part; to wear what I please, and choose conversation with regard only to my own taste; to have no obligation upon me to converse with wits that I don't like, because they are your acquaintance; or to be intimate with fools, because they may be your relations. . . . These articles subscribed, if I continue to endure you a little longer, I may by degrees dwindle into a wife.

Fainall

Fainall's style and wit must be differentiated from Mirabell's. His sentences are not as long or as contemplative as Mirabell's, and his wit is more direct and somewhat crueler: "The coldness of a losing gamester lessens the pleasure of the winner. I'd no more play with a man that slighted his ill fortune than I'd make love to a woman that undervalued the loss of her reputation." Perhaps because of the nature of his part, he is more abrupt in accusation, and his lines may depend on a more obvious parallelism and antithesis: "Could you think, because the nodding husband would not wake, that e'er the watchful lover slept?" And he engages in a more direct attack: "Professed a friendship! Oh, the pious friendships of the female sex!"

Young Witwoud

Since Congreve himself commented that readers and audience could not always distinguish between Witwoud and his true wits, Witwoud's speeches demand especially careful examination.

As Witwoud has no function in the plot of the play, the purpose of his speeches is to characterize him and to provide comedy. The key to his wit is the "similitude." "Truce with your similitudes," says Millamant to him. Each comparison may be clever by itself, amusing, unusual, a little shocking, such as "Friendship without freedom is as dull as love without enjoyment." The lines with which he interrupts Millamant in the second act are each one a comparison, amusing or overburdened. The witticisms are forced; they have been collected and memorized, and at need pulled out of his conjurer's bag of tricks. Irony, if there is any here, is superficial; no one of the witticisms has any particular point. Nor does young Witwoud even realize it should.

Petulant

Petulant's style and wit are included in his name. He has a humour to be angry — that is, he is an example of Jonsonian humour, or, perhaps, he affects a humour.

Lady Wishfort

Lady Wishfort's style, like everything else about her, is of special interest. Her manner is abrupt — a mirror of the arbitrary, petty tyrant she is. Like all Congreve characters, she has, perhaps unconsciously, a fair amount of wit. More than anything else in the play, her verbal attack on others is direct vituperation-"Boudoir Billingsgate," in Meredith's phrase. No unit of thought is longer than a few words. It is clear that she shouts when annoyed or irritated, and she is always in a state of annoyance:

No, fool. Not the ratafia, fool. Grant me patience! I mean the Spanish paper, idiot; complexion, darling. Paint, paint, paint! dost thou understand that, changeling, dangling thy hands like bobbins before thee? Why does thou not stir, puppet? thou wooden thing upon wires!

The term irony has a different meaning when one is discussing Lady Wishfort. It is true that she does indulge in heavy-handed sarcasm, but the unconscious irony is more important. She responds to the accidental images of words in ironical self-revelation. Foible reports that Mirabell said he would "handle" Lady Wishfort. "Handle me, would he durst!" she cries, "such a foul-mouthed fellow." It is clear what the word "handle" means to her — and the reader may or may not catch the ambiguity of "would he durst." Her speech as she repairs her face while waiting for Sir Rowland is a group of short, flustered comments that constitute her regular manner, an unconsciously ironic description of her hypocrisy:

In what figure shall I give his heart the first impression? There is a great deal in the first impression. Shall I sit? — No, I won't sit — I'll walk — aye, I'll walk from the door upon his entrance; and then turn full upon him. — No, that will be too sudden. I'll lie — aye, I'll lie down — I'll receive him in my little dressing-room; there's a couch — yes, yes, I'll give the first impression on a couch. — won't lie neither, but loll and lean upon one elbow, with one foot a little dangling off, jogging in a thoughtful way — yes — and then as soon as he appears, start, aye, start and be surprised, and rise to meet him in a pretty disorder — yes — oh, nothing is more alluring than a levee from a couch, in some confusion. — It shows the foot to advantage, and furnishes with blushes, and recomposing airs beyond comparison.

Examples can be multiplied. One might only add Lady Wishfort's remark when she discovers that her daughter's fortune will not be lost: "'Tis plain thou has inherited thy mother's prudence," a highly ambiguous compliment in the light of Mrs. Fainall's unsatisfactory love affair with Mirabell and Lady Wishfort's misjudgment of Mrs. Marwood and Sir Rowland.

The Way of the World and Restoration Drama

The Restoration, as a period, takes its name from the Restoration of the monarchy, with Charles II assuming the throne in 1660. The Restoration of the monarchy meant the end of the Puritan Parliament's rule, but it also meant the return of the theatre. Because of the theatre's long-standing connection with royalty and aristocracy and because of the Puritans' view of the theatre as licentious and blasphemous, theatrical performances were banned during parliament's rule. In 1662, the theatres re-opened, and play-going became an important part of the reaction against the Puritanism of the previous decades. Restoration theatre, for many cultural historians, epitomizes the era. While many plays from the Shakespearean era were reproduced, new plays commenting on the renewed monarchy and a new culture of performance, wealth, and more open sexuality flourished. In a variety of forms, the entire culture seemed to see itself as a kind of play, as commentators repeatedly emphasized the ways everyone seemed to be playing roles as they negotiated new mores and social conditions.

While the theatre of the Restoration era attempted to return to its earlier form, it innovated on the theatre of the first part of the 17th century in many ways. First, it became accessible and respectable, as the theatres themselves moved into better parts of London and started to attract a broader array of patrons. At the same time, playhouses opened up professionally for women, as they began to appear on stage in large numbers for the first number and several women, most famously, perhaps, Aphra Behn, became successful playwrights. The presence of women on the stage and in larger numbers in the audiences directly contributed to the intensive exploration of sexual themes in the theatre of the period. Actresses were often seen as little more than prostitutes, and many famous actresses were well-known consorts of the king and other nobles. Their performances on stage often played with their supposed sexual availability, while women in the audiences often similarly were seen or displayed themselves as performers as they traded witty conversation laced with double entendre with men about town. In many accounts, the flirtations in the audience mirrored or rivaled the performances on stage.

The Restoration comedy of manners reflected and commented on this culture of performance. These plays often featured rakes—men on the prowl for sexual conquest—who elaborated complicated schemes for bedding as many woman as possible. Over the course of the play, their attempts were often forwarded, rebuffed, and foiled by various women whose sexual knowledge and wit frequently equaled their male counterparts. These comedies usually featured incredibly complex plots and counterplots—emphasizing their characters' ability to manipulate others through their self-display, control of language, and psychological calculations as they attempted to win both sexual favors and wealth. Yet, even as the plays displayed the power of performance that their very audiences indulged in, they often critiqued that culture for its duplicity and depravity. With the Glorious Revolution of 1688 and the return to power of parliament, a reaction against the excesses of the Restoration set in, with much of the focus on the theatre and the culture of performance and display and, in particular, its sexual licentiousness.

Appearing in 1700, Congreve's play represents a late version of the Restoration comedy of manners, one that consolidates many of the features of earlier plays even as it responds to increasing critique of the theatre (the play mentions one of the most famous critiques in Act 3). Implicitly describing the way of the world as one of cynical self-interest, the play follows the reformed rake Mirabell as he attempts to win the hand of Millamant, the woman he actually loves. Before the play begins, Mirabell, we later learn, has had an affair with Mrs. Fainall, whose husband married her only for her wealth and is having an affair with Mrs. Marwood; we only learn most of this in the second act. Millamant is the niece and ward of Lady Wishfort, who is Mrs. Fainall's mother, and stands to inherit a great deal of money, but only if Lady Wishfort approves of her suitor. Mirabell has offended Lady Wishfort, so he needs not only to win Millamant's hand but also to win over Lady Wishfort.

As with most Restoration comedies, Mirabell creates a complicated scheme involving impersonation and artifice to get both wealth and love. He has his valet, Waitwell, pretend to be his uncle and woo Lady Wishfort. His plan is to then rescue Lady Wishfort from being seduced by a servant and thus gain her approval. While Millamant knows of the plot and does love Mirabell, she takes pleasure in teasing him about the uncertainty of their eventual union.

However, things go awry for Mirabell when Mrs. Marwood learns of the plot and of Mirabell's former affair with Mrs. Fainall. Mrs. Marwood informs Mr. Fainall, and they begin a plot against Mirabell. Millamant has accepted Mirabell's proposal, turning down Sir Witful Witwoud (Lady Wishfort's choice). Fainall uncovers the plot to Lady Wishfort and attempts to blackmail her by threatening to reveal her daughter's (Mrs. Fainall's) adultery. He wants all of Millamant's fortune as well as complete control of Mrs. Fainall's potential inheritance. Millamant then decides she will marry Sir Witwoud in order to save her fortune, and Mirabell appears with two servants to prove Mr. Fainall's adultery with Mrs. Marwood. Fainall, however, is not cowed and continues to threaten Mrs. Fainall's reputation. Then, Mirabell plays his last card. Before she married Mr. Fainall, Mrs. Fainall, out of fear of Mr. Fainall's character, had made Mirabell the trustee of her fortune. Without control of that money, Mr. Fainall is left without any resources, and the play ends with Mirabell and Millamant engaged.

The Way of the World exemplifies many of the key features of the Restoration comedy of manners—complex, multi-faceted characters who combine urbanity and wit in treating love and wealth as a game they play through concealment, artifice, and plotting. Unlike some of the plays from the first decade of the Restoration, however, Congreve's play does not end up embracing the cynicism of some of its characters; instead, true love—while far from sentimentalized—wins out and leaves with wealth. His characters have their moral failings and they more than handle themselves in a world of false appearances, banter, and sexual double-dealings, but they are redeemed in the end.

Essay Type Questions with Answers

Q. 1. Comment on the use of Wit in *The Way of the World.*

Ans. Congreve avoids attempting any definition of wit, the latter a product. The author?s comment on wit reflects some light on his practice. In "Concerning Humour in Comedy," he writes:

Every person in a comedy may be allowed to speak them [pleasant things]. From a witty man they are expected and even a fool may be permitted to stumble on 'em by chance. . . . I do not think that humourous characters exclude wit; no, but the manner of wit should be adapted to the humour . . . ; a character of a splenetic and peevish humour should have a satirical wit. A jolly and sanguine humour should have a facetious wit.

He clearly distinguishes between true wit and false wit. Lets come into the definition of wit. Wit is a difficult term to define or translate. In providing an explanation of the term the era of Congreve?s society has to be considered as well because the meaning of the word shifted throughout the history. Gelber mentions that while in the sixteenth century wit stood for genius or wisdom, in the seventeenth century its meaning narrowsed to a "capacity for ingenuity, an ability to make unexpected unions or contrast of generally diverse ideas" (Gelber 269). To discover its most accurate meaning in relation to Congreve?s play, it is best to refer to the critics of the Restoration period themselves and to the way they perceived it. Klára Bicanová points out in her dissertation that wit was seen as something more than humour or cleverness. For both Pope and Addison "wit involved good taste, morality and it was essentially interchangeable with the idea of literary genius.". Hinnant adds that "wit refers to more than just a verbal play (puns, similitudes, antitheses etc.). It also points to a traditional ideal of decorum ("a propriety of words and thoughts") whose theoretical basis provides a standard by which false wit can be judged".

To elaborate more on the concept of true and false wit, characters in The Way of the World that express this notion can be divided into two groups: wits and would-be wits. However, Congreve creates more blurred distinction in dividing the characters into these two groups. In his interpretation, the separation between the two groups is not always clear, neither it is rigid, which makes it more difficult to distinguish the true wits of the play. Hinnant points out that those categories are "not as static, as they tend to be in the earlier comedies [of the Restoration period]" (Hinnant 381). Indeed, Congreve continues with the interest in the notion of wit, but offers a fresh outlook on in. His characters are not black and white. He allows his would-be wits to have some bright moments as well.

The character of Anthony Witwoud can serve as an example, as he represents a rather problematic would-be wit. Hinnant mentions the fact that Witwoud was actually taken for a true wit by his contemporaries as his affectation is focused towards similitudes and his character "balances brilliance with dullness . . . a Witwoud who sparkles and a Witwoud who is tiresome" (Hinnant 375). This allows Congreve to express his sceptical attitude towards the usage of similitudes and its perception as an example of true wit. Witwoud is someone who confesses: "I talk like an old maid at a marriage, I don?t know what I say" (Congreve 1.230-231), but at the same time he tirelessly attempts to express what Kaufman names "the linguistic ease of the wits". As a consequence, the audience can "witness a self-conscious obsession with wit transform a human being into a wit-producing automaton". Witwoud is self-aware of his overindulgence in similitudes, but simply cannot stop himself even though his speeches are found tiresome by others.

Witwoud is conscious of his unstoppable flow of attempted wit, but he still tries to paint himself as a true wit. Kaufman described him as "the logical end product of a society that overvalues appearance". He is a character that focuses predominantly on his rhetorical expressions, but lacks any sense of subtlety or fittingness of his utterances that are essential components of a true wit.

The attempt to present oneself as a true wit is also expressed by female characters in the play. They as well attempt to paint themselves as ingenious players in the game of the society. And just as male characters, they are both successful and failing. Mrs Marwood, Fainall?s mistress, shares with Witwoud the endeavour to present herself as a witty character. But just as he, she is not able to recognize the propriety of some of her expressions. When she is discussing the issue of female friendship with Fainall, she calls it "more sincere, and more enduring, than all the vain and empty vows of men", Fainall immediately reminds her that she is his wife?s friend and at the same time his lover, thus immediately undermining her argument. Her words could express true wit, but they would have to belong to a different character. After such disclosure of her impropriety, she resorts to a less witty and more malicious language that instead of the subtlety of true wit possesses unnecessarily dramatic exclamation such as "I loathe you" or that it is not too late to "detest, abhor mankind . . . and the whole treacherous world". Eventually she has to be reminded by Fainall: "You have a mask, wear it a moment" so she would compose herself once more.

Wit is indeed closely connected to language, but is not expressed solely in words, speeches or similitudes. It is also reflected through action. The central characters of the play Mirabell and Fainall are both very good rhetoricians; therefore it is the deeds rather that discourse that distinguish the true wit that is Mirabell from Fainall, who only feigns it, however masterfully at times, using the language of a gentleman to mask his real spiteful and vicious nature.

Indeed, it is mainly the action that uncovers his false wit. The way they both plot against Lady Wishfort brilliantly highlights the differences that demark the two characters. Fainall is unscrupulously pursuing his ambition to obtain his mother-in-law?s fortune and he is willing to destroy his wife?s reputation, to let her turn "adrift like a leaky hulk to sink or swim" (Congreve 5.1.403-405), thus fully uncovering his absolute lack of morality. Kaufman views Fainall as the "the libertine hero of the early Restoration – a predator whose vision of society is one of man?s animal instincts hidden under the veneer of "honour" or "reputation"" (418). However, those qualities as a result spoil his success and leave him to exit the stage defeated. His instincts are not accurate enough and he gets lost in his schemes. In his final scene, when he is faced with the evidence of the parchment that allocates his wife?s estate "in trust to Edward Mirabell" (Congreve 5.1.500), he cannot control his rage or find words to fight or defend himself, but flees after a failed attempt to assault his wife, which proves his ultimate defeat on the rhetorical battlefield as well.

The world of Congreve?s play is full of false wits, but there still can be found true wit among the characters. Both Mirabell and his love interest Millamant show superiority of wit among others. However, just as would-be wits have their moments of brightness, those two also struggle, but even when they are "laughable at times, in the main they are sympathetic and by the awareness of the way of the world (and a certain degree of luck) they are able to escape its ever-present dangers". They learnt to conduct themselves in the society with sense of propriety and sufficient level of self-discipline. Mirabell does not pursue his scheme unscrupulously as Fainall does, but ensures that it does not pose real danger to Lady Wishfort, when he links her with a suitor that is already married. He pleads that it was an innocent device even though "it had a face of guiltiness" (Congreve 5.1.348-349) and that he has never intended to cause lasting distress to Lady Wishfort. Indeed, through his action he distances himself from Fainall and professes his moral superiority.

While Mirabell thus distances himself from Fainall, who portrays the villain of the play, Millamant is also in control of her own situation. She does not appear in person until the middle of the second act and immediately establishes herself as the character that possesses true wit in contrast to Witwoud, with whom she shares the scene. When he asks her about letters, she responds "I am persecuted with letters – I hate letters – nobody knows how to write letters; and yet one has „em, one does not know why. They serve one to pin up one?s hair" (Congreve 2.1.321-323). She admits that she receives letters from possible admirers and that she finds it rather tiresome, but at the same time she is careful to use "one" instead of "I" that would make her statement more offensive than amusing.

In conclusion, Congreve?s play The Way of the World offers a complex representation of wit in both its true and false forms. He uses typical wit-woulds from the Restoration comedies, but he operates with them in such a way that they do not remain only rigid, laughable characters. The barrier between them and true wits is sometimes so thin that they are almost indistinguishable from each other. However, in comparison to Mirabell or Millamant their affected wit (as Congreve called it in his dedication) proves to be false. The discourse of such characters does not possess sufficient subtlety or propriety and their actions lack sense of morality. As a result their schemes eventually succumb to those flaws, leaving them defeated in the game of society.

Q. 2. Comment on the Women characters in *The Way of the World.*

Ans. The female characters of The Way of the World have much more depth and are more well rounded than the naïve and kind of spastic Margery Pinchwife. Miliamant is a wonderful character that speaks her mind and has her own opinions and seems like a strong woman, something that seems out of the norm for this time period. She is beautiful, has many suitors beyond Mirabell, including Witwoud and Petulant, and also seems to be admired for her personality, the good and bad parts. Mirabell says, "I like her with all her faults; nay, like her for her faults. Her follies are so natural, or so artful, that they become her; and those affectations which in another woman would be odious, serve but to make her more agreeable" (258). One of the most intriguing things about Millamant is her sense of independence and individuality in regards to being a wife. She definitely loves Mirabell and wants to marry him but she is very happy being able to have the freedom of a single woman. She gives Mirabell a list of rules that she requires from him for marriage, including being able to visit or talk to whoever she wants, eat dinner wherever she wants, have all of the clothes she wants, and tells Mirabell, "you shall always knock at the door before you come in" (297). It is probably doubtful that Millamant will get every single wish in her marriage but her request for independence right to her future husband's face is pretty remarkable. She is an easy character to root for and you hope she gets her happy marriage with all her rules intact.

Lady Wishfort is a very powerful character in the play, ultimately making the decision on the marriage between Mirabell and Millamant. She holds Millamant's fortune, which is very interesting decision, to have a female character have all the money and be the decision maker for her family. She really is a pitiable character though, having been duped twice by Mirabell. Before the play, he pretended to love her to get close to Millamant, so she essentially became an older woman cast aside by her younger, more beautiful niece . Then she becomes the unknowing center of a plot to further the marriage to Mirabell and Millamant, ending up totally embarrassed by being led on by a servant Mrs. Marwood and Mrs. Fainall are painted as the less appealing females in the play, but much like Fainall, they aren't truly bad. Mrs. Fainall is having an affair with Mirabell and is in a loveless marriage with her husband. She shouldn't be faulted for her affair, with an unmarried man, if her husband isn't. Fainall even knows about her relationship with Mirabell and doesn't really care. Mrs. Marwood is really unfortunate because she longs for Mirabell when he absolutely only has eyes for Millamant (desspite his affair with Mrs. Fainall). She just really seems to have gotten caught up in the crazy love web and ended up in a bad situation, carrying on an affair with Fainall and being outed to Lady Wishfort. The female characters in The Way of the World are surprisingly three dimensional, independent, and fun to root for.

Q. 3. Comment on the theme of The Amorous and the Predatory in William Congreve's *The Way of the World.*

Ans. The emergence of print capitalism and the rising of the bourgeois is reflected in the ideas of love in Restoration comedy. Restoration comedy uses humour as a mask to cover the seriousness of the issues that it discusses. The audience can laugh at what they can relate to without the play being too didactic in nature. During this time, marriage became more of a social contract and the main aim was always attainment of wealth. This is seen in most of the characters in the play. In fact when we closely examine the characters in the play, we will find that most of them had monetary motives behind their actions and decisions. Lady Wishfort can be seen here as the central source of wealth and the indirect target of all the men who want to marry Millamant. The man who marries Millamant becomes wealthier because of Lady Wishfort's fortune.

Attaining money was the only way that the bourgeois could hope for a better life in terms of finance. This is why money was such an important aspect of the society at the time. If we consider Mirabell, we see that he has a brief affair with Lady Wishfort only so that he can get to Millamant and also obtain money. The nature of this affair is not clearly discussed. In the first Act, Fainall and Mirabell talk about this alleged affair. We find out that Mirabell thought he was just flattering Lady Wishfort a little bit so that she would allow him to marry Millamaunt.

We see that Lady Wishfort interpreted Mirabell's flattery differently. She thought that Mirabell was genuinely trying to woo her. That is why she took such a dislike to him after Mrs. Marwood told her that he was only after Millamant. Marwood also convinces Lady Wishfort to keep her fortune within the family. That is why Lady Wishfort wants Millamant to marry Sir Willfull. Lady Wishfort is determined to keep the money within the family. She wants Willfull Witwoud (a humour name) to marry Millamant instead of Mirabell, whom she now has a personal grudge against. But Mirabell does not take this decision lying down. He creates a plan, which when executed involved Lady Wishfort considering marriage with Mirabell's own personal servant Waitwell (yet another humour name) disguised as Sir Rowland. Mirabell then planned to reveal the true identity of Sir Rowland and would only keep quiet about the situation if Wishfort allowed him to marry Millamant *and* give him Millamant's fortune. However, this plan cannot be completed because of Fainall. He also is after Wishfort's fortune and threatens to reveal the truth about Wishfort's daughter Arabella (his wife) and her affair with Mirabell unless she signed over Arabella's property as well as her own fortune to him. At this point, Mirabell seizes his opportunity and offers to help Wishfort out of her dilemma. In her gratitude, Wishfort grants Mirabell everything that he intended to attain through deception and blackmail.

Mirabell can also be seen as a predatory lover simply because of the number of affairs he has had. He has had an affair with almost every woman in the play. In fact, Mirabell can be compared to the character of Willmore in Aphra Behn's *The Rover.* One of the main differences between Willmore and Mirabell is the way their characters are portrayed. Both men are womanizers but they are shown in contrasting lights. *The Rover* is set during the carnival. The carnival is a time when laws and conventions are openly broken. So what Willmore does is all justified in the spirit of the carnival. He is very open about his sexuality. The same cannot be said for Mirabell. His sexuality is no less than Willmore's, yet is portrayed in a more subdued way. He does not openly accept the fact that he has had affairs with many women. Outwardly, his love for Millamant shines in the spotlight. It is only through the dialogues of the women he has had affairs with that readers come to realize that he is not quite the quintessential Petrarchan lover.

The concept of predatory love is not seen in Mirabell alone. There is a strong undercurrent of jealousy in all the women that he has been with. Each of these women, though married – and in Mrs. Marwood's case, having an affair with Fainall – still feel jealous of Millamant. They express this jealousy in different ways. Lady Wishfort is Millamant's aunt, but she still resents Mirabell.

In many ways, Mrs. Marwood is central to the plot of the play. Her character is anything physically. She simply talks to people and through that she spreads doubt and conflict. She is clever and strategic. She uses manipulation to get what she wants. Her attitude towards Mirabell seems to imply that if she cannot have him, then she will make sure that no one else can have him either. It is she who tells Lady Wishfort that Mirabell was seeming to court her only in order to get Millamant's hand in marriage. She is the one who sends a letter to Lady Wishfort revealing Sir Rowland's true identity. She is the one who plots with Fainall regarding claiming Lady Wishfort's money and property for themselves.

Even Mrs. Fainall is Millamant's rival. She is willing to help Mirabell and not Millamant. This is because she too had an affair with Mirabell and is jealous of Millamant. So we see that the women also play a part in the idea of a predatory lover. There is a constant trope of the hunter and the hunted. Almost everyone is desired by someone but they desire someone else.

Though it is not very apparent, there still remains an amorous aspect to the portrayal of love in the play. When we consider Lady Wishfort, she does not have any mercenary reason for desiring to be loved. She represents the lonely human being who simply wants to be appreciated and desired. However, she holds her reputation above everything else. In fact, one of the reasons she is so eager to get married is to re-establish a reputable position for herself for something other than her money. Nevertheless, she does long for company and this is made apparent by the extensive preparation for receiving Sir Rowland, whom she believes to be a potential husband. This is what makes her so easily gulled by Mirabell. One cannot help but feel sympathy for Lady Wishfort as she is constantly used by Mirabell as a means to an end. It is even sadder that she must compete with her niece for attention from the opposite sex. Mirabell and Millamant seem to be the most desired characters in the play. The love between them is also unconventional. Millamant does not want Mirabell to call her "Love" or any names of that sort. This reflects the slow transition of society from marriages in which the husband dominates to marriages in which both partners are considered equals. Millamant represents women who are trying to establish a place for themselves that subverts patriarchy. Nevertheless, their love is central to the play and the audience is happy when this love triumphs in the end.

Fainall is one character who shows an interesting balance between mercenary and amorous love. He only married Arabella, is wife, in order to attain her property and fortune. But he is willing to spend this property and fortune all on Mrs. Marwood, the woman he truly loves. In fact, he reassures Mrs. Marwood of his intentions in the second act of the play.

Although their love does not triumph in the end, we see that the love between Mrs. Marwood and Fainall was the only one that was closest to the concept of amorous love without greed. Initially they were completely at peace with the fact that they might not inherit money from Lady Wishfort. But they were still willing to persevere in their love.

This amorous aspect of love is not completely devoid of power politics. Kevin J. Gardner talks about Patrician authority in his essay "Patrician Authority and Instability in "The Way of the World"". From Gardner's essay, we see that even amorous love establishes who is superior and inferior. The women are considered inferior because they cannot control their emotions and internalize them. The men are superior because they do not let their emotions control them. He also talks about how amorous love and predatory love are centered around intrigue.

One of the biggest criticisms of this play is that only Mirabell and Millamant's dilemmas are solved. The rest of the characters have unresolved issues that are never dealt with. The main question that arises is the motive behind the behaviour of different characters. One way of analyzing this is by thinking of the play as a reflection of society. In the eighteenth century, men feared cuckoldry, but were not supposed to express it. Affairs happened all the time but they were kept hidden. Through all of this, the main aim of the bourgeois society was to gain social standing. In an essay called "Playhouse Flesh and Blood", Katharine Eisaman Maus talks about how women began to act on stage and largely gained fame because they were the mistress of an aristocrat. The bourgeois were constantly trying to attain the wealth and status of the aristocrats. This is clearly depicted in *The Way of the World.* Money and reputation take priority over selfless love. All the characters represent the typical bourgeois need for climbing to the top of the social ladder and this was a major influence on all their decisions.

Q. 5. Discuss *The Way of the World* as a social satire.

Ans. William Congreve is the best and finest writer of the comedy of manners. His ' The Way of the World' is considered as a pure comedy of manners. Here we find an ironic commentary on the ways of the society of the time. Here Congreve has depicted the social life of the fashionable men and women of the Restoration Age. During this period gravity, spiritual zeal, moral earnestness and decorum were thrown to winds. This was a peculiar age. The king was thorough debauch. He had a number of mistresses and numerous children. He was surrounded by corrupt and degenerate courtiers. There was no moral code for them.

Corruption was rampant in all walks of life. The ladies and gentleman of upper classes were busy in love and lust. The pursuit of women was the main business of men. The man had become licentious animal. The ideal of love was corrupt. There was complete absence of sexual morality. The fond of fashion created a unique type of culture. There was complete freedom among the women. They were like jolly butterflies that fluttered from one flower to another to satisfy their passions. The married women had unfair relations with other men. Their husbands were cuckold. People of this age were frequent visitors of the parks, play houses and hotels. These were the centres of love affairs and love intrigues. The coffee houses were overcrowded. This was the picture of Congreve's age.

In '*The Way of the World* Congreve has presented the true picture of the contemporary society. Here he has described the infidelity of married women, the fashionable life of ladies and gentleman and the intrigues of lovers. All the characters of this play are fond of fashion. Lady like Wishfort uses heavy cosmetics to hide her faded beauty and wrinkles. Public places like Chocolate house and St. James' park are mentioned here. These places provide an opportunity for the lovers to enjoy their games of love, lust and intrigues. The play opens with the scene

In ' The Way of the World' we find that male characters are pursuing female characters. He female characters have unfair relations with other men. They cuckold their husbands. Mrs. Marwood is enjoying sensual pleasure with Mr. Fainall. Mrs. Fainall hates her husband and she has soft corner for mirabell. Millamant loves Mirabell but she has soft corner for Petulant and Witwoud. Mirabell has had an affair with a young widow but he persuades her to marry Fainall. Marriage has no sanctity at all. Thus there is an atmosphere of free love in this play.

Love intrigues occupy an important place in 'The Way of the World'. The entire play deals with the intrigues of Mirabell to win the hand of Millamant. To achieve his aim, he pretends to make love to Lady Wishfort, an elderly lady. When he fails, he hatches a deeper plot. He knows that she is desirous of marrying again. Thus he sends his servant to her as Sir Rowland to deceive her. Mr.

Fainall has illicit relation with Mrs. Marwood. He is also busy in an intrigue to grab the property of his wife's mother. In this way Congreve has presented the spirit of the age.

Millamant's bargain with Mirabell is an important feature of the fashionable society. It shows the true picture of the morality of the age. She thinks that her liberty would be crushed by marriage. Thus before marriage, she wants Mirabell to agree that she would be free to do anything even after marriage.

Thus 'The Way of the World' presents a true picture of the Restoration Age. It reflects the social life of the day. Here the upper class manner is central target of Congreve's attack.

Q. 6. Discuss The Way of The World as a restoration Comedy

Ans. The Restoration, as a period, takes its name from the Restoration of the monarchy, with Charles II assuming the throne in 1660. The Restoration of the monarchy meant the end of the Puritan Parliament's rule, but it also meant the return of the theatre. Because of the theatre's long-standing connection with royalty and aristocracy and because of the Puritans' view of the theatre as licentious and blasphemous, theatrical performances were banned during parliament's rule. In 1662, the theatres re-opened, and play-going became an important part of the reaction against the Puritanism of the previous decades. Restoration theatre, for many cultural historians, epitomizes the era. While many plays from the Shakespearean era were reproduced, new plays commenting on the renewed monarchy and a new culture of performance, wealth, and more open sexuality flourished. In a variety of forms, the entire culture seemed to see itself as a kind of play, as commentators repeatedly emphasized the ways everyone seemed to be playing roles as they negotiated new mores and social conditions.

While the theatre of the Restoration era attempted to return to its earlier form, it innovated on the theatre of the first part of the 17th century in many ways. First, it became accessible and respectable, as the theatres themselves moved into better parts of London and started to attract a broader array of patrons. At the same time, playhouses opened up professionally for women, as they began to appear on stage in large numbers for the first number and several women, most famously, perhaps, Aphra Behn, became successful playwrights. The presence of women on the stage and in larger numbers in the audiences directly contributed to the intensive exploration of sexual themes in the theatre of the period. Actresses were often seen as little more than prostitutes, and many famous actresses were well-known consorts of the king and other nobles. Their performances on stage often played with their supposed sexual availability, while women in the audiences often similarly were seen or displayed themselves as performers as they traded witty conversation laced with double entendre with men about town. In many accounts, the flirtations in the audience mirrored or rivaled the performances on stage.

The Restoration comedy of manners reflected and commented on this culture of performance. These plays often featured rakes—men on the prowl for sexual conquest—who elaborated complicated schemes for bedding as many woman as possible. Over the course of the play, their attempts were often forwarded, rebuffed, and foiled by various women whose sexual knowledge and wit frequently equaled their male counterparts. These comedies usually featured incredibly complex plots and counterplots—emphasizing their characters' ability to manipulate others through their self-display, control of language, and psychological calculations as they attempted to win both sexual favors and wealth. Yet, even as the plays displayed the power of performance that their very audiences indulged in, they often critiqued that culture for its duplicity and depravity. With the Glorious Revolution of 1688 and the return to power of parliament, a reaction against the excesses of the Restoration set in, with much of the focus on the theatre and the culture of performance and display and, in particular, its sexual licentiousness.

Appearing in 1700, Congreve's play represents a late version of the Restoration comedy of manners, one that consolidates many of the features of earlier plays even as it responds to increasing critique of the theatre (the play mentions one of the most famous critiques in Act 3). Implicitly describing the way of the world as one of cynical self-interest, the play follows the reformed rake Mirabell as he attempts to win the hand of Millamant, the woman he actually loves. Before the play begins, Mirabell, we later learn, has had an affair with Mrs. Fainall, whose husband married her only for her wealth and is having an affair with Mrs. Marwood; we only learn most of this in the second act. Millamant is the niece and ward of Lady Wishfort, who is Mrs. Fainall's mother, and stands to inherit a great deal of money, but only if Lady Wishfort approves of her suitor. Mirabell has offended Lady Wishfort, so he needs not only to win Millamant's hand but also to win over Lady Wishfort.

As with most Restoration comedies, Mirabell creates a complicated scheme involving impersonation and artifice to get both wealth and love. He has his valet, Waitwell, pretend to be his uncle and woo Lady Wishfort. His plan is to then rescue Lady Wishfort from being seduced by a servant and thus gain her approval. While Millamant knows of the plot and does love Mirabell, she takes pleasure in teasing him about the uncertainty of their eventual union.

However, things go awry for Mirabell when Mrs. Marwood learns of the plot and of Mirabell's former affair with Mrs. Fainall. Mrs. Marwood informs Mr. Fainall, and they begin a plot against Mirabell. Millamant has accepted Mirabell's proposal, turning down Sir Witful Witwoud (Lady Wishfort's choice). Fainall uncovers the plot to Lady Wishfort and attempts to blackmail her by threatening to reveal her daughter's (Mrs. Fainall's) adultery. He wants all of Millamant's fortune as well as complete control of Mrs. Fainall's potential inheritance. Millamant then decides she will marry Sir Witwoud in order to save her fortune, and Mirabell appears with two servants to prove Mr. Fainall's adultery with Mrs. Marwood. Fainall, however, is not cowed and continues to threaten Mrs. Fainall's reputation. Then, Mirabell plays his last card. Before she married Mr. Fainall, Mrs. Fainall, out of fear of Mr. Fainall's character, had made Mirabell the trustee of her fortune. Without control of that money, Mr. Fainall is left without any resources, and the play ends with Mirabell and Millamant engaged.

The Way of the World exemplifies many of the key features of the Restoration comedy of manners—complex, multi-faceted characters who combine urbanity and wit in treating love and wealth as a game they play through concealment, artifice, and plotting. Unlike some of the plays from the first decade of the Restoration, however, Congreve's play does not end up embracing the cynicism of some of its characters; instead, true love—while far from sentimentalized—wins out and leaves with wealth. His characters have their moral failings and they more than handle themselves in a world of false appearances, banter, and sexual double-dealings, but they are redeemed in the end.

Q. 7. Comment on Various themes in *The Way of The World.*

Ans. The precise statement of the theme of a work of art is always a little unsatisfactory. The pithy sentence must omit a great deal; it always does violence to the whole work. Nevertheless, it is worth making the effort to determine a theme, or themes, in a play as a guide to study or analysis.

As a point of departure, it is valid to say that the theme of this play is given us by Congreve in the title, The Way of the World. All the events and characters of the play can be related to this central theme. The obvious criticism is that the same "theme" can be ascribed to unlimited numbers of other, and quite different, novels and plays. Further, Congreve does not, in this play, seem to take a consistent position. Sometimes he is direct, sometimes ironic; sometimes he deplores, sometimes he approves; at times he is amused; and most of the time his position is a compound of all of these attitudes.

To get a more satisfactory statement we might use a different approach that would give a better sense of the texture of the play. Most Restoration playwrights supplied their plays with alternate titles, or subtitles. Since Congreve did not, we might seek for the different subtitles that are appropriate. Each one would suggest a theme, although not the theme. These may put flesh on the bare bones the title gives us.

Love a la Mode : Certainly, the play can be seen as a dramatic presentation of varieties of love in the England of the year 1700. Central is the delicate handling of the love game as played by Mirabell and Millamant. They represent the ideal of the Restoration attitude, intense yet balanced, their love based on mutual esteem with no surrender of individuality. Contrasted with it are Mirabell's earlier and quite ambiguous love affair with Mrs. Fainall; the illicit love of Fainall and Mrs. Marwood, presumably passionate, but wholly without mutual trust; the spurious court young Witwoud pays to Millamant; the direct and somewhat coarse approach of Sir Wilfull; and, at the opposite extreme completely, the aging and undignified longings of Lady Wishfort, vain, unrealistic, over-eager, desperate, and a little pathetic.

Love and Money: Such an approach is closely related to that of love a la mode, although they are not identical. In the world whose way is presented here, love and money are values to be taken into account at all times. The sincerity of Mirabell's love does not make him lose sight of the importance of Millamant's fortune. Fainall marries for money to support an illicit love; apparently the thought of marrying Mrs. Marwood without adequate money (however "adequate" might be defined) is unthinkable. Money is Lady Wishfort's sole hold over her child and her ward. Even the marriage of the servants is built on a promise of a handsome sum of money. This is the world's way. Love without money is an impossible sentimental dream, although money often corrupts what love there is.

A Gallery of Portraits: Congreve's statements in the dedication, the prologue, and the epilogue suggest that this might be a valid subtitle. Since it is the way of the world to put a premium on youth, Mirabell and Millamant stand at the center, representing all that is to be commended. Mirabell is the beau ideal: polished, poised, rational and balanced, witty and perspicacious without being what we might today call over-intellectual. Millamant is the belle: feminine, beautiful, witty, not prudish, but with a sense of her own worth. She has avoided the messiness and humiliation of sexual intrigue. Opposed to Mirabell are would-be wits, worthy but graceless boors, and deep intriguers. Opposed to Millamant are women who engaged in adultery and an old dowager without decorum. Every character reveals himself in action, and together they produce a gallery of self-portraits.

Jungle of High Intrigue : This subtitle would focus attention on some of the values of London society. Everyone is engaged in intrigue: Mirabell intrigues to gain consent to his marriage from Lady Wishfort, and this involves intrigue within intrigue, for he does not trust Waitwell. Fainall intrigues in turn. Everyone is involved in one or the other of these schemes — Mrs. Fainall, Mrs. Marwood, and the servants. Even Lady Wishfort in her willingness to marry Sir Rowland has a devious purpose — revenge on Mirabell. When Mrs. Fainall married her husband, that was part of an intrigue, as was his marriage to her. And as we see in the play, victory goes to Mirabell, not because of his virtue, but simply because he is the most successful intriguer.

Certainly all these possible subtitles, rather than any one, add up to the ironic commentary on society that is in the title, The Way of the World.

Q. 8. Comment on Style, Wit, and Irony in The Way of the World.

Ans. In the most common use of the word, style describes the author's use of language within the shorter rhetorical units, the sentence or at most the paragraph. It includes the choice of words and the rhythmic and musical quality of the sentences. Since it also includes a discussion of the relations of language to thought, fact, and reality, at some point it becomes identical with a discussion of wit and irony.

If irony is included in the discussion, then arbitrary limits must be set because from some points of view, irony pervades The Way of the World. The title is ironic; the action is ironic; the relationships of the characters to each other are ironic. This section, however, is concerned only with irony as a function of the speeches of characters, not as a function of plot or theme. It is concerned with that kind of irony that is closely related to style and wit.

Congreve avoids attempting any definition of wit, although, in the dedication, he distinguishes between true wit and false wit, the latter a product of affectation. Another comment of Congreve's on wit also casts some light on his practice. In

"Concerning Humour in Comedy," he writes:

Every person in a comedy may be allowed to speak them [pleasant things]. From a witty man they are expected and even a fool may be permitted to stumble on 'em by chance. . . . I do not think that humourous characters exclude wit; no, but the manner of wit should be adapted to the humour . . . ; a character of a splenetic and peevish humour should have a satirical wit. A jolly and sanguine humour should have a facetious wit.

In practice, all of Congreve's characters speak "pleasant things." There is not a speech that does not have its biting edge of wit, satire, or irony.

Discussions of style and wit in a play are in some ways simple. Certain kinds of problems do not have to be discussed since they do not exist. Unlike novels, plays have no long passages of description which may or may not be well written; there are no elaborate expositions of motives. There is no reason to consider whether the author is inside his creatures' minds or external to them. The characters speak; what they say can be examined. To talk of style or wit in a play is to talk of the different styles and different kinds of wit of the characters.

Congreve wrote so that his characters were sharply differentiated by their speech patterns and their wit. As Congreve used style and wit as one of his ways of characterization, the material in this section may be considered additional data for study of the characters, collected here so that a rather technical subject can be treated in one place.

Mirabell: Mirabell's style is not an easy one. We do not feel that he is spontaneous, for his periods are carefully prepared. The sentences are long, flowing, and syntactically intricate. He indulges in no slang or canting expressions. While he can be acid in his judgment, there is no vituperation in his speech. The objects of his disapproval are so deftly lanced in his gracious phrases that they can scarcely feel the knife.

Mirabell's wit and irony are also intricate. His observations about others are shrewd, including a mixture of distaste, tolerance, and amusement. Considerable irony is also directed at himself. There is a strong element of self-criticism that makes him a most unusual hero.

Any number of speeches might serve to reveal these characteristics; this famous speech from the first act about his feelings toward Millamant will do:

I'll tell thee, Fainall, she once used me with that insolence, that in revenge I took her to pieces, sifted her and separated her failings: I studied 'em, and got 'em by rote. The catalogue was so large that I was not without hopes one day or other to hate her heartily: to which end I so used myself to think of 'em, that at length, contrary to my design and expectation, they gave me every hour less and less disturbance, till in a few days it became habitual to me to remember 'em without being displeased. They are now grown as familiar to me as my own frailties, and, in all probability, in a little time longer I shall like 'em as well.

The characteristics can be seen: the long smooth passages (one might read aloud from "to which end" to the end of the sentence), the real wit, the clear vision of the object of the speech, and the wry ability to laugh at himself.

Millamant : The ultimate proof of the individuality of Millamant's style is in this — that to read the passage aloud is immediately to sense the manner and mannerisms of the character. She is flippant, delightfully spoiled, spirited. When, in the fourth act, she reveals a depth that we might not have expected, that, too, is in the style. Her speech in her first appearance is abrupt; she moves not so much from one subject to another as from one feeling to another with an ability to turn anything into wit.

Mrs. Millamant: Oh, aye, letters: I had letters. I am persecuted with letters. I hate letters. Nobody knows how to write letters; and yet one has 'em, one does not know why. They serve one to pin up one's hair.

Witwoud: Pray, madam, do you pin up your hair with all your letters?

Mrs. Millamant: Only with those in verse, Mr. Witwoud; I never pin up my hair with prose. I think I tried once, Mincing.

Mincing: O mem, I shall never forget it.

After a series of short, flippant statements, there comes an inspired thought: "They serve one to pin up one's hair." She then pursues the train of thought that this conceit suggests: "Only with those in verse." It is incidentally pleasant that Mincing can pick up her cue and proceed further.

The passage "One makes lovers as fast as one pleases" is similar, as is "Now I think on't, I'm angry. No, now I think on't, I'm pleased; for I believe I gave you some pain!" The style and wit are the character of Millamant.

In the proviso scene, more serious in content, the pace changes. There is still a teasing element, but there is less skipping from point to point. Millamant is stating her conditions for marriage:

Trifles — as liberty to pay and receive visits to and from whom I please; to write and receive letters, without interrogatories or wry faces on your part; to wear what I please, and choose conversation with regard only to my own taste; to have no obligation upon me to converse with wits that I don't like, because they are your acquaintance; or to be intimate with fools, because they may be your relations. . . . These articles subscribed, if I continue to endure you a little longer, I may by degrees dwindle into a wife.

Fainall: Fainall's style and wit must be differentiated from Mirabell's. His sentences are not as long or as contemplative as Mirabell's, and his wit is more direct and somewhat crueler: "The coldness of a losing gamester lessens the pleasure of the winner. I'd no more play with a man that slighted his ill fortune than I'd make love to a woman that undervalued the loss of her reputation." Perhaps because of the nature of his part, he is more abrupt in accusation, and his lines may depend on a more obvious parallelism and antithesis: "Could you think, because the nodding husband would not wake, that e'er the watchful lover slept?" And he engages in a more direct attack: "Professed a friendship! Oh, the pious friendships of the female sex!"

Young Witwoud: Since Congreve himself commented that readers and audience could not always distinguish between Witwoud and his true wits, Witwoud's speeches demand especially careful examination.

As Witwoud has no function in the plot of the play, the purpose of his speeches is to characterize him and to provide comedy. The key to his wit is the "similitude." "Truce with your similitudes," says Millamant to him. Each comparison may be clever by itself, amusing, unusual, a little shocking, such as "Friendship without freedom is as dull as love without enjoyment." The lines with which he interrupts Millamant in the second act are each one a comparison, amusing or overburdened. The witticisms are forced; they have been collected and memorized, and at need pulled out of his conjurer's bag of tricks. Irony, if there is any here, is superficial; no one of the witticisms has any particular point. Nor does young Witwoud even realize it should.

Petulant: Petulant's style and wit are included in his name. He has a humour to be angry — that is, he is an example of Jonsonian humour, or, perhaps, he affects a humour.

Lady Wishfort: Lady Wishfort's style, like everything else about her, is of special interest. Her manner is abrupt — a mirror of the arbitrary, petty tyrant she is. Like all Congreve characters, she has, perhaps unconsciously, a fair amount of wit. More than anything else in the play, her verbal attack on others is direct vituperation-"Boudoir Billingsgate," in Meredith's phrase. No unit of thought is longer than a few words. It is clear that she shouts when annoyed or irritated, and she is always in a state of annoyance:

No, fool. Not the ratafia, fool. Grant me patience! I mean the Spanish paper, idiot; complexion, darling. Paint, paint, paint! dost thou understand that, changeling, dangling thy hands like bobbins before thee? Why does thou not stir, puppet? thou wooden thing upon wires!

The term irony has a different meaning when one is discussing Lady Wishfort. It is true that she does indulge in heavy-handed sarcasm, but the unconscious irony is more important. She responds to the accidental images of words in ironical self-revelation. Foible reports that Mirabell said he would "handle" Lady Wishfort. "Handle me, would he durst!" she cries, "such a foul-mouthed fellow." It is clear what the word "handle" means to her — and the reader may or may not catch the ambiguity of "would he durst." Her speech as she repairs her face while waiting for Sir Rowland is a group of short, flustered comments that constitute her regular manner, an unconsciously ironic description of her hypocrisy:

In what figure shall I give his heart the first impression? There is a great deal in the first impression. Shall I sit? — No, I won't sit — I'll walk — aye, I'll walk from the door upon his entrance; and then turn full upon him. — No, that will be too sudden. I'll lie — aye, I'll lie down — I'll receive him in my little dressing-room; there's a couch — yes, yes, I'll give the first impression on a couch. — won't lie neither, but loll and lean upon one elbow, with one foot a little dangling off, jogging in a thoughtful way — yes — and then as soon as he appears, start, aye, start and be surprised, and rise to meet him in a pretty disorder — yes — oh, nothing is more alluring than a levee from a couch, in some confusion. — It shows the foot to advantage, and furnishes with blushes, and recomposing airs beyond comparison.

Examples can be multiplied. One might only add Lady Wishfort's remark when she discovers that her daughter's fortune will not be lost: "'Tis plain thou has inherited thy mother's prudence," a highly ambiguous compliment in the light of Mrs. Fainall's unsatisfactory love affair with Mirabell and Lady Wishfort's misjudgment of Mrs. Marwood and Sir Rowland.

Q. 9. Comment on the significance of the title of *The Way of the World*.

Ans. It was perhaps sheer pedantic myopia that, when Jeremy Collier published his essay A Short View of the Immorality and Profaneness of the English Stage in 1698, he made Congreve a particular target of his criticism. That Collier had a case is undeniable, but he forgot that a true artist does have as sincere obligation to society as a churchman. Had he waited before publishing his essay till the production of *The Way of the World* (1770), he could have perhaps understood that truth; for, in the play *The Way of the World* Congreve seems to understand the "immorality and profaneness" of a society, upon the matrices of which Restoration plays were made. He was seriously thinking of an alternative pattern of behaviour and an alternative set of codes of conduct.

The very title of the play, *The Way of the World* points to the 'way' the hero and heroine (and by implication the spectators) should adopt in order to come out of the grip of the fashionable society. The whole story is an illustration of the process, by following which Mirabell and Millament seek a resolution, that is, to gain their own world by using and manipulating the existing social norms, through the winding lanes of that society. Congreve constructed the plot of the play accordingly with this aim in mind. One can discern a definite pattern in the movement of the play. At the beginning of the play, Mirabell is trying to shape up a situation so that he can win both hands of Millament and her estate from Lady Wishfort. He has married his servant, Waitwell off to Lady Wishfort's maid, Foible and plans to have Waitwell disguise himself as a noble man, court, and marry Lady Wishfort. Then Mirabell would blackmail her by threatening to disclose that she has married a servant and would offer her to release her if she will let him marry Millament plus the estate. But Mrs. Marwood discovers the plan and tells Lady Wishfort. Mrs. Marwood also tells Fainwall of his wife, Mrs. Fainwall's former relationship with Mirabell. From all these Fainwall plans to blackmail Lady Wishfort by threatening to reveal all unless she signs over to him not only his wife's but also Millament's estate and even the conversation of Lady Wishfort's own estate after her death.

As the action of the play gets momentum and the plot becomes more and more complicated, Congreve loads the stage by introducing confusing figures like Mr. Wilful Witwood. While it adds to the comedy of the play, it complicates the plot further. However, certain hidden facts of the past are revealed through the conversations of the characters: for instance, Mrs. Marwood's desire for Mirabell, Mrs. Marwood's relationship with Fainall, Mirabell's past affair with Mrs. Fainall etc. Congreve measures these secrets slowly person by person, until the final revelation in Act V, where all pretences are destroyed Mr. Fainall's and Mirabell's revelations, and the bringing out from a black box of the deed renders Mr. Fainall powerless. The complexities and complications are, however, deliberate on Congreve's part; for he wanted to present his Restoration audience a play that can coincide artistically with the artificialities and complexities in the human affairs of the period. The chief aim of the dramatist is to demonstrate "the way of the world". Following this way Mirabell and Millament, through their own peculiar balance of wit and generosity of spirit, reduce the bumbling Witwood and Mr. Fainall to the same level of false wit. Thus the pair dramatise the true wit that is carefully and symmetrically defined through their opposition. They are aware of the fact that they are making compromises in their marriage. Mirabell says, "...I like her with all her faults: nay, I like her for her faults...They are now grown familiar to me as my own frailties..." And Millament charmingly declares, "Well, if Mirabell should not make a good husband, I am lost thing—find I love him violently." These confidences do not prevent their own chances for honesty in marriage. In the *Proviso Scene* they arrange an agreement for their marriage. The reason is obvious: that is, marriage is a social contract that would enable them to rise above the cant and hypocrisy that surround them.

The triumph of the play is in the emergence of lovers who through a balance of intense affection and cool self-knowledge achieve an equilibrium that frees them from the world's power. As the title of the play The Way of the World suggests, they have assimilated the rational lucidity of sceptical rake so that they can use the world and reject its demands.

Q.10. How would you apply the main features of 'Comedy of Manners' in the play *The Way of the World* ?

Or, How would you justify the dictum that *The Way of the World* offers a vast vista of contemporary social morality and principles?

Or, *The Way of the World,* has been considered the reflection of the civilized Comedy of Manners which is quite reversed of the Shakespear's natural sentiments and idiosyncracy; it is affectation of fashionable society. Give reasons for supporting this dictum.

Ans. *The Way of the World* is considered to be one of the most remarkable works of Comedy of Manners. These comedies of Manners were quite in vogue during the Restoration period. Sheridan and Oscar Wilde also followed this genre in their writings. Some of the distinguished personalities of the Comedy of Manners were Wycherley, Etherege, Congreve and Vanbrugh.

Although Comedy of Manners became very popular because of its artistic presentation, the chief speciality of this form was related to its technical aspect. The main target of the writers of Comedy of Manners was the social follies prevalent in their time. Comedy of Manners is primarily satirical in its approach. *The way of the World* contains satirical elements, including the elements of love, marriage, treacherous persons, romantic dialogues, wit and humour; which are essential ingredients of Restoration Comedy.

The Way of the World is most suitable example of *Comedy of Manners.* Actually, this comedy contains almost all the qualities of a Restoration Comedy. It presents a vast vista of contemporary social morality and principles. This play maintains a satirical tone from the beginning to the end. It gives us valuable informations about the sophisticated class of society in England at that time. How they were involved in their life style; and how woman of that period were crazy about fashions and love-affairs, such sort of things have been brilliantly depicted in *The Way of the World.*

It is very clear after the study of *The Comedy of Manners* that the Restoration period was devoid of moral values. When we go through *The Way of the World* we get a clear idea about the moral backwardness of the society. The characters of Mrs. Fainall, Mirabell, Mrs. Marwood and Mr. Fainall give a clear picture of the moral impoverishment of their contemporary society. It looks very funny when Mirabell suggests Mrs. Fainall to marry Mr. Fainall in order to conceal her pregnancy, because she had an illicit love-affair with him. It is very surprising to note that Fainall inspite of his awareness of Mrs. Fainall's extra-marital affair, doesn't take it very seriously. Although when he speaks to Mrs. Marwood he reacts to his wife's behaviour and calls himself a cuckold.

When we minutely observe the play *The Way of the World,* we notice that Mr. Fainall ignores the treachery of his wife because he is no way better than her. He has an extra-marital affair with Mrs. Marwood. But, when this immoral affair is exposed he faces it without any feeling of shame and puts his arguments in order to defend himself. We can judge the moral degradation of Mrs. Marwood that inspite of maintaining a love-affair with Mr. Fainall she is also involved with Mirabell. Here we can laugh at Mr. Fainall's condition, because he thinks himself an over-intelligent fellow and fabricates intrigues for others but he is himself being deceived by his wife and Mrs. Marwood.

The Way of the World depicts a wonderful picture of the affectations of the people particularly women, in fashionable society. The author is very clear-minded when he portrays the inclination of women for fashion. He ridicules them for obsession for fashion. We get a clearer picture when we read the "provisio-scene". Mirabell presents a broad analysis about women's habit of visiting theatres without their husband's consent, extra-marital affairs and tea parties and so many other habits which were in vogue in fashionable circle of that society.

Apart from this, when Millamant puts some conditions before Mirabell for their marriage, one observes that she talks about her habit of sleeping late in the morning, receiving letters from her well-wishers, writing them replies even after her marriage, entertaining her visitor and she tells Mirabell that she doesn't want any interference on his part in her activities. It shows that how fashion was dominant in the upper class of society.Further we see that wearing tight dresses was very much in fashion in that period. So Mirabell warns Millamant that she can't wear such type of garments during the time of pregnancy because it might cause harm to the forthcoming child.

Congreve is very successful when he describes the fashionable society of that period. He tells us about *Cabal nights,* when women of the upper class of society assemble and gossip about various scandalous affairs. Anyone can imagine the craze for fashion in the Restoration Period when Lady Wishfort appears on the scene. Inspite of being an old lady of fifty five, she is very serious about her make-up and chides her attendant because of inefficiency in the art of make-up.

The affectation for fashion was so acute in Restoration Period that everybody was under its grip, there was no age-factor for this obsession. Even an old lady like Lady Wishfort tries to keep herself maintained like a young girl.

Further the feeling of vanity and jealousy was very much prevalent among the women of Restoration society. In course of the study of the play we notice that Mrs. Marwood is very jealous of Millamant although it is justified, because she has a deep inclination for Mirabell. However, it has been mentioned as an inevitable fact of Restoration Comedy but truly speaking, it has been a weakness of women in every age.

In the Restoration society there was absolute dominance of intrigues and conspiracy. Men and women were deeply involved in plotting and scheming. Such kind of intrigues were in vogue and young men wanted to marry rich women in order to acquire maximum fortune. In *The Way of the World* we find that Mr. Fainall is not very much interested in Mrs. Fainall. He doesn't love her but he marries her only to acquire her property. He also wants to usurp the whole property of Lady Wishfort on the basis of an illegal document, but we notice that Mirabell foils his attempt and saves the property and reputation of Mrs. Fainall and Lady Wishfort.

Mirabell pretends to be in love with Lady Wishfort in order to marry her niece Millamant. Mrs. Marwood and Fainall both fabricate an intrigue to exploit Lady Wishfort and similarly, even Sir Wilful too, joins Millamant in an intrigue when he declares that Millamant is ready to marry him.

So we observe that the Comedy of Manners of the Restoration period is packed with intrigues and conspiracies. William Congreve has handled these elements with mastery and presented a clear picture of the age before its readers.

The most remarkable feature of the comedies of the Restoration Period is the use of witty dialogues and *The way of the World* contains this feature in a unique manner.

False wits and fops are other elements which dominate the comedies of the Restoration Period. They always try to exhibit their capability of using witty dialogues and pass vulgar remarks to prove their false wit.

Congreve is remarkable when he exhibits this capability. He has portrayed the characters of Petulant, Witwoud and Wilfull only to maintain this trend. Witwoud and Petulant are actually a false wit. We find a beautiful display of witty dialogues in the conversation of Petulant Witwoud and Sir Wilfull. When Witwoud doesn't want to recognise Sir Wilfull simply because he comes from the countryside, Sir Wilfull loses his temper. But Witwoud says, that it is not the fashion here to recognise relatives, then Sir Wilfull replies by saying that fashion is foolish; and Witwoud is not better than a fop.

The dialogues of Petulant and Witwoud are full of humour elements :

Petulant : "Witwoud, are you even an attorney's clerk? Of the family of the Furnivalas, Ha, ha, ha!"

Witwoud : "But that was just for a while. Not long, not long. I was not in my own power then. An Orphan and this fellow was my guardian".

Further when Witwoud talks to Mrs. Marwood he says to her that Petulant is my good friend but when he contradicts me I also contradict him. Petulant says in reply that if they are not in good mood then if Witwood calls a black colour black then he (Petulant) certainly contradict him and calls it blue.

So an overall study of the play shows that as a *Comedy of Manner, The Way of the World* presents a vast-vista of contemporary Restoration society. It satirises the follies of the people of upper class of society. In a nutshell, it can be maintained that Congreve has proved his capability and presented a true picture of his contemporary society in *The Way of the World.*

Q.11. "*The Way of the World* is not consistent in its nature, hence subplots are more significant than the main plot." Comment.

Or, "*The Way of the World* has complexity of plot and is perhaps a little lose in its fabrication." Illustrate,

Or,"The plot of *The Way of the World* lacks order in thoughts and speech." Discuss.

Ans. William Congreve's plots have been a nightmare for the readers and the play, *The Way of the World* also has followed the same pattern. Truly speaking, *The Way of the World* has more complexity and inconsistency in its plot in comparison with other play like *Love for Love,* although his play *Double Dealer* is even more intricate in its plot construction. The plot of *The Way of the World* is baffling and readers got confused when they come across a number of intrigues and conspiracies. In fact, the plot of this play is so complicated that one feels a little confused.

The plot of this comedy is packed with intrigues and conspiracies which make it so complicated that sometimes readers find themselves lost in confusion. Mirabell, who is the hero of this play plots a conspiracy to dupe Lady Wishfort because he wants to win Millaments hand. So he arranges the marriage of his servant Waitwell with Foible, the maid servant of Lady Wishfort. But the plot becomes more confusing when the servant of Mirabell, presents himself in form of Mirabell's uncle. (Sir Rowland) and reaches Lady Wishfort's house to woo her. He (Waitwell) does all these things on the advice of Mirabell and Foible gives her full co-operation to him. But unfortunately Mrs. Marwood who is very close to Lady Wishfort becomes aware of all these things and informs Lady Wishfort about it. Lady Wishfort loses her temper and asks Foible about her involvement; but there is no end to these intrigues here as the plot further develops. We see that Mr. Fainall who is the son-in-law of Lady Wishfort prepares a plan alongwith Mrs. Marwood. According to this plan they are to usurp the property of Lady Wishfort, Mrs. Fainall and Millamant. But this plot also proves a failure because now Mirabell comes forward to their rescue and foils the treacherous plan of Mr. Fainall and Mrs. Marwood. The sequence of intrigues does not end here, Mirabell once again fabricates a plan to save Millaments property. This time he takes the help of Sir Wilfull, who is the nephew of Lady Wishfort. As it was the condition for Millaments' marriage that if she doesn't get the consent of her aunt (Lady Wishfort) for her marriage she would lose half of her fortune; but Mirabell, very cleverly prepares a plan. According to that plan, Sir Wilfull and Millamant, falsely inform Lady Wishfort that they are ready to marry each other. Lady Wishfort, gives her consent without causing any further delay and this way, Mirabel saves that half of the fortune of Millamant and here also Fainall miserably fails in his evil design to acquire Millamants' property. But Lady Wishfort now is well-aware of this fact that Millamant and Sir Wilfull are not actually going to marry. Earlier, she was not in favour of Millamant's marriage with Mirabell but, now her mind is completely changed because of Mirabell's efforts and she, without any hesitation, gives her consent regarding their marriage.

The plot of *The Way of the World* further gets more complex when we go through the various love-affairs mentioned in this comedy. The plot of this comedy revolves around the love affairs. The various love affairs are as follows:

1. Love affair between Mirabell and Millamant
2. Love-affair between Mrs. Marwood and Mirabell.
3. Love-affair between Mrs. Marwood and Fainall
4. Love-affair between Mirabell and Mrs. Fainall, and
5. Love-affair between Mr. Fainall with Mrs. Fainall.

As far as the love-affair of Millamant and Mirabell is concerned, it is the only genuine relationship among the others mentioned in the play. The rest of these relationships are only based on selfish motives.

But unfortunately, the aunt of Millament is not in favour of this relationship and she hated Mirabell because of his treachery in pretending to be her suitor when he was actually in love with Millamant. So in order to win Millamant's hand, Mirabell hatches a conspiracy in which he takes the help of his servant Waitwell and Foible, the maid servant of lady Wishfort. But it is very unfortunate for Mirabell because Mrs. Marwood happens to see Foible in conservation with Mirabell. She smells a rat and immediately informs Lady Wishfort about it Lady Wishfort becomes outrageous and warns Millament because if she (Millament) marries Mirabell without her (Lady Wishfort) consent she might lose her half of the fortune.

When we go through the play we find that Mrs. Marwood keeps a soft corner in her heart for Mirabell. In fact, she wants to win his favour but Mirabell never takes her seriously. His neglect causes annoyance to Mrs. Marwood and she decides to teach him a lesson; so she informs Lady Wishfort about his conspiracy. But readers get confused when they come to know that Mrs. Marwood is also involved in a love-affair with Mr. Fainall, who is the husband of Mrs. Fainall.Mrs. Fainall is also not fully innocent however she looks very simple. She has had a love-affair with Mirabell. Not only this, she is pregnant because of her relation with Mirabell, and in order to conceal her pregnancy she married Mr. Fainall and in this way, deceived him (Fainall). Although, the character of Mr. Fainall is villaineous in nature because he nurtures an evil desire. But he is also a victim of his wife; because even after their marriage his wife (Mrs. Fainall) maintains an illicit relation with Mirabell. This is very confusing for the readers and the plot of the comedy, becomes more and more incoherent. It is devoid of a proper order in its thought and speech.

The above-mentioned descriptions are sufficient to support this logic that the plot of this comedy are so numerous that it creates a problem for the reader. However, these subplots contain a lot of significance and contribute immensely in the development of the mainplot. All these subplots are like a garland and these are so interlinked with each other that if we miss any one of them, it becomes very difficult to understand this comedy as a whole. And this is one of the reasons that this play was a failure on stage because it is undoubtedly, very difficult to digest all these subplots in their proper sequence. We realise that it is very difficult to understand the play without careful concentration.

Therefore, it is quite clear after this analysis that the plot of *The Way of the World* is not only full of complex circumstances but it is absolutely scattered as far as the compactness of thoughts and actions is concerned.

When we go through the comedy, *The Way of the World* we find a number of relationships prevailing among different characters. Everybody is related to everyone in some or other respect. We see that lady Wishfort is the aunt of Sir Wilfull. She also has the same relation with Witwoud. Further it can be noticed that Sir Wilfull and Witwoud are the son of same mother but from different fathers and this way they are half-brothers.

When we talk about the heroine of the play, Millament, she is the niece of Lady Wishfort and half of her fortune is under the trusteeship of her aunt. Again we find that Millamant is related with Mrs. Fainall and Mr. Fainall also because Mrs. Fainall is the daughter of Lady Wishfort. So naturally when Mrs. Fainall faces adverse circumstances in the play, Lady Wishfort becomes perplexed. When we read about Mirabell we notice that he is virtually, surrounded by women characters. He is already in love with Millamant but Mrs. Marwood also has a feeling of affection for him. However he always has a kind of hatred for her. Mrs. Fainall, inspite of being a married woman maintains relation with him. Such kind of relations among these characters create a confusion and complicate the plot to a great extent; because as this play proceeds these relations come to the surface and baffle the readers.

It is speciality of Congreve to introduce some interesting characters in his play who deliver witty and humorous dialogues. They provide a particular type of strength to the plot of the play. They are very vocal people and capable enough to ridicule the follies of other characters. These types of characters such as Sir Wilfull, Witwood, Petulant and to some extent Millamant make the plot lively and interesting to read. That is why it is well justified to affirm that in *The Way of the World,* subplots or small scenes are as significant as the play as a whole'. Particularly, some of the scenes of this play, are the soul of the whole plot. The Proviso Scene' between Millamant and Mirabell is packed with witty conversation. Readers can fully enjoy the effect of wit and humour in this scene. Similarly, the dialogue between Petulant and Sir Wilfull and between Witwoud and Petulant are rare example of witty exposition. Another scene which adds vigour to the plot of the play is the conversation between Mrs.

Marwood and Mr. Fainall. Mr. Fainall very strongly reacts to Mrs. Marwood's behaviour and alleges that she is in love with Mirabell and similarly Mrs. Marwood threatens him to disclose his affairs.

Apart from these significant small subplots, there are some other scenes which are very important. Among these scenes, the behaviour of Lady Wishfort creates an amusing atmosphere in the play especially when she prepares herself to receive Sir Rowland, who is actually the servant of Mirabell. In the next scene we are amused when Waitwell in disguise of Sir Rowland talks to Lady Wishfort and displays a rare kind of wit and humour.

As a whole it can easily be affirmed that the plot of *The Way of the World* is incoherent and a little lose in its fabrication. But the main strength of this comedy is its subplots which provide vigour and vitality to this play.

Q.12. "In his plays, Congreve has displayed a unique sense of the art of characterization" . Support this statement with special reference to *The Way of the World.*

Or, "In *The Way of the World* Congreve's characters are realistic in their approach." Justify

Or "Congreve has exhibited a masterly approach in the art of characterization in *The Way of the World.*" Discuss.

Ans. As far the art of characterization is concerned, Congreve has displayed an outstanding capability in almost every play but particularly, in *The Way of the World,* he is at the height of his glory. His characters leave a mark upon the readers mind and also in their hearts. He has presented them in such an excellent manner that they seem very close to us. His approach in this play is absolutely realistic. However, his characters somehow, look over-ingenious but nevertheless, readers find them very lively.

William Congreve, very dexterously introduces the satirical elements in his characterization. In *The Way of the World,* infact, he has fabricated a kind of puzzle for his readers. He has inter-mingled his characters in such a way and they are related to one another in such a manner that readers of this play have a very tough time in establishing their identity. He is so remarkable in his character portrayal that he paints the characters of high and low society with equal dexterity. He is brilliant when he portrays the character of Lady Wishfort and Millamant and again he shows the same brilliance in the portrayal of Waitwell and Foible's character. Congreve is so exceptional in his presentation, that if we study his characters carefully, we can easily trace the nature and mentality of those characters through their dialogue-delivery.

Importance of Characters in the Comedy

Although Congreve's *The Way of the World* is considered a brilliant piece of *Comedy of Manners,* the characters of this play individually, are so well-sketched that it can easily be called a *Comedy of Characters* instead of *Comedy of Manners.* As far as the proceedings of the plot in this comedy is concerned, characters dominate the scenes. Events and subplots are not as significant and important as these characters are. These characters help in the development of scenes in the play *The Way of the World.* He has done justice to every character. They display such an originality that they appear to be exact replicas of the role which they play. In other words it can be said that in *The Way of the World* characters rule the roost.

Although Congreve has portrayed his characters with equal vitality, he is exceptionally brilliant when he presents his hero and heroine in *The Way of the World.* His hero and heroine that is Mirabell and Millamant, occupy a distinct position in this comedy. The hero and heroine of this comedy represent the upper strata of society. They never face the hard reality of this world and always spend a life full of mirth and comfort. In other words it can be said that if they are mentally disturbed it is not because of adverse situations rather they are themselves accountable for their difficulties.

The Way of the World we find a unique style of the art of characterization. Most of the characters have their partners. First of all we can cite the example of the hero of the play, Mirabell, who enjoys the position of the hero of this comedy. He is paired with Millamant, the heroine of this play. Although there are two other young women who pursue him-the wife of Mr. Fainall, who even after her marriage, enjoys the friendship of Mirabell and the other one is Mrs. Marwood. Although Mirabell doesn't pay any attention to her, she has a soft-corner for him. Readers find some element of surprise when they come to know that Lady Wishfort also wanted to win the favour of Mirabell. But, Mirabell was in fact only pretending to love her, as a cover for his love for her niece, Millamant. So Lady Wishfort gets duped in this manner.

As far as other characters are concerned, we notice that Mr. Fainall, although married to Mrs. Fainall, is in love with Mrs. Marwood Foible, who plays the role of maid-servant of Lady Wishfort is paired with Waitwell, a servant of Mirabell. One the other hand, Petulant accompanies Witwoud in the play.

So we see that Congreve is very zealous in his characterization. He projects his characters according to the demand of the scene. It certainly proves his master-mind approach in the art of characterization.

Congreve handles his characters with an immense insight. This is the reason why his characters appear realistic and life-like. He is undoubtedly, a wonderful painter of characters. Congreve gives them a right direction in this comedy and that is why he is tremendously successful in his art of character portrayal. William Congreve is simply unparalleled in this area. When we go through the comedy, we find that each and every characters of this play follow a guideline and they never deviate from their path. This is Congreve's speciality; and it is a concrete evidence of his unique sense of the art of characterization.

At times Congreve appears a little careless in his character portrayal we observe this in the characters of Mrs. Fainall and to some extent Sir Wilfull and Waitwell. These characters have been neglected to some extents.

In *The Way of the World* Congreve is extremely terrific,-as far as his selection of the words is concerned. His characters speak those dialogues which very accurately suit their personality. The characters of Lady Wishfort, Millamant and Mirabell have been brilliantly presented by Congreve. They speak those dialogues which are typical of their nature and attitudes. Similarly, the characters of Petulant and Witwoud are brought out in their witty conservations. They speak in a most humourous and witty manner; because they have been presented in this comedy as fops.

Congreve is absolutely marvelous in the characterization of Sir Wilfull and Fainall. Sir Wilfull is the half-brother of Witwoud and nephew of lady Wishfort buy he lives in the countryside so he is not very familiar with the urban lifestyle; therefore, he speaks and behaves in a rustic manner. Here, we can observe the masterly approach of Congreve's art of characterization.

On the other hand, Mr. Fainall, the, son-in-law of Lady Wishfort tries to usurp her fortune and fabricates a plan in this regard. Here, Congreves has presented him as the villain of this play and readers can easily identify him as a villain through his way of speaking.

So, we see that Congreve's selection of dialogues for his characters, is par-excellence. This speciality contributes to the realism of his characters in his comedies.

William Congreve's characters are successful representatives of their age. It is well known-fact that Restoration period was full of follies and vices and the society was in the grip of immoral practices. Infidelity and treachery was prevalent among men and women. And all these defects of that society can easily be seen in the characters of *The Way of the World*. These characters are typical of the Restoration society. Women are licentious and their behaviour is very disgraceful. Mr. Fainall, is completely immoral and reprobate in nature. Similarly, although Mrs. Marwood, shows that she is a good friend of Lady Wishfort, she, infact, cheats her and gives her wrong information. Lady Wishfort, inspite of her advanced age, behaves like a young girl. She puts on so much make up at her in this age. Not only this, she also wants to get married even in this age.

As far as the character-portrayal of Millamant is concerned, Congreve has presented her as a multi-faceted personality. She sometimes comes across as a very impressive character but at times, she falters and behaves like a strange woman and readers get confused because of this transformation.

Mrs. Fainall, the daughter of Lady Wishfort, however, looks very innocent but in fact, she is not as innocent as she looks like. She maintains illicit relation with Mirabell and not only this, she becomes pregnant because of it, This behaviour of Mrs. Fainall is one of the features of her age. Such sort of relations were prevalent in that Restoration Society. Congreve through her characters has very successfully painted the social fabric of his age. When we go through the comedy, we find that besides Mrs. Fainall, Mrs. Marwood also has crossed the limit of immoral behaviour not just because she is in love with Mr. Fainall but also because, she wants to win the favour of Mirabell also.

As far as Mirabell's character is concerned, Congreve presents him as the hero of the play. In this role he is surrounded by four women. He is actually in love with Millamant but, he maintains secret relation with Mrs. Fainall also Mrs. Marwood and Lady Wishfort also pursue him, although he is not interested in them.

So we observe that Congreve has painted a realistic picture of Restoration Society through his unique sense of character portrayal.

In the play *The Way of the World* almost all the characters of Congreve indulge in one or the other conspiracy. Right from the hero to the maid servant all are involved in intrigues and conspiracies .Although, Millamant does not directly indulged in any conspiracy, she knows everything. This is strength of Congreve's pen that he has very successfully painted the picture of his age through his characterization. Conspiracy and intrigues were the order of the day during the Restoration period. So we see that even husband and wife fabricate a intrigue against each other. Mother and daughter are rivals in love. Women keep their illicit relations intact even after their marriages. So, when we go through Congreve's play the real picture of the Restoration period appears before our eyes.

Apart from these above-mentioned traits of Congreve's art of characterization, there are some other noteworthy features of his characterization.

Congreve has very successfully portrayed both the round and flat types of characters. Although most of his characters which have been portrayed by him are of flat nature but certainly the characters of Millament and Mirabell including the character of Lady Wishfort are very much alive and full of vitality.

Congreve is an excellent architect of wit and humour and *The Way of the World* is packed with these qualities. We get a complete picture of the contemporary society which Congreve has presented in *The Way of the World.*

A special quality of this play of Congreve is the dominance of women characters. Congreve's women characters have certainly an edge over their male counterpart. They are full of boldness, vigour and stamina. In fact these female characters dominate their male counterpart in the entire comedy. If Mr. Fainall deceives her wife, she also maintains illicit relations even after her marriage and in this way she is not weak. Similarly, Millamant is such a type of female character who is full of vigour and vitality. She would never tolerate any male domination over her way of life.

In a nutshell, it can easily be affirmed that as far as Congreve's ability of character-portrayal in *The Way of the World* is concerned, it is absolutely magnificent. He has, undoubtedly, exhibited a masterly approach in this regard; and has presented a realistic picture of his contemporary society. His vision is broad and his characters are the true representatives of his age.

Q.13. "In *The Way of the World,* playwright has highlighted the relations of men and women in marriage." Do you agree with his dictum?

Or "*The Way of the World* is a replica of Congreve's contemporary society; Congreve ridicules the prevalent mode of relationships and suggests a remedy for it." Elucidate.

Or, "*The Way of the World* is a serious document of its age." Comment.

Or,"Although *The Way of the World,* appears to be a light-hearted comedy, it contains a seriousness in the plot," Elaborate,

Ans. Relation of Men and Women as Focal Point

The Way of the World is a comedy which mainly deals with the relations of men and women in marriage. Restoration comedy, contains the element of sex and love in abundance. In other words we can say that the sexual relation of men and women is the focal point of Restoration comedy. Restoration dramatists are mainly concerned with the upper and polished class of society.

Although, Etherege, Dryden, Wycherley and Vanbrugh are some of the noted writers of this age but William Congreve occupies a special status when he deals with the subject of love and marriage. He is absolutely brilliant in the portrayal of his contemporary society.

Congreve, in *The Way of the World,* has presented the relations of men and women in a realistic manner. When we go through the comedy, it becomes clear to us that immoral practices and infidelity dominate the society. Men and women are engaged in extra-marital affairs. They are suffering from moral degradation. No body is reliable, husbands and wives cheat each others. Daughter is involved in conspiracy against mother. Lover deceives his beloved and vice-versa.

So, a through analysis of the play strengthens this idea that *The Way of the World* deals with the relations of men and women in marriage. But a closer study of this comedy reveals the fact that it also deals with the extra-marital relations of men and women.

As we go through the play we notice that the hero of this comedy, Mirabell, is in love with Millamant, who is the niece of Lady Wishfort, but as the play progresses we detect the demerits of Restoration period even in Mirabell's personality. He is cheating Millamant because he is also involved with the daughter of Lady Wishfort, Mrs. Fainall. Although, Mirabell is the hero of the play but his attitude in love can not be said proper. He further maligns the image of a hero when he advices Mrs. Fainall to Marry Fainall in order to cover her pregnancy because she is pregnant and Mirabell is responsible for her pregnancy. Inspite of being a married woman, Mrs Fainall maintains an illicit relation with Mirabell. It shows that in Restoration period the human relations were in its lowest ebb. We feel a little surprised because although Mirabell is fully accountable for the pregnancy of Mrs. Fainall, she never protests against his act; and treats her husband as a scapegoat. Further we see that Mrs. Fainall has appointed Mirabell as a trustee of her entire fortune. It shows that she is very intimate with him.

Human relationship is Congreve's primary concern in *The Way of the World* and the relation between Mrs. Marwood and Mr. Fainall is another example of an illicit relationship. Although Mrs. Marwood is very much interested in Mirabell, but when she shows her love, she miserably fails, because Mirabell does not take any notice of her. So obviously she is annoyed with him and because of her annoyance she always wants to teach Mirabell a lesson. Consequently, she develops a relation with Mr. Fainall. However, she doesn't like him in reality. In course of her discussion with Mr. Fainall we notice that Mr. Fainall, appears to know the truth when he accuses Mrs. Marwood of being inclined towards Mirabell, but Mrs. Marwood reacts strongly and threatens to expose his illicit relation if he continues his rude behaviour. Then we see that Mr. Fainall is afraid of being exposed and tries to pacify her in every possible manner. Because if Mrs. Marwood reveals this affair it would land him in adverse circumstances.

Thus, we can easily understand that Congreve wants to ridicule the relationships in his contemporary society which is totally based on money. Reader of this comedy can understand this fact that neither Mrs. Marwood nor Mr. Fainall is devoted to each other. They maintain a false love-affair in order to usurp the huge fortune of Lady Wishfort and her niece including Mrs. Fainall. In fact, Congreve makes a fun of such relationships which are completely based on selfish motives.

Although *The Way of the World* appears to be a light-hearted comedy which is full of witty and humourous dialogues, infact, a minute observation of the plot, shows its seriousness.

Undoubtedly, Congreve has used wit and humour in abundance but his purpose behind this comedy is very serious. He exposes the degradation of social norms. Human values are in its lowest ebb. Men and women are absolutely shameless and devoid of all moral values. Society is completely in the grip of vices and follies. Treachery and infidelity are the order of the day. Even a mother doesn't have faith in her daughter, and daughter plots a conspiracy against her mother. Even the sacred relation of lover and beloved is based on selfish motives.

It shows that the society of Restoration period was absolutely corrupted. Congreve, infact, presents the gloomy picture of contemporary period in lighter vein.

The proviso scene is one of the most remarkable aspects of Congreve's *The Way of the World.* Although, *Prima facie* it looks like a light-hearted and comic conversation between Millament and Mirabell but in reality, it is a serious and thought-packed analysis which reflects the gravity of the play. We enjoy the witty dialogues of Millamant and Mirabell but actually, Congreve has very skillfully painted the depression and perplexity of Millamant. She is very nervous because she is well-aware of those adverse circumstances which a women faces after her marriage. Millamant is putting her conditions before Mirabell. It is not that she is vain but she only seeks proper conduct on the part of Mirabell; because she knows that men always exploit their wives after their marriage. She doesn't want to face that situation which her cousin, Mrs. Fainall is facing. It shows the inner plight of Millamant. She doesn't want to be dominated by her husband, Mirabell after marriage; because it was the general trend in the Restoration period that men always exploit their wives after marriage. Millamant is very upset because of Mr. Fainall's attitude to his wife, who is her cousin. So she, very intelligently, and frankly explains all her doubts and wishes to Mirabell so that after their marriage they might spend a happy life together.

Although, Mirabell also puts his conditions before her, it is only a matter of mutual understanding. They both want to respect each others' feelings and thus they simply want to clear their doubts.

Thus, the scenes, in a sense contains the essence of what Congreve has to say about ideal marriage.

Congreve has presented the relation of Millamant and Mirabell in a different manner. As we know that the Restoration age was absolutely devoid of human values and there was no place for devotion and dedication. Lovers were not loyal to each other in love-affairs. But we feel a pleasant surprise when we come to know about the relation of Millamant and Mirabell. The love-story of Millamant and Mirabell is the central point of this play. Millamant and Mirabell love each other very honestly; but here one can raise a question about Mirabell's behaviour, because he maintains an illicit relation with Mrs. Fainall. But truly speaking, Millamant is aware of this fact and she tolerates it. As far as Millamant's attitude in love is concerned, she is absolutely spotless. She is fully devoted to Mirabell and readers 'do not detect any defect in her love. The character of Millamant is an exception because she is quite aloof from the immoral love-practices of her society. Her dedication is only confined to Mirabell.

As far as Mirabell is concerned, it is true that he is involved with Mrs. Fainall but infact his honesty in love for Millamant can not be questioned. He ignores all the weaknesses of Millamant and confesses his love for her. He is also devoted to her that once he says that Millamant's faults suit her personality. In the "Proviso scene" we see that Millamant puts a bundle of conditions before him but he accepts all those conditions without making any hue and cry.

So it is very clear from this description that although Congreve has exposed the infidelities and treacheries of lovers and beloveds prevalent in his society but the relation of Mllamant and Mirabell has been treated in different way.

By the character portrayal of Lady Wishfort, Congreve gives us a clear picture of his contemporary society: in which unconventional and eccentric behaviour are at its peak.

He presents a ridiculous picture of Lady Wishfort. She, inspite of her advanced age has a strong desire for marriage. She is so weak at this point that she is ready to do anything to fulfill her desire. She wants to present herself as a young girl of twenty and for this, she devotes a lot of time before the dressing table. A number of people exploit her because of this weakness. Mirabell has already deceived her by showing false love for her. Similarly, Waitwell in disguise of Sir Rowland, exploits her although Mirabell plays a key-role behind all this. Lady Wishfort appears before us like an eccentric character. Her behaviour is strange. A minute study of her character reveals the other aspect of her personality. Actually, she is a pitiable character. She needs our sympathy because she behaves in that manner out of frustration. We can observe her pitiable condition, when Mr. Fainall tries to exploit her and threatens her that if she doesn't agree with his conditions he will definitely divorce Mrs.Fainall, who is the daughter of Lady Wishfort. She cries for help and at that stage she appears to be one of the weakest characters of the play.

So, it is obvious after this broad analysis that although Congreve ridicules

Lady Wishfort's behaviour, infact, a close study of her character unfolds her inner plight.

In *The Way of the World* Congreve has presented the real picture of his contemporary society. All the vices which were prevalent in that period have been depicted in a skilfull manner. The treachery of married women, craze for fashion, immoral attitude of men; feeling of jealousy, scandalous life of characters both men and women, conspiracy and intrigues can easily be detected in the plot of the play. It is true that Congreve has presented all these elements in his play but it doesn't mean that Congreve is in favour of these wrong practices.

In the "Proviso Scene", his character, Millamant, reacts strongly against these social evils. Congreve, through the character of Millamant, denounces the immoral practices of the age. Again Congreve very skillfully portrays the character of Sir Wilfull who inspite of being a absolute drunkard, protests against these prevalent practices.

Congreve has successfully depicted the scenes of scandal. When we go through the comedy we come across the name of some places where men and women gather and talk about scandals such as "Chocolate House" and St. James's Park are the places where such kind of conversations take place. Similarly we get the description of play houses and coffee houses, where scandals and intrigues are discussed.

Besides this, Congreve is unparalleled when he presents the element of wit and humour in his play. Although, it is a noteworthy aspect that he has very intelligently and smartly satirise the follies and vices which were prevalent in that society, a minute observation of his dialogues enable us to understand his main purpose. Infact, through his witty dialogues he exposes the follies of society and provides a remedy for this moral degradation. But if we want to grasp his main ideas we need a•keen insight.

On the whole, *The Way of the World* is quite successful in picturising the contemporary society. It is certainly a replica of the Restoration Society. The playwright has very successfully portrayed and highlighted the relations of men and women of his age. Although, *prima facie* it looks like a light-hearted comedy but infact, it has a serious aspect which is hidden under a comic subject matter.

Q.14. "In *The Way of the World* although the Proviso scene, appears comic in presentation, it contains valuable suggestions for a happy conjugal life." Explain.

Or,"The Proviso scene between Millamant and Mirabell is a significant event which strengthens the plot of the play." Illustrate.

Or,"In *The Way of the World,* the Bargaining scene defines the true meaning of love". Discuss.

Or,"Wit and humour are the dominating elements in the Proviso scene." Elaborate.

Ans. The Proviso scene in *The Way of the World* is an outstanding mixture of fun and facts. This scene has been widely and simulta-neously admired by the critic and readers alike. Infact, it serves as an excellent medium through which Congreve conveys his message to his readers. It is a thought-packed and meaningful conversation between the two leading characters of the play, Millamant and Mirabell, which contains valuable suggestions for a happy conjugal life. The Proviso scene contains the central idea of the play. It is undoubtedly the focal point of the comedy *The Way of the World.*Although Congreve has followed the tradition of Restoration comedy in the presentation of Proviso scene but he succeeds in satirising the prevalent mode of a married life, while at the same time suggesting the remedy for its ills.

When we go through the various conditions of Millamant and Mirabell which they put before each other, we see the brilliant use of wit and humour in their dialogues. But a serious study of this scene exposes the follies and vices related to a married life as it had become in that society. Congreve, here, wants to depict the fear and problems of both husband and wife after marriage. Millamant and Mirabell simply want to make themselves clear about each other's behaviour after their marriage.

The most noteworthy aspect of the Proviso scene is Millamants witty style in which she puts her conditions before her lover Mirabell. Readers find a magnificent Exhibition of Witty dialogues when she starts putting her conditions before Mirabell.

According to her first condition, she wants equal amount of love and affection on the part of her would-be husband throughout her life. Behind her above mentioned condition we notice the pitable condition of a wife after marriage. Just before marriage when men and women are lovers they declare full support and love for each other but things take a turn when they marry each other. So, Millamant appears anxious because of this reason and that is why she puts this condition. Again, Millamant says that she hates those lovers who do not take a proper care of his beloved. She further wants that her husband must be a loyal and good-natured man.

Millamant is quite brilliant and witty in this scene when she puts her conditions before Mirabell. She says,

"Ay, as wife, spouse, my dear, joy, jewel, love sweet heart, and the rest of that nauseous can't, in which men and their wives are so fulsomely familiar-I shall never bear that, Good Mirabell, don't let us be familiar or found, nor kiss before folks, like my lady Fadler and Sir Francis, nor go to Hyde Park together, the first Sunday in new chariot, to provoke eyes and whispers; and then never be seen there together again; as if we were proud of one another the first week and ashamed of one another even after."

Millamant puts down these conditions in a witty and a humourous manner but certainly her conditions reflect that inner agony which a woman faces after her marriage. When she talks about her liberty after the marriage, Millamant appears before us as 'a witty character when she informs Mirabell that she can not forgo her independence, she has used the words like, 'faithful solitude', 'darling contemplation', 'morning thoughts', 'agreeable wakings', 'indolent slumbers' etc,, which are proof of her sparkling wit, although the readers might misjudge her viewpoint when she says, that "Let us be as strange and unfamiliar as if we had been married a long time ago. Millamant's opinion as expressed here is that there should be a certain distance between husband and wife, as it strengthens and intensifies their love.

She puts a lot of condition before Mirabell but he is so much in love with her that he asks if she has any more conditions? Millament further informs him that she doesn't want any interference in the regular routine. At her tea-table she will be the "sole empress", and even Mirabell cannot enter her room without knocking at the door. Although these last conditions are not acceptable to Mirabell but ultimately he agrees.

Mirabell listens to all the conditions of Millament with patience. Although he is not very happy with some of the conditions, he doesn't raise any objection. Now he informs Millamant about some of his own conditions. When we go through his conditions we observe that it is a witty satire on the affectations of women in that society. It can be said that Congreve, through the mouth of his character Mirabell portrays a ridiculous picture of women's activity in that society. Although his satire is directed at his contemporary society but his satirical approach is still relevant.

Mirabell wants that after their marriage Millamant should follow some guidelines. Millamant should not be in company of any woman who has a nefarious background or who indulges in scandalous activities.

He further informs her that he expects her to stay away from the theatre. Mirabell here appears to be a very simple natured-person who doesn't like activities which are related to fashionable society. So he says to her that she should not wear those oil-skinned masks which are in fashion because it covers the actual appearance of a woman. Again a further study of Mirabell's condition makes us aware of his hatred for those activities in which women are accustomed to wear tight and skin fit dresses. He strongly opposes Millamant's wearing such kind of clothes during her pregnancy because it might have harmful consequences for the unborn child. So he informs Millamant that after her marriage, he will not allow her to wear such tight dresses.

Mirabell's conditions are a comment on the ridiculousness of the activities of women in Congreve's time. Both the characters, Mirabell and Millamant are intelligent enough to understand the necessity of rising above such ridiculousness in order to live a happy married life. While putting down their conditions they display extensive wit and humour which dominate the proceedings of the play and add to its charm.

Although *Prima-facie,* the scene appears comic in its presenta-tion, but actually it is a serious document which contains a lot of valuable suggestions for a happy conjugal life.

If we study the scene carefully, we find that these conditions, although they seem very funny and light-hearted at first, are actually a serious comment on the degradation of conjugal relations. At the same time they also convey a feeling of optimism that an ideal marriage is still possible. The conditions as set down by the two lovers, therefore confirm the sincerity of their motives and their wish to live a married life which is different from the kind which was prevalent at that time. Millamant expresses her wish to retain her liberty and independence after marriage, while Mirabell forbids her to follow the silly practices of affectations ladies. Both accept each other's conditions and it is expected that an understanding has been achieved between them as far as such matters are concerned. In other words it is a guideline or memorandum of understanding between husband and wife, which would enable them to spend a happy married life. After following these guidelines there is no any possibility of misunderstanding. Although Millamant has put down some harsh conditions which would not be normally acceptable in an ordinary situation, Congreve, here, defines love in its true spirit. Mirabell loves Millamant without any reservations. His love for her is without any selfish motives. So he does not object to her extravagant demands and accepts them.

So we see that Congreve, in the Proviso scene has a serious purpose. Actually, Congreve throws light on the vital aspects of a happy married life. Through this scene he conveys this idea that if a man or a woman wants to spend a tension -free and satisfied married life he or she must not be egoistic. It requires a certain amount of sacrifice from both men and the women. Another important aspect of the scene is that it exposes the suspicious nature of men and women. A complete study of the bargaining scene strenghthens this idea that a happy conjugal life is possible only, when both husband and wife are not too suspicious of each other. A happy conjugal life requires a complete sacrifice on the part of both husband and wife. They must respect their privacy so that both husband and wife can enjoy a certain amount of freedom. But certainly there should be a limit to it. If a wife does not respect and follow the guidelines of her husband does not like cosmetics and fashionable dresses, she must not use these things because she must win her partner's heart in order to preserve her married life. And these above mentioned rules and regulations should strictly be followed by husbands also.

In the Proviso scene, love has been defined in a unique manner. In the course of their conversation Millamant says to Mirabell that she does not want momentary love from him. She wants to be lived by Mirabell in equal proportion throughout her life. Here we can easily judge the mental state of Millamant. She is very upset because of Mr. Fainall's attitude to her cousin, Mrs. Fainall. She is very intelligent and smart lady so she tells Mirabell that a lover should be very careful in his behaviour towards the beloved. A careless man cannot be a true lover. Besides, she thinks that a lover should allow a certain amount of liberty and privacy to his beloved.

Some critics are of the opinion that the love between Mirabell and Millamant is absolutely devoid of emotions. According to them this kind of love is only based on term and conditions. Both Millamant and Mirabell talk like tradesmen. They are absolutely very conscious people and understand their social conditions so they want to keep themselves secure. But if we carefully go through the words of Millamant we can notice that although she puts a lot of conditions before Mirabell, ultimately she affirms that if he will follow these conditions sincerely; she would try her best to prove herself a perfect wife. Actually, she knows that a married woman cannot spend her life against the wishes of her husband. She has to obey and respect the feelings of her life-partner.

So through this Proviso scene we see that Congreve has given a new philosophy of love, which requires complete devotion and dedication on the part of both men and women in an equal proportion.

As far as the importance of Proviso scene is concerned it is undoubtedly one of the most significant events of the play. In other words it can be said that it is the climax of the comedy. In this scene Congreve exposes the follies and vices prevalent in a married life. We know that the love and marriage are the central theme of the comedy of Restoration age; and in this scene we notice that the playwright has elaborated the matter of love and marriage in a broad and clear manner.

The Proviso scene is significant event in the play because a thorough study of this scene presents a true picture of Restoration Society. Millamant and Mirabell are the leading characters of this comedy and both of them have been fully highlighted by the playwright in this scene. Although such type of scenes are the part and parcel of the comedy of that age, but Congreve is undoubtedly unparalleled in his presentation. Dryden in his *Secret love* and *The Wild Gallant* has presented such sort of scenes but Congreve is more lucid and vivid in his presentation. His wonderful depiction of wit and the boldness of the characters are some of the salient features of Proviso scene. So an overall analysis of this scene presents a clear picture of the contemporary society. It is, although full of comic elements, it also contains very serious suggestions for a happy conjugal life.

Q. 15. "*The Way of the World* is not very vivid and vigorous as far as its movement and action is concerned but it is certainly delightful in its subject matter." Elucidate.

Or,"The Comedies of Restoration period lack sharpness, they are insensible and immoral." Support your answer with special reference to *The Way of the World*.

Or,"*The Way of the World* provides a crystal-clear picture of the loose morals of the upper classes of the Restoration Society." Illustrate.

Ans. The Restoration Comedy has always been the target of criticism right from the beginning. A prominent critic of English literature L.C. Knight has criticised the comedies of the Restoration period on the basis of their insensivity. He is of the opinion that these comedies are dull and devoid of emotions. Before this, these comedies have always been criticised because of its lack of morality. In his criticism, Charles Lamb has said that these comedies are completely based on imaginary concepts. They are far from reality, but another critic Macaulay opposed this view point and considers it a reflection of contemporary society.

So we see that Restoration Comedies have been criticised by various critics.

As far as *The Way of the World* is concerned, it is not insensitive and dull.

Although, this play has some shortcomings but nonetheless, it is a delightful work of art by Congreve. When we talk about the drawbacks of this play we find that inspite of a lively plot, this play lack the intensity of action and movement. Some characters are completely flat and frigid. They do not possess any vigour and vitality in their actions. Mrs. Fainall and Sir Wilfull are the characters which are absolutely typical. To some extent the characters of Mrs. Marwood and Mr. Fainall also lack the intensity. They are only confined to intrigues and conspiracies. Another loophole of this comedy is the intricacy and complexity of its plot. Characters in this play are intermingled with one another in such a confusing manner that it baffles the readers. It is a very difficult task for the readers to trace out the relation of one character with another. In other words, it can be said that each and every characters in this comedy is related to one another in some or other manner. This situation is extremely bewildering for the readers.

The Way of the World can also be criticised on the basis of its conclusion. When the play ends, readers find themselves in a dilemma because still there are number of unsolved mysteries. For example, what action would Fainall take against Mirabell and Mrs. Fainall? Lady Wishfort still continues her search for a young husband and even the situation of Millamant and Mirabell is not very clear because they are not very sure about the durability of their married life.

So we observe that though *The Way of the World* is undoubtedly delightful and entertaining, it lacks the intensity of movement clarity of actions. Despite above-mentioned flaws there are some special features which fascinate its readers to a great extent. We can classify them in the following manner.

1. A typical example of Comedy of Manners
2. Brilliant characterization technique
3. Appealing comic element
4. Praise-worthy style

In *The Way of the World* we find all the elements of the Restoration Comedy, in the Comedy of Manners. In this comedy, Congreve has painted a true picture of his contemporary society which is corrupted with immoral practices. Relations between husband, wife, lovers and beloves are based on selfish motives. In the characters of Mrs. Fainall and Mrs. Marwood we can easily find this selfish attitude. Congreve has shown his brilliance in presenting the fashions and affectation prevalent in the upper strata of society.

On the whole, Congreve is highly successful in satirising the follies of his contemporary society but besides this, he has a serious purpose too. He, very cleverly, portrays the characters of Millamant and Mirabell, who in the Proviso scene, present a valuable suggestions for a happy married life. A minute study of this scene shows the seriousness of the playwright's purpose.

This play succeeds in conveying to the readers, awareness about the vices and follies prevalent in their society. Through the Proviso scene Congreve wants to clarify that husbands and wives are themselves responsible for their unpleasant married lives. If they forget their egoistic attitude and co-operate with their life-partner in day to day life, then there is no question of an unpleasant situation. Actually, the playwrights here wants to suggest that a successful and harimonious married life requires a lot of sacrifice, capability for adjustment and mutual understanding.

The other aspect of Congreve's *The Way of the World* is related to the exposure of the loose morals which was part and parcel of the upper strata of society in the Restoration age.

The characters of *The Way of the World* are very bold and enthusiastic in nature. They are also very excited and always keep themselves alert to face any critical condition. Even the maid servant of Lady Wishfort is capable of defending herself against any critical situation. When Lady Wishfort asks about her involvement with Mirabell, we see how shrewdly she replies to her Lady Wishfort inspite of being an old lady, draws our attention because of her eccentric behaviours. Millamant and Mirabell who are respectively the heroine and hero of this play impress the readers because of their attractive personality. Even the characters of Mrs. Marwood and Mr. Fainall, although they are villainous in their attitude, keep the readers' interest alive throughout the play. Witwoud, Petulant and Sir Wilfull including Waitwell are remarkable characters because they have got excellent quality of wit and humour.

Further, this play is full of comic elements which are appealing in its nature. Thus inspite of a slow action and dull movement, this comedy fascinates us because of its delightful conversations.

The conversations between Witwoud and Petulant and Petulant and Sir Wilfull are full of comic and humorous elements.

As far as the style of this play is concerned it is lively and energetic. Congreve's technique is appealing. He is a master as far as the using of words is concerned. His characters speak according to the demand of the situation. That is why he is simply unparalleled as far as his style is concerned. In his depiction of the characters of Millamant and Mirabell he is especially brilliant.

So, these are some of the reasons why inspite of the charges leveled against the Comedy of Manners, *The Way of the World* is a delightful work of art.

The Way of the World presents a true picture of the upper class of society. In other words it can easily be said that it is a replica of Congreve's contemporary society. It contains all those elements such as infidelity of women, conspiracy and intrigues, scandalous gossip, sex, marriage and many other evils prevalent in the society. Besides these he satirises the fashions and follies of that age.

In the play we find characters like Mrs. Marwood, Lady Wishfort and Mrs. Fainall who have abnormal sexual appetite. Mrs. Fainall maintains illicit relation even after her marriage. Similarly we see that Mrs. Marwood deceives Mr. Fainall in her love affair. Lady Wishfort is so eccentric in her behaviour that even in her old age, she wants to get married, and we know that all these women are from the upper class of society.

We further see that, Congreve has beautifully presented the element of conspiracy and intrigue which were part and parcel of the upper strata of society. Almost all the characters of this play indulge in conspiracy in a direct or indirect manner. Mrs. Marwood who is very close to Lady Wishfort plots a conspiracy against her with Mr. Fainall. Mr. Fainall, inspite of his close relation with Lady Wishfort, exploits her and threatens to divorce her wife who is the daughter of Lady Wishfort. Infact, he wants to usurp the huge fortune of Lady Wishfort along with Millamant and Mrs. Fainall and for this purpose he and Mrs. Marwood devise this plan.

A further study of the play shows that even the hero of the comedy, Mirabell is involved in a conspiracy against Lady Wishfort although his purpose is not malicious. He simply wants to win Millamant's hand because both he and Millamant love each other but Lady Wishfort opposes the union of these lovers.

During the Restoration period, scandals and intrigues were very much prevalent in upper class of society. And for these kind of activities there were some special places such as Hyde park, or St.Jame's park, coffee houses, chocolate houses, and play houses, where such scandalous matter used to be discussed. Women of the upper class of society used to assembled at a certain place on a particular night to discuss the scandalous affairs. No man was allowed in such meetings and such a night was known as "Cabal Night."

So it is quite obvious after this analysis that this element has been skillfully highlighted by Congreve in the comedy *The Way of the World*.

A thorough study of the play *The Way of the World* throws light on the immoral practices which were prevalent in society. At that time husband and wife used to deceive each other. Both of them had illicit love-affairs and money was the main reason behind every sort of relationships. Here, we can cite an example from *The Way of the World*. When we go through the play, we see that Mr. Fainall is the husband of Mrs. Fainall but both these husband and wife have extra-marital affairs-Mr. Fainall is in love with Mrs. Marwood and Mrs. Fainall has an illicit relationship with Mirabell. She even became pregnant because of her relations with Mirabell.

The society was so corrupt and degraded that even daughters and son-in law were involved in the intrigues against their mother. In the entire play we can not find a single event of a genuine love- affair. All the love-affairs are false and based on selfish motives. In the Proviso scene even Millamant and Mirabell talk like business-men. Although they love each other, none of them wants to sacrifice his or her liberty. It can not be called emotional love because we know that a true lover or beloved would never talk in this manner. Love requires complete devotion and surrender; which is nowhere visible in this play.

When we read this scene carefully, we notice how the Restoration Society was in the grip of immoral practices. Millamant puts her conditions and says that even after her marriage, she will write letters to her well-wishers and receive their replies. She further says that Mirabell should have no objection to her paying a visit to her admires. These kind of conditions cannot be considered moral in a civilized society. Similarly other characters like Mrs. Fainall and Mrs. Marwood are also immoral in their attitude.

So an overall analysis of the play strengthens this notion that Congreve has presented a panoramic view of Restoration world which is full of immoral practices. Scandals, intrigues, gambling, adultery and debauchery were the order of the day. Everybody was engaged in selfish activities. Women and men were not loyal to each other. We see that even the maid servant of Lady Wishfort, is involved in nefarious activities against her mistress.

In a nutshell, it can easily be affirmed that in *The Way of the World* Congreve has very successfully presented the moral degradations of the people of upper class of society. But inspite of above-mentioned facts, Congreve's play *The Way of the World* sustains our interest. It fascinates us because of its charming style and its excellent witty dialogues.

Q.16. "Congreve has imitated the earlier mode of writings in *The Way of the World*." Discuss

Or,"We notice a great influence of earlier drama on *The Way of the World*". Explain.

Ans. A serious study of the play *The Way of the World* reveals that Congreve has imitated the earlier mode of writings in this comedy. First of all we can see the influence of Elizabethan style of writing in *The Way of the World.* As in the style of Ben Jonson, Congreve has depicted women, who with the help of their lovers, foil the evil purpose of their husband who had married to them only for their property. Mrs. Fainall, for example, is one such woman. She resembles the woman character of Ben Jonson, who wrote during Elizabethan age. Again we come across the character of Sir Wilfull who comes from countryside and is a little rustic in his behaviour. This character has been deeply influenced by the Elizabethan mode of characterization.

In the comedy, *The Way of the World* Congreve has imitated the earlier mode of writings to a great deal, especially in the Proviso. For example, we can cite the example of the character Melantha scene, whose behaviour and nature in *Marriage a la mode,* very much resembles Millamant's in this comedy. Millamant's hatred for a prototype married life style is very much similar to the attitude of Isabella. In other words it can easily be affirmed that Millamant has been portrayed by Congreve like Isabella, in *The Wild Gallant.* Her character is a reflection of the character of Isabella. Like her, Millamant also doesn't like those endearing words which husbands call their wives, such as sweetheart, jewel, spouse, my dear etc. When we study the character of Mirabell we observe that he resembles the character of Isabella's lover, because after listening to all the conditions put down by Millamant, he accepts everythings. But in the final round, like Isabella's lover he feels that in later part of her (Millamant) demands, she is a little unjustified to her lover. After Millamant's conditions, Mirabell comes forward with his own conditions although he has very reasonable demands and he puts them forward in a very formal style. The scene is very much close in conception to those scenes which had earlier been portrayed in the drama *Secret Love in Amphitryon.*

Undoubtedly, Congreve has imitated the earlier dramas but he has improved upon the earlier elements. His Proviso scene is the most skillfully handled work of art and it is certainly the best among all the Proviso scenes of the Restoration age. His poetic style is vivid and both lovers and beloved display a free minded attitude approach. Congreve has achieved perfection in the presentation of such scenes. Like Dryden he has also used such Proviso scenes in his writings very successfully.

The witty characters like Witwoud, Sir Wilfull and Petulant resemble the characters of Worm and Cutter who had earlier been portrayed by Cowley in *The Cutter of Coleman Street.* The characters of Witwoud and Petulant have been presented as a pair. Readers find that both these charaters, although fops, always want to underestimate each other on various occasions. They think them selves to be highly intelligent but actually their behaviour is quite nonsensical. But nonetheless, they are friend and enjoy each others company.

Mirabell, the hero of the comedy has an affinity with many other women characters like Mrs. Fainall, Mrs. Marwood and Lady Wishfort. He has followed the tradition of the heroes of earlier Restoration Comedies who were earlier involved in such sort of relations. Mirabell, before marrying Millamant maintains these illicit relations according to the practice in the comedy of manners.

Lady Wishfort in this play, exhibits affectations and eccentric nature which is very much close to the behaviour of Mrs. Loveit who is a character of Etherege in *The Man of Mode.* Shadwell has also portrayed the characters of Lady Loveyouth in *The Humorists* who has left her impression on Lady Wishforts' character. The scene, in which Lady Wishfort is in romatic conversation with Sir Rowland resembles the scene, which has been drawn by Thomas Shadwell in *The Amorous Bigot,* in which Belica talks with Bernado in the same manner. Though Congreve has drawn inspiration for the character of Lady Wishfort from all these sources, it must be admitted that he has shown his originality while portraying this character.

The character of Mrs. Fainall has been portrayed by Congreve in such a way that she seems to be different from other women characters. The character of Mrs. Marwood has been deeply influ-enced by the character of Mrs. Loveit, a women character in *The Man of Mode* a magnificent play by Etherge.

Congreve is splendid in his picturisation of the wooing scene in *The Way of the World.* Such kind of scenes were in fashion during that time. It is a tradition which has been followed by Congreve. In Shakespeare's "Much Ado About Nothing" we come across the characters of Benetick and Beatrice who are just like the characters of Millamant and Mirabell. Apart from this, Congreve has drawn inspiration from other Jacobean comedy like "Hyde Park".

A thorough study of the play *The Way of the World* shows that it has been deeply influenced by Moliere, a great French comedy writer. Moliere had very successfully painted the picture of fashionable society whose faults he satirised but he did not offer any remedy for the ills of the society. Similarly Congreve is excellent in portraying the follies of fashionable society. Congreve very lightheartedly paints out the vices and follies, prevalent in his contemporary society. He creates laughter. His characters conspire against one another and do not care for moral values.

Therefore, obviously Congreve has imitated Moliere in his writings to some extent. Etherege had very successfully and dexterously presented the reality of that age and Congreve has followed the same pattern in *The Way of the World.*

Infact, inspite of his imitation of the style of earlier dramatists, Congreve appears somewhat different. His style is unique and original, although very much influenced by other dramatists of earlier periods. Congreve is different because of his witty approach. Though his characters, resemble many of the earlier characters who had already been portrayed by earlier dramatists but Congreve has presented them in such an artistic manner that there is a touch of novelty in them. Wit and humour, are the elements which give life to the plot and style of the play and make it special.

Congreve is extraordinary inspite of his traditional approach, because he presents an improved and novel subject-matter before its readers. As mentioned earlier, the characters of Lady Wishfort, Millamant, Mirabell and many others remind us those characters who had already been portrayed by Shakespeare, Moliere, Ben Jonson and many other Jacobean and Elizabethan dramatists. Congreve is so witty and humourous in his style that his characters produce real fun for us. Although these characters are in a sense devoid of emotional depth, they certainly are appealing.

As a whole it can be easily affirmed that though Congreve has imitated earlier mode of writing in his play, *The Way of the World* but he fascinates his readers through his original manner of presentation. The characters are so lively and energetic that we cannot underestimate them.

Q.17. Present a critical analysis of Restoration Comedy with a reference to *The Way of the World.*

Or, Describe different aspects of the Comedy of Manners illustrating some of the points from Congreve's *The Way of the World.*

Ans. Restoration Comedy mainly deals with the upper classes of society. There are some specific places where the scenes are planted. Such places are: St. James's Park, Hyde Park, Westminister's Hall etc where people discuss fashions and manners prevalent in high and sophisticated society. The main theme of the comedies of this age was love (illicit or genuine), marriage and money. These matters were not condemned, instead they served as a pastime and source of entertainment for the people. The plots of Restoration Comedy were very intricate and complicated, and baffled its readers. Wit and humour always played an important role and maintained the interest of readers.

Characters in the comedies of the Restoration age were much criticised for their immorality. Jeremy Colliere condemned these plays on the basis of their lack of moral and human values. This immorality was in fact a reaction to the puritan world view which prescribed all kinds of entertainment, and prescribed a disciplined, religious life. So, after the Restoration, libertinism and licentiousness became the order of the day as a consequence of the sudden freedom from all restraints.

As far as the plots of Restoration comedy is concerned, it has been neglected by the playwrights. Plot, as a whole, was not so important. Scenes and events in the comedy of Manners were much more vital and delightful than the entire plot. Plots were so bewildering and intricate that readers of these comedies often found themselves in a maze. In this context, we can take the example of Congreve's *The Way of the World* in which plot is so complex that until Act IV, readers are not able to understand the situation. Although, ultimately, everybody feels satisfied because we see that the play ends in a happy note, with callous people falling in their evil designs and the good people triumphant over the bad.

Almost all the characters in Restoration Comedy display wit in their conversation. The dramatists of this age gave a lot of importance to wit and humour. It was the backbone of the characters of Restoration Comedies. Because of this quality the comedies of this age were more lively than that of Elizabethan period. Although it is true that these witty dialogues lack depth of feeling and emotions, it cannot be denied that they help sustain the reader's interest. But truely speaking, these witty elements sometimes produce the harsh reality of the time. In Proviso scene, we notice that Mirabell has satirised the vices and follies, prevalent among the women of Restoration Age. But behind that light hearted banter, there is also a note of seriousness. We are made aware of the gravity of the situation, especially when little follies and foibles, and affectatious are stretched too far-as in when a pregnant woman wears tight dresses to show her good figure, without any care for the child who is inside her womb. Witwould has been portrayed as a false wit and fop but in the course of the play we see that he presents himself as an intelligent person on the basis of his sensible and logical statements. In Act-III, while talking to Millamant he says, "how an illiterate man dares to make love". Further while telling Millamant about his friendship with Petulant he says that although occasionally they contradict each other but infact they are good friends.

Critics are of different opinion about the serious aspect of Restoration Comedy. Some of them think that these comedies are only a satirical description of its age. We notice that Congreve, in *The Way of the World,* ridicules the follies prevalent in his contemporary society. But besides this, it also appears in his that he may have some serious purpose behind it. He has exposed the unconventional and immoral practices which were prevalent among men and women of that society. Particularly, in the Proviso scene, Mirabell ridicules the fashionable trend of women in Restoration Society.

According to some other critics like Bateson, and L.C. Knight, the writers of Comedy of Manners have a rational attitude towards love and sex. These writers have satirised the conventional attitude in order to create a comic effect.

In this context, we can cite the example of the Proviso scene between Millamant and Mirabell in which sex has been treated in an intelligent manner

The most salient feature of Restoration Comedies is its treatment of marriage and sexual behaviour. When we go through the Bargaining scene between Millamant and Mirabell it becomes clear to all of us that woman is not a slave after her marriage. She is as strong as her husband. A man cannot dominate in his married life on the basis of his masculinity. Congreve, through his characters, has shown that women inevitably emerge as the loser in a marriage. Through Mirabell and Millamant, he puts forth his definition of an ideal marriage, which is of the kind in which neither of the partner will exert disproportionate and undue claims over the other. Congreve maintains that marriage is a kind of compromise between men and women. Both of them are expected to play an important role and they must have a feeling of respect for each other.

Restoration Comedies, are primarily, known for their entertaining qualities. If we are ready to forget moral and human values for a shortwhile, Restoration Comedies can be quite entertaining. For example in *The Way of the World,* we see that Lady Wishfort is a great source of entertainment for the readers when she exhibits her eccentric nature. She wants to depict herself like a teenaged girl when she prepares herself to receive Sir Rowland. She is not satisfied with her make-up and tries to appear very young, although she is about fifty-five. This situation is very amusing for readers because they know the reality of Sir Rowland, who is actually the servant of Mirabell. Similarly, conservations between witwoud and Petulant contain sufficient materials for amusement. Commenting on the purpose of Restoration Comedy, Dryden has maintained that writers of this age have displayed splendid quality of wit; the prime purpose being to entertain the readers. And the Restoration Comedy is successful in its purpose.

In fact, Comedy of Manners received both praise and condemnation alike. As mentioned earlier critics are divided on this issue. Some of them have praised it but there a number of critics who have condemned it because of its immoral attitude. Those critics who were orthodox in their approach, criticized it bitterly but critics with liberal temperament treated it in a different way. These kind of comedies have been criticised by the critics, because of their lack of depth and emotions. Love has been presented in a cheap manner. The elements of selfishness and licentiousness in love has been widely highlighted in such comedies.

The characters in such sort of comedies have been portrayed brilliantly Restoration Comedies are devoid of emotion but it is very sophisticated in its presentation. Wit and humour are the special features of these comedies.

Restoration Comedy mainly, contains an urban and high polished social atmosphere. Actually, such kind of comedies present a society in its whole. These are not concerned with any individual.

As far as the difference between Comedy of Manners and the Comedy of Humour is concerned, it is mainly in its stagecraft. Prima facie, both these comedies are similar in nature but Comedy of Manner doesn't give much attention to moral value. Another difference between these two comedies is related to its subject matter. Comedy of Manners portrays the superficial aspect of a man or woman but Comedy of Humour deals with the inner traits of an individual.

The most remarkable characteristic of Restoration Comedy is its dialogues. In Restoration Comedy, dialogues appear to be highly satirical and critical, and expose the follies of the people.

Archer, a critic of Restoration Comedy has criticised it on the ground of its exclusiveness. He is of the view that such comedies are very much confined in its approach.

The most interesting criticism of Restoration Comedy has been done by Leight Hunt. He very interestingly comments that in "Restoration Comedies, we could see an assembling of stone-hearted and selfish ladies and gentlemen of high society, who are moving here and there, exchanging witty dialogues and fabricating conspiracies against one another." But, in fact, Restoration Comedy can be regarded as a reflection of its contemporary society; which was full of immoral practices.

To conclude it can easily be maintained that Restoration Comedy is valuable work of art from the historical point of view; because we notice that it is a direct reflection of the age in which it has been written.

As far as William Congreve is concerned, he is undoubtedly, superb. His style of writing Comedy of Manners is exclusive and that is why Dryden has many things to say in his praise. His comic characters appear real and make us thoughtfull. Particularly, Congreve is excellent in his portrayal of his women characters in *The Way of the World*. His women characters are lively and bold; and typical women of the Restoration Age. Although Etherege and Wycherley are other writers who are considered to be noteworthy names in writers of Restoration comedy; but Congreve stands out as the greatest master of the art of Comedy of Manners. Congreve is simply unparalleled in the Portrayal of Restoration Society.

Novel	GULLIVER'S TRAVELS (Book-I & II) -Jonathan Swift

❖ An Introduction to Jonathan Swift:

Jonathan Swift was born in Dublin, Ireland, on November 30, 1667. The son of an English lawyer, he grew up there in the care of his uncle before attending Trinity College at the age of fourteen, where he stayed for seven years, graduating in 1688. In that year, he became the secretary for Sir William Temple, an English politician and member of the Whig party. In 1694, he took religious orders in the Church of Ireland and then spent a year as a country parson. He then spent further time in the service of Temple before returning to Ireland to become the chaplain of the Earl of Berkeley. Meanwhile, he had begun to write satires on the political and religious corruption surrounding him, working on A Tale of a Tub, which supports the position of the Anglican Church against its critics on the left and the right, and The Battle of the Books, which argues for the supremacy of the classics against modern thought and literature. He also wrote a number of political pamphlets in favor of the Whig party. In 1709 he went to London to campaign for the Irish church but was unsuccessful. After some conflicts with the Whig party, mostly because of Swift's strong allegiance to the church, he became a member of the more conservative Tory party in 1710.

Unfortunately for Swift, the Tory government fell out of power in 1714 and Swift, despite his fame for his writings, fell out of favor. Swift, who had been hoping to be assigned a position in the Church of England, instead returned to Dublin. During his brief time in England, Swift had become friends with writers such as Alexander Pope, and during a meeting of their literary club, the Martinus Scriblerus Club, they decided to write satires of modern learning. The "third voyage" described in his best-known work, Gulliver's Travels, is assembled from the work Swift did during this time. However, the final work was not completed until 1726, and the narrative of the third voyage was actually the last one completed. After his return to Ireland, Swift became a staunch supporter of the Irish against English attempts to weaken their economy and political power, writing pamphlets such as the satirical A Modest Proposal, in which he suggests that the Irish problems of famine and overpopulation could be easily solved by having the babies of poor Irish subjects sold as delicacies to feed the rich.

Swift's Ireland was a country that had been effectively controlled by England for nearly 500 years. The Stuarts had established a Protestant governing aristocracy amidst the country's relatively poor Catholic population. Denied union with England in 1707 (when Scotland was granted it), Ireland continued to suffer under English trade restrictions and found the authority of its own Parliament in Dublin severely limited. Swift, though born a member of Ireland's colonial ruling class, came to be known as one of the greatest of Irish patriots. He, however, considered himself more English than Irish, and his loyalty to Ireland was often ambivalent in spite of his staunch support for certain Irish causes. The complicated nature of his own relationship with England may have left him particularly sympathetic to the injustices and exploitation Ireland suffered at the hands of its more powerful neighbor.

Although Swift's disgust with the state of the nation continued to increase, A Modest Proposal was the last of his essays about Ireland. Swift wrote mostly poetry in the later years of his life, and he died in 1745.

❖ An Introduction to *Gulliver's Travels (Bk. I & II)*

Although in its abridged form Gulliver's Travels (1726) is known as a classic children's adventure story, it is actually a biting work of political and social satire by an Anglican priest, historian, and political commentator. Anglo-Irish author Jonathan Swift parodied popular travelogues of his day in creating this story of a sea-loving physician's travels to imaginary foreign lands. Structurally, the book is divided into four separate adventures, or travels, which Dr. Lemuel Gulliver undertakes by accident when his vessel is shipwrecked or taken over by pirates. In these fantastic tales, Swift satirizes the political events in England and Ireland in his day, as well as English values and institutions. He ridicules academics, scientists, and Enlightenment thinkers who value rationalism above all else, and finally, he targets the human condition itself.

Like all of Swift's works, Gulliver's Travels was originally published without Swift's name on it because he feared government persecution. His criticisms of people and institutions are often scathing, and some observers believe he was a misanthrope (one who hates mankind). Other critics have suggested that while Swift criticized humans and their vanity and folly, he believed that people are capable of behaving better than they do and hoped his works would convince people to reconsider their behavior. Swift himself claimed he wrote Gulliver's Travels "to vex the world rather than divert it." He succeeded in that aim, as the book is considered one of the best examples of satire ever written. Swift's sharp observations about the cor-ruption of people and their institutions still ring true today, almost three hundred years after the book was first published.

❖ Historical Background of *Gulliver's Travels (Bk. I & II)* :

England in the 1720s : While Swift was writing Gulliver's Travels in the 1720s, England was undergoing a lot of political shuffling. George I, a Hanoverian prince of Germany, had ascended the British throne in 1714 after the death of Queen Anne ended the Stuart line. Although he was not a bad or repressive king, he was unpopular. King George had gained his throne with the assistance of the Whig party, and his Whig ministers subsequently used their considerable gains in power to oppress members of the opposition Tory party. Swift had been a Tory since 1710, and bitterly resented the Whig actions against his friends, who often faced exile or worse. Understanding how events in Europe and England led to this political rivalry can help the reader of Swift's novel better understand his satire.

The Restoration : The Restoration era began in 1660, a few years before Swift was born. At this time Charles Stuart (King Charles II) became king of England, restoring the Protestant Stuart family to the throne. Charles II supported a strong Church of England, also known as the Anglican Church. He was supported by the Tories, a political party made up mostly of church officials and landowning noblemen. Protestants who did not support the Anglican church teamed with Roman Catholics to form the opposing Whig party. The main source of contention between the parties was the Test Act of 1673, which forced all government employees to receive communion according to the Anglican church's customs. In effect, this prevented non-An-glicans from holding government jobs. Swift himself supported the act, and even switched from Whig to Tory in 1710 because he believed a strong Church of England was necessary to keep the balance of power in the government. Throughout his life, he felt that institutions such as the church and government had to be strong in order to rein in people's tendency toward chaos and sin; he explored this idea in Gulliver's Travels. Over the years, however, Swift came to believe the Tories were as much to blame as the Whigs for engaging in partisan politics, locking horns over minor issues and bringing the government to a stalemate. Whenever one party was in favor with the reigning king and in power in the Parliament, it attacked the other party, exiling and imprisoning the opposition's members. Swift satirized their selfish and petty politics in Part I of Gulliver's Travels, where the Lilliputian heir (who represented George II, the future king of England) has to hobble about with one short heel and one high as a compromise between the two parties that wear different heights of heels.

The Glorious Revolution and War of Spanish Succession : Charles II's brother King James II, a Catholic, came to the British throne in 1685. He immediately repealed the Test Act and began to hire Whigs for his government. The Anglican-dominated Parliament secretly negotiated with William of Orange, the Protestant Dutch husband of James's Protestant daughter Mary, to take over the throne. In December 1688, William did so, and James II fled to France without a fight. This was called the Glorious Revolution because no one was killed in the coup.

Soon after King William III and Queen Mary II came to power, the Catholic Louis XIV of France declared war on Spain over trade and religious issues. William entered the war on the side of Spain, a war the English called William's War. This conflict was satirized by Swift in the war between the Lilliputians (England) and Blefuscudians (England with the Spanish, Dutch, and Germans as allies) was fighting France, it was also warring with Ireland. Irish Catholics wanted freedom from British rule, and England feared that France could invade their country through a sympathetic Ireland. Peace came about in 1697, but England got almost none of the spoils of war—land in Spain. In order to appear strong, William declared war again, this time on the Spanish and the French. This began the War of Spanish Succession.

In 1702 William died and his daughter Queen Anne ascended the throne. The war waged on while at home the Whigs and Tories fought amongst themselves. Many of the Whigs were merchants who were profiting from the war, and they wanted the fighting to continue. The landowning Tories wanted the war to cease, because it devalued their property. Swift helped the Tories in their efforts to stop the war by becoming editor of their newspa-per, the Examiner. His influential writings, along with his friend Bolingbroke's secret negotiations with France, helped end the war in 1713 with the Treaty of Utrecht. Queen Anne seemed ungrateful for these efforts, as she later exiled Bolingbroke and destroyed Swift's chances of a career in the Church of England. Swift was forced to return to Ireland to find a job as an Anglican priest.

Ireland : Catholic Ireland had been dominated by the British since the fifteenth century, because England had always been paranoid about a French or Spanish invasion coming through Catholic Ireland. England's restrictive policies had driven Ireland and its people into poverty, which angered Swift. He was incensed when the scientist Sir Isaac Newton, given the task of overseeing the economics of Ireland, supported a currency law that would further destroy the economy of the Irish. His anonymously written The Drapier's Letters, inspired the Irish people to unite against England and force the law to be repealed. The Irish protected Swift's anonymity, and for his role, Swift is a hero in Ireland to this day.

The Enlightenment : In the midst of all this political back and forth, the optimistic Age of Enlightenment was flourish-ing. Intellectuals, philosophers, and scientists such as John Locke, Francis Bacon, and Isaac Newton were opening the doors to exploration in many fields, asking new questions, and experimenting. They discarded the old idea that man is by nature sinful because of Adam and Eve's fall from grace in the Garden of Eden. Man's ability to reason, they claimed, could save him from his tendency to sin. Man could create a utopia, or perfect society, that solved the problems of humankind. Swift vehemently disagreed. He felt that reason could just as easily be misused for foolish or selfish purposes as good ones, and man could never rise above the tendency toward sin to be able to create utopia on earth. His satire of the folly of Enlightenment scientific and theological musings and experiments in Part III of Gulliver's Travels is followed by his portrayal of a utopian society, the Houyhnhnm's, into which man can never fit.

❖ The Story of *Gulliver's Travels (Bk. I & II)*

BOOK-I

When the ship Gulliver is traveling on is destroyed in a storm, Gulliver ends up on the island of Lilliput, where he awakes to find that he has been captured by Lilliputians, very small people — approximately six inches in height. Gulliver is treated with compassion and concern. In turn, he helps them solve some of their problems, especially their conflict with their enemy, Blefuscu, an island across the bay from them. Gulliver falls from favor, however, because he refuses to support the Emperor's desire to enslave the Blefuscudians and because he "makes water" to put out a palace fire. Gulliver flees to Blefuscu, where he converts a large war ship to his own use and sets sail from Blefuscu eventually to be rescued at sea by an English merchant ship and returned to his home in England.

BOOK-II

As he travels as a ship's surgeon, Gulliver and a small crew are sent to find water on an island. Instead they encounter a land of giants. As the crew flees, Gulliver is left behind and captured. Gulliver's captor, a farmer, takes him to the farmer's home where Gulliver is treated kindly, but, of course, curiously.

The farmer assigns his daughter, Glumdalclitch, to be Gulliver's keeper, and she cares for Gulliver with great compassion. The farmer takes Gulliver on tour across the countryside, displaying him to onlookers. Eventually, the farmer sells Gulliver to the Queen. At court, Gulliver meets the King, and the two spend many sessions discussing the customs and behaviors of Gulliver's country. In many cases, the King is shocked and chagrined by the selfishness and pettiness that he hears Gulliver describe. Gulliver, on the other hand, defends England. Gulliver tries to maintain his dignity with little success. He offers to help the Brobdingnagian king strengthen his power by using gunpowder and is puzzled by the king's disgust, concluding that, though the Brobdingnagians are a good-hearted people, they are just not as sophisticated as humans. One day, the box Gulliver is carried around in for outings gets snatched up by a bird on the beach and, dumped in the sea, he is picked up by a human ship and carried back to England. Back among humans, Gulliver is astonished by their littleness.

❖ A Detailed Actwise Summary of *Gulliver's Travels (Bk. I & II)* :

BOOK-I

The novel begins with Lemuel Gulliver recounting the story of his life, beginning with his family history. He is born to a family in Nottinghamshire, the third of five sons. Although he studies at Cambridge as a teenager, his family is too poor to keep him there, so he is sent to London to be a surgeon's apprentice. There, under a man named James Bates, he learns mathematics and navigation with the hope of traveling. When his apprenticeship ends, he studies physics at Leyden.

He then becomes a surgeon aboard a ship called the Swallow for three years. Afterward, he settles in London, working as a doctor, and marries a woman named Mary Burton. His business begins to fail when his patron dies, so he decides to go to sea again and travels for six years. Although he has planned to return home at the end of this time. he decides to accept one last job on a ship called the Antelope.

In the East Indies, the Antelope encounters a violent storm in which twelve crewmen die. Six of the crewmembers, including Gulliver, board a small rowboat to escape. Soon the rowboat capsizes, and Gulliver loses track of his companions. They are never seen again. Gulliver, however, swims safely to shore.

Gulliver lies down on the grass to rest, and soon he falls asleep. When he wakes up, he finds that his arms, legs, and long hair have been tied to the ground with pieces of thread. He can only look up, and the bright sun prevents him from seeing anything. He feels something move across his leg and over his chest. He looks down and sees, to his surprise, a six-inch-tall human carrying a bow and arrow. At least forty more little people climb onto his body. He is surprised and shouts loudly, frightening the little people away. They return, however, and one of the little men cries out, "Hekinah Degul."

Gulliver struggles to get loose and finally succeeds in breaking the strings binding his left arm. He loosens the ropes tying his hair so he can turn to the left. In response, the little people fire a volley of arrows into his hand and violently attack his body and face. He decides that the safest thing to do is to lie still until nightfall.

The noise increases as the little people build a stage next to Gulliver about a foot and a half off the ground. One of them climbs onto it and makes a speech in a language that Gulliver does not understand.

Gulliver indicates that he is hungry, and the little people bring him baskets of meat. He devours it all and then shows that he is thirsty, so they bring him two large barrels of wine. Gulliver is tempted to pick up forty or fifty of the little people and throw them against the ground, but he decides that he has made them a promise of goodwill and is grateful for their hospitality. He is also struck by their bravery, since they climb onto his body despite his great size.

An official climbs onto Gulliver's body and tells him that he is to be carried to the capital city. Gulliver wants to walk, but they tell him that that will not be permitted. Instead, they bring a frame of wood raised three inches off the ground and carried by twenty-two wheels. Nine hundred men pull this cart about half a mile to the city. Gulliver's left leg is then padlocked to a large temple, giving him only enough freedom to walk around the building in a semicircle and lie down inside the temple.

Gulliver's narrative begins much like other travel records of his time. The description of his youth and education provides background knowledge, establishes Gulliver's position in English society, and causes the novel to resemble true-life accounts of travels at sea published during Swift's lifetime. Swift imitates the style of a standard travelogue throughout the novel to heighten the satire. Here he creates a set of expectations in our minds, namely a short-lived belief in the truth of Gulliver's observations. Later in the novel, Swift uses the style of the travelogue to exaggerate the absurdity of the people and places with which Gulliver comes into contact. A fantastical style—one that made no attempt to seem truthful, accurate, or traditional—would have weakened the satire by making it irrelevant, but the factual, reportorial style of Gulliver's Travels does the opposite.

Gulliver is surprised to discover the Lilliputians but is not particularly shocked. This encounter is only the first of many in the novel in which we are asked to accept Gulliver's extraordinary experiences as merely unusual. Seeing the world through Gulliver's eyes, we also adopt, for a moment, Gulliver's view of the world. But at the same time, we can step back and recognize that the Lilliputians are nothing but a figment of Swift's imagination. The distance between these two stances—the gullible Gulliver and the skeptical reader—is where the narrative's multiple levels of meaning are created: on one level, we have a true-life story of adventure; on another, a purely fictional fairy tale; and on a third level, transcending the first two and closest to Swift's original intention, a satirical critique of European pretensions to rationality and goodwill.

Swift wrote Gulliver's Travels at a time when Europe was the world's dominant power, and when England, despite its small size, was rising in power on the basis of its formidable fleet. England's growing military and economic power brought it into contact with a wide variety of new animals, plants, places, and things, but the most significant change wrought by European expansion was the encounter with previously unknown people—like the inhabitants of the Americas—with radically different modes of existence. The miniature stature of the Lilliputians can be interpreted as a physical incarnation of exactly these kinds of cultural differences.

The choice of physical size as the way of manifesting cultural differences has a number of important consequences. The main consequence is the radical difference in power between Gulliver and the Lilliputian nation. His physical size and strength put Gulliver in a unique position within Lilliputian society and give him obligations and capabilities far beyond those of the people who keep him prisoner. Despite Gulliver's fear of the Lilliputians' arrows, there is an element of condescension in his willingness to be held prisoner by them. The power differential may represent England's position with respect to the people it was in the process of colonizing. It may also be a way for Swift to reveal the importance of might in a society supposedly guided by right. Finally, it may be a way of destabilizing humanity's position at the center of the universe by demonstrating that size, power, and significance are all relative. Although the Lilliputians are almost pitifully small in Gulliver's eyes, they are unwilling to see themselves that way; rather, they think of themselves as normal and of Gulliver as a freakish giant. That Gulliver may himself be the Lilliputian to some other nation's Englishman—a notion elaborated fully in Part II—is already implied in the first chapter.

Summary of Chapter II

Once the Lilliputians chain Gulliver to the building, he is finally allowed to stand up and view the entire countryside, which he discovers is beautiful and rustic. The tallest trees are seven feet tall, and the whole area looks to him like a theater set.

Gulliver meticulously describes his process of relieving himself, which initially involves walking inside the building to the edge of his chain. After the first time, he makes sure to relieve himself in open air, and servants carry away his excrement in wheelbarrows. He says that he describes this process in order to establish his cleanliness, which has been called into question by his critics.

The emperor visits on horseback from his tower. He orders his servants to give Gulliver food and drink. The emperor is dressed plainly and carries a sword to defend himself. He and Gulliver converse, though they cannot understand each other. Gulliver tries to speak every language he knows, but nothing works. After two hours, Gulliver is left with a group of soldiers guarding him. Some of them, disobeying orders, try to shoot arrows at him. As a punishment, the brigadier ties up six of these offenders and places them in Gulliver's hand. Gulliver puts five of them into his pocket and pretends that he is going to eat the sixth, but then cuts loose his ropes and sets him free. He does the same with the other five, which pleases the court.

After two weeks, a bed is made for Gulliver. It consists of 600 small beds sewn together. News of his arrival also spreads throughout the kingdom and curious people from the villages come to see him. Meanwhile, the government tries to decide what to do with him. Frequent councils bring up various concerns: that he will break loose, for instance, or that he will eat enough to cause a famine. Some suggest that they starve him or shoot him in the face to kill him, but others argue that doing so would leave them with a giant corpse and a large health risk.

Officers who witnessed Gulliver's lenient treatment of the six offending soldiers report to the council, and the emperor and his court decide to respond with kindness. They arrange to deliver large amounts of food to Gulliver every morning, supply him with servants to wait on him, hire tailors to make him clothing, and offer teachers to instruct him in their language.

Every morning Gulliver asks the emperor to set him free, but the emperor refuses, saying that Gulliver must be patient. The emperor also orders him to be searched to ensure that he does not have any weapons. Gulliver agrees to this search, and the Lilliputians take an inventory of his possessions. In the process, all of his weapons are taken away.

Summary of Chapter III

Gulliver hopes to be set free, as he is getting along well with the Lilliputians and earning their trust. The emperor decides to entertain him with shows, including a performance by Rope-Dancers, who are Lilliputians seeking employment in the government. For the performance, which doubles as a sort of competitive entrance examination, the candidates dance on "ropes"—slender threads suspended two feet above the ground. When a vacancy occurs, candidates petition the emperor to entertain him with a dance, and whoever jumps the highest earns the office. The current ministers continue this practice as well, in order to show that they have not lost their skill.

As another diversion for Gulliver, the emperor lays three silken threads of different colors on a table. He then holds out a stick, and candidates are asked to leap over it or creep under it. Whoever shows the most dexterity wins one of the ribbons.

Gulliver builds a platform from sticks and his handkerchief and invites horsemen to exercise upon it. The emperor greatly enjoys watching this new entertainment, but it is cut short when a horse steps through the handkerchief, after which Gulliver decides that it is too dangerous for them to keep riding on the cloth.

Some Lilliputians discover Gulliver's hat, which washed ashore after him, and he asks them to bring it back. Soon after, the emperor asks Gulliver to pose like a colossus, or giant statue, so that his troops might march under Gulliver.

Gulliver's petitions for freedom are finally answered. Gulliver must swear to obey the articles put forth, which include stipulations that he must assist the Lilliputians in times of war, survey the land around them, help with construction, and deliver urgent messages. Gulliver agrees and his chains are removed.

In these chapters, Gulliver learns more about Lilliputian culture, and the great difference in size between him and the Lilliputians is emphasized by a number of examples, many of which are explicit satires of British government. For instance, Lilliputian government officials are chosen by their skill at rope-dancing, which the Lilliputians see as relevant but which Gulliver recognizes as arbitrary and ridiculous. The would-be officials are almost literally forced to jump through hoops in order to qualify for their positions. Clearly, Swift intends for us to understand this episode as a satire of England's system of political appointments and to infer that England's system is similarly arbitrary. Gulliver, however, never suggests that he finds the Lilliputians ridiculous. Throughout the entire novel, Gulliver tends to be very sympathetic in his descriptions of the cultures he visits, never criticizing them or finding anything funny, no matter how ludicrous certain customs seem to us. Nor does Gulliver point out the similarities between the ridiculous practices he observes in his travels and the ridiculous customs of Europe. Instead, Swift leaves us to infer all of the satire based on the difference between how things appear to us and how they appear to Gulliver.

The difference in size between Gulliver and the Lilliputians helps to emphasize the importance of physical power, a theme that recurs throughout the novel. Over time, Gulliver begins to earn the Lilliputians' trust, but it is clearly unnecessary: for all their threats, Gulliver could crush the Lilliputians by simply walking carelessly. The humor comes from the Lilliputians' view of the situation: despite the evidence before their eyes, they never realize their own insignificance. They keep Gulliver tied up, believing that they can control him, while in truth he could destroy them effortlessly. In this way, Swift satirizes humanity's pretensions to power and significance.

In these chapters, Swift plays with language in a way that again pokes fun at humanity's belief in its own importance. When the Lilliputians draw up an inventory of Gulliver's possessions, the whole endeavor is treated as if it were a serious matter of state. The contrast between the tone of the inventory, which is given in the Lilliputians' own words, and the utter triviality of the possessions that are being inventoried, serves as a mockery of people who take themselves too seriously. Similarly, the articles that Gulliver is forced to sign in order to gain his freedom are couched in formal, self-important language. But the document is nothing but a meaningless and self-contradictory piece of paper: each article emphasizes the fact that Gulliver is so powerful that, if he so desires, he could violate all of the articles without much concern for his own safety.

Summary of Chapter IV

After regaining his freedom, Gulliver goes to Mildendo, the capital city of the Lilliputians. The residents are told to stay indoors, and they all sit on their roofs and in their garret windows to see him. The town is 500 feet square with a wall surrounding it, and can hold 500,000 people. The emperor wants Gulliver to see the magnificence of his palace, which is at the center of the city, so Gulliver cuts down trees to make himself a stool, which he carries around with him so that he can sit down and see things from a shorter distance than a standing position allows.

About two weeks after Gulliver obtains his liberty, a government official, Reldresal, comes to see him. He tells Gulliver that two forces, one rebel group and one foreign empire, threaten the kingdom. The rebel group exists because the kingdom is divided into two factions, called Tramecksan and Slamecksan. The people in the two factions are distinguished by the heights of their heels.

Reldresal tells Gulliver that the current emperor has chosen to employ primarily the low-heeled Slamecksan in his administration. He adds that the emperor himself has lower heels than all of his officials but that his heir has one heel higher than the other, which makes him walk unevenly. At the same time, the Lilliputians fear an invasion from the Island of Blefuscu, which Reldresal calls the "Other Great Empire of the Universe." He adds that the philosophers of Lilliput do not believe Gulliver's claim that there are other countries in the world inhabited by other people of his size, preferring to think that Gulliver dropped from the moon or a star.

Reldresal describes the history of the two nations. The conflict between them, he tells Gulliver, began years ago, when the emperor's grandfather, then in command of the country, commanded all Lilliputians to break their eggs on the small end first. He made this decision after breaking an egg in the old way, large end first, and cutting his finger. The people resented the law, and six rebellions were started in protest. The monarchs of Blefuscu fueled these rebellions, and when they were over the rebels fled to that country to seek refuge. Eleven thousand people chose death rather than submit to the law. Many books were written on the controversy, but books written by the Big-Endians were banned in Lilliput. The government of Blefuscu accused the Lilliputians of disobeying their religious doctrine, the Brundrecral, by breaking their eggs at the small end. The Lilliputians argued that the doctrine reads, "That all true believers shall break their eggs at the convenient end," which could be interpreted as the small end.

Reldresal continues that the exiles gained support in Blefuscu to launch a war against Lilliput and were aided by rebel forces inside Lilliput. A war has been raging between the two nations ever since, and Gulliver is asked to help defend Lilliput against its enemies. Gulliver does not feel that it is appropriate to intervene, but he nonetheless offers his services to the emperor.

Summary of Chapter V

Gulliver spies on the empire of Blefuscu and devises a plan. He asks for cables and bars of iron, out of which he makes hooks with cables attached. He then wades and swims the channel to Blefuscu and catches their ships at port. The people are so frightened that they leap out of their ships and swim to shore. Gulliver attaches a hook to each ship and ties them together. The Blefuscu soldiers fire arrows at him, but he keeps working, protecting his eyes by putting on the spectacles he keeps in his coat pocket. He tries to pull the ships away, but they are anchored too tightly, so he cuts them away with his pocketknife and pulls the ships back to Lilliput.

In Lilliput, Gulliver is greeted as a hero. The emperor asks him to go back to retrieve the other ships, intending to destroy Blefuscu's military strength and make it a province in his empire. Gulliver dissuades him from this action, saying that he does not want to encourage slavery or injustice. This position causes great disagreement in the government, with some officials turning staunchly against Gulliver and calling for his destruction.

Three weeks later, a delegation arrives from Blefuscu, and the war ends with Blefuscu's surrender. The Blefuscu delegates are privately told of Gulliver's kindness toward the Lilliputians, and they ask him to visit their kingdom. He wishes to do so, and the emperor reluctantly allows it.

As a Nardac, or person of high rank, Gulliver no longer has to perform all the duties laid down in his contract. He does, however, have the opportunity to help the Lilliputians when the emperor's wife's room catches fire. He forgets his coat and cannot put the flames out with his clothing, so instead he thinks of a new plan: he urinates on the palace, putting out the fire entirely. He worries afterward that since the act of public urination is a crime in Lilliput he will be prosecuted, but the emperor tells him he will be pardoned. He is told, however, that the emperor's wife can no longer tolerate living in her rescued quarters.

Despite the fact that the history of the conflict between Lilliput and Blefuscu is blatantly ridiculous, Gulliver reports it with complete seriousness. The more serious the tone, the more laughable this conflict appears. But Swift expects us to understand immediately that the entire history Gulliver relates parallels European history exactly, down to the smallest details. The High-Heels and the Low-Heels correspond to the Whigs and Tories of English politics. Lilliput and Blefuscu represent England and France. The violent conflict between Big-Endians and Little-Endians represents the Protestant Reformation and the centuries of warfare between Catholics and Protestants.

By recasting European history as a series of brutal wars over meaningless and arbitrary disagreements, Swift implies that the differences between Protestants and Catholics, between Whigs and Tories, and between France and England are as silly and meaningless as how a person chooses to crack an egg. Once we make this connection, though, we face the question of why Swift thinks that these conflicts are trivial and irrelevant. After all, religion, politics, and national identity would have been considered the most important issues in Swift's time, and we continue to think of these things as important today. The answer to this question is less obvious, and the text does not give us a simple explanation. The debate between the Big-Endians and Little-Endians does provide some clues, however. The egg controversy is ridiculous because there cannot be any right or wrong way to crack an egg, so it is unreasonable to legislate how people must do it. Similarly, we may conclude that there is no right or wrong way to worship God—at least, there is no way to prove that one way is right and another way is wrong. Moreover, the Big-Endians and Little-Endians both share the same religious text, but they disagree on how to interpret a passage that can clearly be interpreted two ways. Similarly, Swift is suggesting that the Christian Bible can be interpreted in more than one way, and that it is ridiculous for people to fight over how to interpret it when no one can really be certain that one interpretation is right and others are wrong.

The text contains a number of allusions to events in Swift's life and to the politics of Europe. For instance, it has been suggested that the empress represents Queen Anne of England, Gulliver's urination on her quarters represents Swift's work A Tale of a Tub, and the empress's disgust at Gulliver's urination is analogous to Queen Anne's criticism of Swift's work and her attempts to limit his prospects in the Church of England. Within the story, Gulliver's urination on the palace is not merely an offense to the Lilliputians' sense of decency, it is also a suggestion of their insignificance, to which they respond indignantly. Although Gulliver's urination is intended to prevent a disaster, it is also an assertion of his ability to control the Lilliputians—even by the most profane of actions. The episode illustrates again the importance of physical power, which can turn a normally insignificant and vulgar action into a lifesaving act.

Gulliver's refusal to obey the emperor's orders to destroy the fleet of Blefuscu is a sign that he feels some responsibility toward all beings. However small, the inhabitants of Blefuscu still have rights, one of which is freedom from tyranny. Granted almost godlike power by his unusual size, Gulliver finds himself in a position to change the Lilliputians' society forever.

Summary of Chapter VI

Gulliver describes the general customs and practices of Lilliput in more detail, beginning by explaining that everything in Lilliput— their animals, trees, and plants—is sized in proportion to the Lilliputians. Their eyesight is also adapted to their scale: Gulliver cannot see as clearly close-up as they can, while they cannot see as far as he can.

The Lilliputians are well educated, but their writing system is odd to Gulliver, who jokes that they write not left to right like the Europeans or top to bottom like the Chinese, but from one corner of the page to the other, "like the ladies in England."

The dead are buried with their heads pointing directly downward, because the Lilliputians believe that eventually the dead will rise again and that the Earth, which they think is flat, will turn upside down. Gulliver adds that the better-educated Lilliputians no longer believe in this custom.

Gulliver describes some of the other laws of Lilliput, such as a tradition by which anyone who falsely accuses someone else of a crime against the state is put to death. Deceit is considered worse than theft, because honest people are more vulnerable to liars than to thieves, since commerce requires people to trust one another. The law provides not only for punishment but also for rewards of special titles and privileges for good behavior.

Children are raised not by individual parents but by the kingdom as a whole. They are sent to live in schools at a very young age. The schools are chosen according to the station of their parents, whom they see only twice a year. Only the laborers' children stay home, since their job is to farm. There are no beggars at all, since the poor are well looked after.

Summary of Chapter VII

Gulliver goes on to describe the "intrigue" that precipitates his departure from Lilliput. While he prepares to make his trip to Blefuscu, a court official tells Gulliver that he has been charged with treason by enemies in the government. He shows Gulliver the document calling for his execution: Gulliver is charged with public urination, refusing to obey the emperor's orders to seize the remaining Blefuscu ships, aiding enemy ambassadors, and traveling to Blefuscu.

Gulliver is told that Reldresal has asked for his sentence to be reduced, calling not for execution but for putting his eyes out. This punishment has been agreed upon, along with a plan to starve him to death slowly. The official tells Gulliver that the operation to blind him will take place in three days. Fearing this resolution, Gulliver crosses the channel and arrives in Blefuscu.

Summary of Chapter VIII

Three days later, he sees a boat of normal size—that is, big enough to carry him—overturned in the water. He asks the emperor of Blefuscu to help him fix it. At the same time, the emperor of Lilliput sends an envoy with the articles commanding Gulliver to give up his eyesight. The emperor of Blefuscu sends it back with the message that Gulliver will soon be leaving both their kingdoms. After about a month, the boat is ready and Gulliver sets sail. He arrives safely back in England, where he makes a good profit showing miniature farm animals that he carried away from Blefuscu in his pockets.

Throughout much of Part I, Swift satirizes European practices by implicitly comparing them to outrageous Lilliputian customs. In Chapter VI, however, Gulliver describes a number of unusual Lilliputian customs that he presents as reasonable and sensible. This chapter, which describes improvements that could be made in European society, is less satirical and ironic than the previous chapters. We may infer that Swift approves of many of these institutions. Clearly, there is a good case to be made for treating fraud as a more serious crime than theft and for making false testimony a capital crime. The very fabric of society depends upon trust, so dishonesty may be even more damaging than theft and violence.

In general, the customs of Lilliput that Swift presents as good are those that contribute to the good of the community or the nation as opposed to those that promote individual rights or freedoms. Ingratitude is punishable by death, for instance, because anybody who would treat a benefactor badly must be an enemy to all mankind. Children are raised by the community rather than by their parents because parents are thinking only of their own appetites when they conceive children. Children are raised in public nurseries, but parents are financially penalized if they burden society by bringing children for whom they cannot pay into the world.

Gulliver's analysis of Lilliputian customs also serves to illuminate the arbitrary nature of such practices, as well as the fact that societies tend to assume, nonetheless, that certain customs are simply natural. The Lilliputians do not question their cultural norms because they have no reason to believe that there is any other way to conduct affairs. When alternatives are discussed, as in the case of the egg-breaking controversy, the discussion ends in violent conflict.

The articles of accusation against Gulliver, like the inventory of his possessions and the articles of his freedom in the previous chapters, are written in formal language that serves only to emphasize their absurdity. Swift makes a mockery of formal language by showing how it can be used to mask simple fears and desires, such as the Lilliputians' desire to eliminate the threat that Gulliver poses. The help that Gulliver gets from Reldresal is an illustration of a persistent motif in Gulliver's Travels: the good person surrounded by a corrupt society.

Book-II

Summary of Chapter I :

Two months after returning to England, Gulliver is restless again. He sets sail on a ship called the Adventure, traveling to the Cape of Good Hope and Madagascar before encountering a monsoon that draws the ship off course. The ship eventually arrives at an unknown land mass. There are no inhabitants about, and the landscape is barren and rocky. Gulliver is walking back to the boat when he sees that it has already left without him. He tries to chase after it, but then he sees that a giant is following the boat. Gulliver runs away, and when he stops, he is on a steep hill from which he can see the countryside. He is shocked to see that the grass is about twenty feet high.

He walks down what looks like a high road but turns out to be a footpath through a field of barley. He walks for a long time but cannot see anything beyond the stalks of corn, which are forty feet high. He tries to climb a set of steps into the next field, but he cannot mount them because they are too high. As he is trying to climb up the stairs, he sees another one of the island's giant inhabitants. He hides from the giant, but it calls for more people to come, and they begin to harvest the crop with scythes. Gulliver lies down and bemoans his state, thinking about how insignificant he must be to these giant creatures.

One of the servants comes close to Gulliver with both his foot and his scythe, so Gulliver screams as loudly as he can. The giant finally notices him, and picks him up between his fingers to get a closer look. Gulliver tries to speak to him in plaintive tones, bringing his hands together, and the giant seems pleased. Gulliver makes it clear that the giant's fingers are hurting him, and the giant places him in his pocket and begins to walk toward his master.

The giant's master, the farmer of these fields, takes Gulliver from his servant and observes him more closely. He asks the other servants if they have ever seen anything like Gulliver, then places him onto the ground. They sit around him in a circle. Gulliver kneels down and begins to speak as loudly as he can, taking off his hat and bowing to the farmer. He presents a purse full of gold to the farmer, which the farmer takes into his palm. He cannot figure out what it is, even after Gulliver empties the coins into his hand.

The farmer takes Gulliver back to his wife, who is frightened of him. The servant brings in dinner, and they all sit down to eat, Gulliver sitting on the table not far from the farmer's plate. They give him tiny bits of their food, and he pulls out his knife and fork to eat, which delights the giants. The farmer's son picks Gulliver up and scares him, but the farmer takes Gulliver from the boy's hands and strikes his son. Gulliver makes a sign that the boy should be forgiven, and kisses his hand. After dinner, the farmer's wife lets Gulliver nap in her own bed. When he wakes up he finds two rats attacking him, and he defends himself with his "hanger," or sword.

Summary of Chapter II

The farmer's nine-year-old daughter, whom Gulliver calls Glumdalclitch, or "nursemaid," has a doll's cradle that becomes Gulliver's permanent bed. Glumdalclitch places the cradle inside a drawer to keep Gulliver safe from the rats. She becomes Gulliver's caretaker and guardian, sewing clothes for him and teaching him the giants' language.

The farmer begins to talk about Gulliver in town, and a friend of the farmer's comes to see him. He looks at Gulliver through his glasses, and Gulliver begins to laugh at the sight of the man's eyes through the glass. The man becomes angry and advises the farmer to take Gulliver into the market to display him. He agrees, and

Gulliver is taken to town in a carriage, which he finds very uncomfortable. There, he is placed on a table while Glumdalclitch sits down on a stool beside him, with thirty people at a time walking through as he performs "tricks."

Gulliver is exhausted by the journey to the marketplace, but upon returning to the farmer's house, he finds that he is to be shown there as well. People come from miles around and are charged great sums to view him. Thinking that Gulliver can make him a great fortune, the farmer takes him and Glumdalclitch on a trip to the largest cities.

The three arrive in the largest city, Lorbrulgrud, and the farmer rents a room with a table for displaying Gulliver. By now, Gulliver can understand their language and speak it fairly well. He is shown ten times a day and pleases the visitors greatly.

In Gulliver's adventure in Brobdingnag, many of the same issues that are brought up in the Lilliputian adventure are now brought up again, but this time Gulliver is in the exact opposite situation. Many of the jokes from Gulliver's adventure in Lilliput are played in reverse: instead of worrying about trampling on the Lilliputians, Gulliver is now at risk of being trampled upon; instead of being feared and admired for his gargantuan size, he is treated as a miniscule and insignificant curiosity; instead of displaying miniature livestock in England to make money, he is put on display for money by the farmer. As a whole, the second voyage serves to emphasize the importance of size and the relativity of human culture.

Gulliver's initial experiences with the Brobdingnagians are not positive. First they almost trample him, then the farmer virtually enslaves him, forcing him to perform tricks for paying spectators. This enslavement emphasizes the fundamental humanity of the Brobdingnagians—just like Europeans, they are happy to make a quick buck when the opportunity arises—and also makes concrete Gulliver's lowly status. Whereas in Lilliput, his size gives him almost godlike powers, allowing him to become a hero and a Nardac to the Lilliputian people, in Brobdingnag his different size has exactly the opposite effect. Even his small acts of heroism, like his battle against the rats, are seen by the Brobdingnagians as, at best, "tricks."

Swift continues to play with language in a way that both emphasizes his main satirical points about politics, ethics, and culture and makes fun of language itself. In the first few pages of this section, while Gulliver is still at sea, he describes in complicated naval jargon the various attempts his ship makes to deal with an oncoming storm. The rush of words is nearly incomprehensible, and it is meant to be so—the point is to satirize the jargon used by writers of travel books and sailing accounts, which in Swift's view was often overblown and ridiculous. By taking the tendency to use jargon to an extreme and putting it in the mouth of the gullible and straightforward Gulliver, Swift makes a mockery of those who would try to demonstrate their expertise through convoluted language. Attacks like this one, which are repeated elsewhere in the novel, are part of Swift's larger mission: to criticize the validity of various kinds of expert knowledge that are more showy than helpful, whether legal, naval, or, as in the third voyage, scientific.

Summary of Chapter III

The strain of traveling and performing "tricks" takes its toll on Gulliver, and he begins to grow very thin. The farmer notices Gulliver's condition and resolves to make as much money as possible before Gulliver dies. Meanwhile, an order comes from the court, commanding the farmer to bring Gulliver to the queen for her entertainment.

The queen is delighted with Gulliver's behavior and buys him from the farmer for 1,000 gold pieces. Gulliver requests that Glumdalclitch be allowed to live in the palace as well. Gulliver explains his suffering to the queen, and she is impressed by his intelligence. She takes him to the king, who at first thinks he is a mechanical creation. He sends for great scholars to observe Gulliver, and they decide that he is unfit for survival, since there is no way he could feed himself. Gulliver tries to explain that he comes from a country in which everything is in proportion to himself, but they do not seem to believe him.

Glumdalclitch is given an apartment in the palace and a governess to teach her, and special quarters are built for Gulliver out of a box. They also have clothes made for him from fine silk, but Gulliver finds them very cumbersome. The queen grows quite accustomed to his company, finding him very entertaining at dinner, especially when he cuts and eats his meat. He finds her way of eating repulsive, since her size allows her to swallow huge amounts of food in a single gulp.

The king converses with Gulliver on issues of politics, and laughs at his descriptions of the goings-on in Europe. He finds it amusing that people of such small stature should think themselves so important, and Gulliver is at first offended. He then comes to realize that he too has begun to think of his world as ridiculous.

The queen's dwarf is not happy with Gulliver, since he is used to being the smallest person in the palace and a source of diversion for the royal court. He drops Gulliver into a bowl of cream, but Gulliver is able to swim to safety and the dwarf is punished. At another point, the dwarf sticks Gulliver into a marrowbone, where he is forced to remain until someone pulls him out.

Summary of Chapter IV

Gulliver describes the geography of Brobdingnag, noting first that since the land stretches out about 6,000 miles there must be a severe error in European maps. The kingdom is bounded on one side by mountains and on the other three sides by the sea. The water is so rough that there is no trade with other nations. The rivers are well stocked with giant fish, but the fish in the sea are of the same size as those in the rest of the world—and therefore not worth catching.

Gulliver is carried around the city in a special traveling-box, and people always crowd around to see him. He asks to see the largest temple in the country and is not overwhelmed by its size, since at a height of 3,000 feet it is proportionally smaller than the largest steeple in England.

Summary of Chapter V

Gulliver is happy in Brobdingnag except for the many mishaps that befall him because of his diminutive size. In one unpleasant incident, the dwarf, angry at Gulliver for teasing him, shakes an apple tree over his head. One of the apples strikes Gulliver in the back and knocks him over. Another time, he is left outside during a hailstorm and is so bruised and battered that he cannot leave the house for ten days.

Gulliver and his nursemaid are often invited to the apartments of the ladies of the court, and there he is treated as a plaything of little significance. They enjoy stripping his clothes and placing him in their bosoms, and he is appalled by their strong smell, noting that a Lilliputian told him that he smelled quite repulsive to them. The women also strip their own clothes in front of him, and he finds their skin extremely ugly and uneven.

The queen orders a special boat to be built for Gulliver. The boat is placed in a cistern, and Gulliver rows in it for his own enjoyment and for the amusement of the queen and her court.

Yet another danger arises in the form of a monkey, which takes Gulliver up a ladder, holding him like a baby and force-feeding him. He is rescued from the monkey, and Glumdalclitch pries the food from his mouth with a needle, after which Gulliver vomits. He is so weak and bruised that he stays in bed for two weeks. The monkey is killed and orders are sent out that no other monkeys be kept in the palace.

Gulliver's continued adventures in Brobdingnag serve to illustrate the importance of physical size. Reduced to a twelfth of the size of the people who surround him, Gulliver finds all of his pride and importance withering away. Without physical power to back him up—whether the normal level that he experiences in England or the extraordinary level of his time in Lilliput—it is impossible for Gulliver to maintain the illusion of his own importance.

These chapters contain, in addition to the continuing satire of European culture, some of the most entertaining portions of the novel. Gulliver is treated like a doll, tormented by the court dwarf, and adopted, briefly, by a monkey. For the most part, these scenes serve to hammer home the image of Gulliver's miniscule size as compared to the Brobdingnagians, but they also achieve several more significant accomplishments. The conflict with the dwarf is a good example of such a point. The dwarf, unable to gain the power that generally accompanies great physical size, has tried to make a place for himself in society by capitalizing instead on the distinctive lack of power that accompanies his tiny size. When Gulliver enters the court, he challenges the dwarf's distinctiveness, and the dwarf responds aggressively. If there is a moral to the episode, it is that the politics of those who attempt to achieve power not through physical strength but through their distinctiveness can be just as immoral as the mainstream.

Another key episode takes place with Gulliver's visit to the ladies of the court. The fantasy of domination and submission—realized when Gulliver becomes the sexual plaything of the ladies—is overshadowed by his outright disgust at their smell and appearance. He knows, theoretically, that if he were their size they would be just as attractive as the well-pampered court ladies of England, but since he is not, their flaws are literally magnified, and they appear to him malodorous, blemished, and crude. Swift's point is that anything, even the smoothest skin or the most appealing political system, has imperfections, and these imperfections are bound to be exposed under close enough scrutiny. In a sense, what looks perfect to us is not actually perfect—it is simply not imperfect enough for our limited senses to notice.

At the time that Swift was writing Gulliver's Travels, however, technology that could accentuate these imperfect senses was burgeoning, and Gulliver's microscopic view of flies and flesh may be a reference to the relatively recent discovery of the microscope. The late seventeenth century saw the first publication of books containing magnified images illustrating that various items—fleas, hair, skin—contained details and flaws that had previously been hidden. Gulliver lives this microscopic experience directly. In a magnified world, everything takes on new levels of complexity and imperfection, demonstrating that the truth about objects is heavily influenced by the observer's perspective.

Summary of Chapter VI

Gulliver makes himself a comb from the stumps of hair left after the king has been shaved. He also collects hairs from the king and uses them to weave the backs of two small chairs, which he gives to the queen as curiosities. Gulliver is brought to a musical performance, but it is so loud that he can hardly make it out. Gulliver decides to play the spinet for the royal family, but must contrive a novel way to do it, since the instrument is so big. He uses large sticks and runs over the keyboard with them, but he can still strike only sixteen keys.

Thinking that the king has unjustly come to regard England as insignificant and laughable, Gulliver tries to tell him more about England, describing the government and culture there. The king asks many questions and is particularly struck by the violence of the history Gulliver describes. He then takes Gulliver into his hand and, explaining that he finds the world that Gulliver describes to be ridiculous, contemptuous, and strange, tells him that he concludes that most Englishmen sound like "odious Vermin."

Summary of Chapter VII

Gulliver is disturbed by the king's evaluation of England. He tries to tell him about gunpowder, describing it as a great invention and offering it to the king as a gesture of friendship. The king is appalled by the proposal, and Gulliver is taken aback, thinking that the king has refused a great opportunity. He thinks that the king is unnecessarily scrupulous and narrow-minded for not being more open to the inventions of Gulliver's world.

Gulliver finds the people of Brobdingnag in general to be ignorant and poorly educated. Their laws are not allowed to exceed in words the number of letters in their alphabet, and no arguments may be written about them. They know the art of printing but do not have many books, and their writing is simple and straightforward. One text describes the insignificance and weakness of Brobdingnagians and even argues that at one point they must have been much larger.

Summary of Chapter VIII

Gulliver wants to recover his freedom. The king orders any small ship to be brought to the city, hoping that they might find a woman with whom Gulliver can propagate. Gulliver fears that any offspring thus produced would be kept in cages or given to the nobility as pets. He has been in Brobdingnag for two years and wants to be among his own kind again.

Gulliver is taken to the south coast, and both Glumdalclitch and Gulliver fall ill. Gulliver says that he wants fresh air, and a page carries him out to the shore in his traveling-box. He asks to be left to sleep in his hammock, and the boy wanders off. An eagle grabs hold of Gulliver's box and flies off with him, and then suddenly Gulliver feels himself falling and lands in the water. He worries that he will drown or starve to death, but then feels the box being pulled. He hears a voice telling him that his box is tied to a ship and that a carpenter will come to drill a hole in the top. Gulliver says that they can simply use a finger to pry it open, and he hears laughter. He realizes that he is speaking to people of his own height and climbs a ladder out of his box and onto their ship.

Gulliver begins to recover on the ship, and he tries to tell the sailors the story of his recent journey. He shows them things he saved from Brobdingnag, like his comb and a tooth pulled from a footman. He has trouble adjusting to the sailors' small size, and he finds himself shouting all the time. When he reaches home, it takes him some time to grow accustomed to his old life, and his wife asks him to never go to sea again.

In the previous section, Gulliver's personal insignificance is illustrated by his reduction to the status of a plaything in the court. In this section, the same lesson is repeated on a larger scale when he describes the culture and politics of Europe to the king of Brobdingnag. Suddenly, all of the life-and-death issues that seemed so important when Gulliver was in Europe are revealed to be the trivial conflicts of miniscule people. They are not only insignificant, but the king also derides them as "odious." In his eyes, the tiny size of the Europeans is matched by their moral weakness. Gulliver's long discussions with the king leave him feeling humiliated.

Nonetheless, Gulliver manages to maintain some sense of the importance of England in the face of the king's criticisms. But his protests seem so transparently groundless that each argument he gives for England's superiority, including his argument that the king is too dull-witted to see the beauty of English culture, serves only to emphasize the futility of his resistance. In the end, the king's assessment of the Europeans as "odious vermin" wins the day. Gulliver's personality plays an important role in pushing this satirical point home. His naïveté, his gullibility, and his ingenuous praise for England all accentuate his similarity to the Lilliputians: convinced of his own significance, he is unable to realize the pettiness and imperfection of the society he represents.

This imperfection is not just one of organization or law. If that were the only problem with English society as Swift saw it, then Gulliver's Travels would have been a much more boring and less significant work. The imperfection, rather, is fundamentally one of morals: the British, and by extension humanity in general, are not only bad at getting what they want, they also want bad things. This truth is illustrated in Gulliver's offer of the secret of gunpowder to the king. The king refuses without a second thought, not because the Brobdingnagians have superior technology, but because he is horrified by the potential moral and physical consequences of gunpowder. Most preindustrial societies would treat gunpowder as an achievement of high order. But the king indicates that he feels it would be better to live where violence and destruction are minimized instead of exaggerated. Gulliver's inability to understand the king's position—he sees the refusal as a weakness in the king's understanding—illustrates how the values of a violent society are deeply ingrained in Gulliver. Observing both the king and Gulliver, we are invited to choose between them.

Nevertheless, the Brobdingnagians are not perfect, however much more developed their moral sense may be than Gulliver's. They are, rather, humans who have achieved a gargantuan level of moral achievement. Unlike the petty and miniscule Lilliputians, in whom the human vices of pride and self-righteousness are exaggerated, the Brobdingnagians have constructed a society in which those vices are minimized as much as possible. They still exist—for instance, the farmer exploits Gulliver by showing him off for profit—but they are not, as they are in England, encoded in the structure of government itself. The Brobdingnagians—more moral than the Lilliputians, more practical than the Laputans of the third voyage, and more human than the Houyhnhnms of the fourth voyage—are in some ways the most admirable of the societies Gulliver encounters.

❖ ***Gulliver's Travels (Bk. I & II)*-এর সারাংশের বঙ্গানুবাদ :**

প্রথম ভাগ

(লিলিপুটদের দেশে)

গুলিভারের যাত্রাকারী জাহাজটি যখন ঝড়ে ধ্বংস হয়ে যায়, গুলিভার গিয়ে পৌঁছায় লিলিপুটদের দেশে, যেখানে সে জ্ঞান ফিরে দেখে যে লিলিপুটবাসীরা তাকে বন্দী করেছে, যারা ছিল আকারে অত্যন্ত ক্ষুদ্র-উচ্চতায় মোটামুটি ছয় ইঞ্চি। গুলিভারের সাথে ভালো ব্যবহার করা হল। তার পরিবর্তে, সে তাদের কিছু সমস্যার সমাধানে সাহায্য করল, বিশেষত তাদের শত্রু ব্লেফুস্কুর সাথে দ্বন্দ্বের বিষয়ে, যেটি ছিল তাদের সাগরের অপর পাড় বরাবর অবস্থিত অপর একটি দ্বীপপুঞ্জ। এসব সত্ত্বেও, গুলিভার তাদের পক্ষপাত হারাল, কারণ সে ব্লেফুস্কুবাসীদের বন্দী করার জন্য লিলিপুট সম্রাটের ইচ্ছাকে পালন করতে অস্বীকার করল আর যেহেতু সে প্রাসাদের আগুন নিভাতে মুত্রত্যাগ করেছিল। গুলিভার ব্লেফুস্কুতে পালিয়ে গেল, যেখানে সে একটি বৃহদাকার যুদ্ধ জাহাজকে নিজের প্রয়োজন অনুযায়ী রূপান্তরিত করল আর ঘটনাচক্রে সমুদ্রে তাকে উদ্ধার করল একটি ইংরেজ বাণিজ্য তরী আর সে ইংল্যান্ডে নিজের গৃহে প্রত্যাবর্তন করল।

দ্বিতীয় ভাগ

(ব্রবডিংন্যাগদের দেশে)

যখন সে একটি জাহাজের অধিনায়ক হিসাবে যাত্রা করছিল, গুলিভার ও তার ক্ষুদ্র নাবিকদলকে একটি দ্বীপে জল সন্ধান করতে পাঠানো হল। পরিবর্তে তারা দানবদের দ্বীপে গিয়ে পৌঁছাল। নাবিকদল পালিয়ে গেলে, গুলিভার সেখানে একা হয়ে পড়ে আর বন্দী হয়। গুলিভারকে বন্দীকারী ছিল একজন চাষী, সে তাকে তার নিজের বাড়ি নিয়ে গেল যেখানে গুলিভারের সাথে ভালো ব্যবহার করা হল, কিন্তু, অবশ্যই অনুসন্ধিৎসার সাথে। চাষীটি তার মেয়ে গ্লমডালক্লিচকে গুলিভারকে দেখাশোনার দায়িত্ব দিল আর মেয়েটি গুলিভারের সাথে অত্যন্ত সহৃদয়পূর্ণ ব্যবহার করতে লাগল। চাষীটি গুলিভারকে গ্রামে ঘুরতে নিয়ে গেল, পথযাত্রীদের তাকে দেখালো। ঘটনাচক্রে, চাষীটি রানীর কাছে গুলিভারকে বিক্রি করে দিল। রাজসভাতে, গুলিভারের সাথে রাজার সাক্ষাৎ হল, আর দুইজনে অনেকটা সময় কাটাল গুলিভারের দেশের রীতি ও আচরণের বিষয়ে আলোচনা করে। অনেক ক্ষেত্রেই, রাজা হতভম্ব ও বিরক্ত বোধ করল গুলিভারের বর্ণিত তাদের দেশের স্বার্থপরতা ও হীণচেতার কথা শুনে। অপরদিকে, গুলিভার ইংল্যান্ডের পক্ষ অবলম্বন করল। গুলিভার নিজের সম্মান রাজসভায় ধরে রাখার আপ্রাণ চেষ্টা করে। গুলিভার ব্রবডিংন্যাগ রাজাকে নিজের শক্তি বাড়াতে বারুদের ব্যবহার শিখিয়ে সাহায্য করতে চায় আর রাজার বিরক্তি দেখে হতবাক হয়ে যায় আর শেষে এই সিদ্ধান্তে উপনীত হয় যে তারা (ব্রবডিংন্যাগরা) ভালো হৃদয়সম্পন্ন হলেও মানুষের মত বাস্তব বুদ্ধিসম্পন্ন নয়। একদিন যে বাক্সটিতে করে গুলিভারকে এক জায়গা থেকে অন্য জায়গায় নিয়ে যাওয়া হত সেটিকে

একটি পাখি ছিনিয়ে নিয়ে উড়ে চলে যায় এবং শেষে সাগরের মধ্যে ফেলে দেয়। একটি মানববাহী জাহাজ তাকে সেখান থেকে উদ্ধার করে এবং তাকে নিজের দেশ ইংল্যান্ডে ফিরিয়ে নিয়ে যায়। মানুষদের মাঝে পুনরায় ফিরে এসে, গুলিভার তাদের ক্ষুদ্র আকারে অবাক অনুভব করতে থাকে।

❖ A Critical Analysis of *Gulliver's Travels (Bk. I & II)* :

Gulliver's Travels was quite a success in its time. The first printing sold out immediately and the book was translated into French, Dutch, and German. It appealed to people from all social classes and ages, and readers thought the book was a humorous adventure tale, suitable even for children to read (the separate category of books especially for children did not come about until a generation after Swift's death). Gulliver was perceived as a "happy fellow." (Note, however, that the original editor of the work had toned down some of the satire, which was not restored to the text until 1735.) By the end of the 1700s, however, people were beginning to see past the fun adventure plot and become aware of Swift's hidden messages. Many were shocked by the negativity of the book and condemned it. Writer William Makepeace Thackeray said the message of the book was "horrible, shameful, blasphemous ... filthy in word, filthy in thought" and "obscene," and certainly proof that Jonathan Swift was "about the most wretched being in God's world."

Sir Walter Scott obviously thought Gulliver's Travels had some merit or he wouldn't have published a collection of Swift's works in 1814. He noted that the work was "unequalled for the skill with which [the narrative] is sustained, and the genuine spirit of satire of which it is made the vehicle." He also declared, however, that the book was "severe, unjust and degrading" and dismissed early fans as people who, like Swift, had obviously been in a "state of gloomy misanthropy." Swift was accused again and again of being a bitter misanthrope who hated mankind, a pessimist who wouldn't acknowledge the good qualities of human beings. For a time only Part III was considered acceptable reading, and Part IV was considered exceptionally offensive right up through the 1800s. In 1889, Edmund Gosse urged "decent" people to avoid reading Part IV because of the "horrible foulness of this satire." And in 1882 Leslie Stephen speculated that the "oppressive" tone of "misanthropy" in Parts III and IV must have been the result of Swift's bitterness over ill health and dashed ambitions and suggested that readers skip them altogether. His contemporary, Churton Collins, said the book had "no moral, no social, no philosophical purpose." The novel's controversial messages about politics and the nature of man even led to censorship. In later editions, right up until 1899, the Lindalinian revolt at the end of Part III was excised because it was (probably correctly) interpreted as a symbol of the righteousness of a potential Irish revolt.

However, despite the early controversies, critics over the years have come to hail Gulliver's Travels as the greatest satire by the greatest prose satirist in the English language. An early fan, William Hazlitt, said in 1818 that Swift's object had not been to spew venom but to "strip empty pride and grandeur" and "to show men what they are, and to teach them what they ought to be." Novelist Aldous Huxley (author of the anti-utopian novel Brave New World) said in the early twentieth century that Swift was an incurable sentimentalist and romantic who resented reality. Indeed, most critics today think that Swift has been misunderstood, probably since many readers have mistakenly assumed that Gulliver, who certainly is a misanthrope at the end, is a mouthpiece for Swift.

Swift's bitterness, contemporary critics argue, is not the product of insanity or illness but the inevitable result of a caring, compassionate, religious man who had seen the worst side of human nature. As a young man, Swift had tried to serve his country through work with political parties, and wanted to serve in the Church of England, but petty politics destroyed his and his friends' plans and drove them into exile. In Ireland, Swift saw the greed of the British drive a country of people to poverty and desperation. He tried, in Gulliver's Travels, to alert people to the ugliness of human behavior. Yet at the same time, he hoped that the novel, and his other works, would rouse them to strive to do better. Swift denied that he hated people. He wrote, "I have ever hated all Nations, professions, and Communityes and all my love is toward individuals." His inclusion of the kindly, charitable Captain Pedro de Mendez in the end of the book supports Swift's claim that he believed there are good, admirable individuals in the world.

As for novel itself, critics have generally agreed that Part III is the weakest and least unified of the four sections, possibly because it was the last written. Some have claimed the fourth section of Part III is an unnecessary departure from the major themes of the book, focusing as it does on Swift's fears of growing old and senile (which, in fact, he did). Also, in Part III, Gulliver is merely an observer, which makes the voyage less engaging than the others.

Critics have agreed about what Swift was satirizing in each of the first three voyages. They have disagreed, however, on how to interpret the fourth voyage. Do the Houyhnhnm and Yahoos represent the dual nature of humanity, good and evil? Or do the Houyhnhnm represent Swift's view that utopian thinkers are foolish in their attempts to imagine a perfect human society? Critics since 1950 have generally agreed that the Houyhnhnm are symbols of unattainable human perfection which can be the ideal we strive for, even if we fall short, and the Yahoos represent how far into ugliness we can fall if we lose sight of our ideals.

Critics have suggested that Swift intended the novel to be both an attack on mankind and its follies and a honest assessment of mankind's positive and negative qualities. It is also considered a critique of the greatest moral, philosophical, scientific, and political ideas of Swift's time. The greatest and most lasting accomplishment of Gulliver's Travels may be its ability to encourage readers of any society at any time to raise important questions about mankind's limitations, how we can structure our institutions to bring out the best in people, and what it means to be human.

Essay Type Questions with Answers

Q.1. Discuss Liliputian History, Politics, Culture & Satire.

Ans. Lilliput and Blefuscu are island nations that appear in the first part of Gulliver's Travels by Jonathan Swift. The two islands are neighbors in the South Indian Ocean, separated by a channel eight hundred yards wide. Both are inhabited by tiny people who are about one-twelfth the height of ordinary human beings.

Both kingdoms are empires,The capital of Lilliput is Mildendo. Swift gives the location of Lilliput and Blefuscu as Latitude 30°2'S, to the northwest of Van Diemen's Land. Because this area is actually occupied by Australia, and on the basis of other textual evidence, some have concluded that Swift intended to place Lilliput in the Pacific Ocean, to the northeast, not northwest, of Van Diemen's Land. Lilliput is said to extend 5,000 blustrugs, or twelve miles in circumference. Blefuscu is located northeast of Lilliput, across an 800-yard channel. The only cities mentioned by Swift are Mildendo, the capital of Lilliput, and Blefuscu, capital of Blefuscu.

Lilliput is ruled by an Emperor, Golbasto Momarem Evlame Gurdilo Shefin Mully Ully Gue. He is assisted by a first minister (who carries a white staff) and several other officials (who later bring articles of impeachment against Gulliver on grounds of treason): the galbet or high admiral, Skyresh Bolgolam; the lord high treasurer, Flimnap; the general, Limnoc; the chamberlain, Lalcom; and the grand justiciary, Balmuff.

The Lilliputian court customs are very interesting. Men seeking political office demonstrate their agility in rope dancing. How long and how skillfully a candidate can dance upon a rope determines his tenure in office. Reldresal, Gulliver's friend, and Flimnap, are two of the candidates that are most adept in this. Other diversions include noblemen competing for official favor by crawling under or leaping over a stick, a feat for which they are then rewarded with various colored threads. The disbelief of a Divine Providence renders a man incapable of holding any public station; for, since kings avow themselves to be the deputies of Providence, the Lilliputians think nothing can be more absurd than for a prince to employ such men that disown the authority under which he acts.

There are quarrels between the High Heel Party and the Low Heel Party. The conflict originated over a religious question "Which end should the faithful break their eggs, at the big end or at the little end?" The Blefuscudians break theirs, in the original style, at the big end. But, by royal edict, the Lilliputians must break their eggs at the little end.

All crimes in Lilliput are punished with utmost severity. False accuser are treated as severely as a traitor and put to death and, out of his goods, or lands, the innocent person is quadruply recompensed for the loss of his time and for the danger he underwent,. Fraud is considered a greater crime than theft and is punished with death. Ingratitude is a capital crime, as whoever makes ill returns to his benefactor, must needs be a common enemy to the rest of mankind.

Lilliputians believe that parents are the last of all others to be trusted with the education of their own children; and, therefore, they have, in every town, public nurseries, where all parents are obliged to send their children to be reared and educated. These schools are of several kinds, suited to different qualities, and to both sexes. They have certain professors, well skilled in preparing children for such a condition of life as befits the rank of their parents, and their own capacities as well as inclinations.

Lilliput and Blefuscu were intended as, and understood to be, satirical portraits of the kingdom of Great Britain and the kingdom of France, respectively, as they were in the early 18th century. Only the internal politics of Lilliput are described in detail; these are parodies of British politics, in which the great central issues of the day are belittled and reduced to unimportance.

Lilliput is reputedly named after the real area of Lilliput on the shores of Lough Ennell in Dysart, Mullingar, Co. Westmeath in Ireland. Swift was a regular visitor to the Rochfort family at Gaulstown House. It's said that it was when Swift looked across the expanse of Lough Ennell one day and saw the tiny human figures on the opposite shore of the lake that he conceived the idea of the Lilliputians featured in Gulliver's Travels. There is also an early Christian association - St. Patrick's sister, Lupita is known to the Lilliput area, which may recall her name. In fact, the townland known from ancient times as Nure was renamed Lileput or Lilliput shortly after the publication of Gulliver's Travels in honour of Swift's association with the area. Lilliput House has stood in the locality since the Eighteenth Century.

Q.2. Discuss the Satirical interpretations of Lilliput and Blefuscu.

Ans. Lilliput and Blefuscu were intended as, and understood to be, satirical portraits of the Kingdom of Great Britain and the Kingdom of France, respectively, as they were in the early 18th century. Only the internal politics of Lilliput are described in detail; these are parodies of British politics, in which the great central issues of the day are belittled and reduced to unimportance.

For instance, the two major political parties of the day were the Whigs and the Tories. The Tories are parodied as the Tramecksan or "High-Heels" (due to their adhesion to the high church party of the Church of England, and their exalted views of royal supremacy), while the Whigs are represented as the Slamecksan or "Low-Heels" (the Whigs inclined toward low church views, and believed in parliamentary supremacy). These issues, generally considered to be of fundamental importance to the constitution of Great Britain, are reduced by Swift to a difference in fashions.

The Emperor of Lilliput is described as a partisan of the Low-Heels, just as King George I employed only Whigs in his administration; the Emperor's heir is described as having "one of his heels higher than the other", which describes the encouragement by the Prince of Wales (the future George II) of the political opposition during his father's life; once he ascended the throne, however, George II was as staunch a favourer of the Whigs as his father had been.

The novel further describes an intra-Lilliputian quarrel over the practice of breaking eggs. Traditionally, Lilliputians broke boiled eggs on the larger end; a few generations ago, an Emperor of Lilliput, the Present Emperor's great-grandfather, had decreed that all eggs be broken on the smaller end after his son cut himself breaking the egg on the larger end. The differences between Big-Endians (those who broke their eggs at the larger end) and Little-Endians had given rise to "six rebellions... wherein one Emperor lost his life, and another his crown". The Lilliputian religion says an egg should be broken on the convenient end, which is now interpreted by the Lilliputians as the smaller end. The Big-Endians gained favour in Blefuscu.

The Big-Endian/Little-Endian controversy reflects, in a much simplified form, British quarrels over religion. England had been, less than 200 years previously, a Catholic (Big-Endian) country; but a series of reforms beginning in the 1530s under King Henry VIII (ruled 1509–1547), Edward VI (1547–1553), and Queen Elizabeth I (1558–1603) had converted most of the country to Protestantism (Little-Endianism), in the episcopalian form of the Church of England. At the same time, revolution and reform in Scotland (1560) had also converted that country to Presbyterian Protestantism, which led to fresh difficulties when England and Scotland were united under one ruler, James I (1603–25).

Religiously inspired revolts and rebellions followed, in which, indeed, one king, Charles I (1625–49) lost his life, and his son James II lost his crown and fled to France (1685–1688). Some of these conflicts were between Protestants and Catholics; others were between different branches of Protestantism. Swift does not clearly distinguish between these different kinds of religious strife.

Swift has his Lilliputian informant blame the "civil commotions" on the propaganda of the Emperor of Blefuscu, i.e. the King of France; this primarily reflects the encouragement given by King Louis XIV of France to James II in pursuit of his policies to advance the toleration of Catholicism in Great Britain. He adds that "when (the commotions) were quelled, the (Big-Endian) exiles always fled for refuge to that empire (Blefuscu/France)". This partially reflects the exile of King Charles II on the Continent (in France, Germany, the Spanish Netherlands, and the Dutch Republic) from 1651 to 1660, but more particularly the exile of the Catholic King James II from 1688–1701. James II was dead by the time Swift wrote Gulliver's Travels, but his heir James Francis Edward Stuart, also Catholic, maintained his pretensions to the British throne from a court in France (primarily at Saint-Germain-en-Laye) until 1717, and both Jameses were regarded as a serious threat to the stability of the British monarchy until the end of the reign of George II. The court of the Pretender attracted those Jacobites, and their Tory sympathizers, whose political activity precluded them staying safely in Great Britain; notable among them was Swift's friend, the Anglican Bishop of Rochester Francis Atterbury, who was exiled to France in 1722.

Swift's Lilliputian claims that the machinations of "Big-Endian exiles" at the court of the Emperor of Blefuscu have brought about a continuous war between Lilliput and Blefuscu for "six and thirty moons" (Lilliputians calculate time in 'moons', not years; their time-scale, while not one-twelfth the size of normal humans, appears to be somewhat faster, since the emperor was stated to be "past his prime" before he was thirty.) This is an allusion to the wars fought under King William III and Queen Anne against France under Louis XIV, the War of the Grand Alliance (1689–97) and the War of the Spanish Succession (1701–13).[10]:30 In both cases, the claims of the exiled House of Stuart were marginal to other causes of war, but were an important propaganda point in Great Britain itself, as both James II and James Francis Edward were accused of allying with foreigners to force Catholicism on the British people.

In the novel, Gulliver washes up on the shore of Lilliput and is captured by the inhabitants while asleep. He offers his services to the Emperor of Lilliput in his war against Blefuscu, and succeeds in capturing the (one-twelfth sized) Blefuscudian fleet. Despite a triumphant welcome, he soon finds himself at odds with the Emperor of Lilliput, as he declines to conquer the rest of Blefuscu for him and to force the Blefuscudians to adopt Little-Endianism.

Gulliver's position reflects the decision of the Tory government to withdraw from the War of the Spanish Succession. Britain's allies considered the important objects of the war to have been met, and that the Whigs' larger claims were excessive. The withdrawal was seen by the Whigs as a betrayal of British interests. Swift (a Tory) is here engaged in an apology.

Gulliver is, after further adventures, condemned as a traitor by the Council of Lilliput, and condemned to be blinded; he escapes his punishment by fleeing to Blefuscu. This condemnation parallels that issued to the chief ministers of the Tory government that had made peace with France, Robert Harley, 1st Earl of Oxford and Mortimer, who was impeached and imprisoned in the Tower of London from 1715 to 1717; and Henry St John, 1st Viscount Bolingbroke, who, after his political fall, received vague threats of capital punishment and fled to France in 1715, where he remained until 1723.

Q.3. Compare and Contrast the Lilliputian Emperor with the King of Brobdingnag.

Ans. "A dark picture of political institutions and manners" has been presented in Gulliver's Travels by the supreme satirist of English literature, Jonathan Swift. He had practical experience in politics and politicians. This experience had shown him the hidden springs of power and the part played by corruption and intrigue. Gulliver's Travels throws the light of superior and destructive irony upon the smallness of means, the verity of motives, the illusion of the catchwords through which kings retained thrones. These elements of the contemporary politics and politicians have been reflected in the characters and philosophies of the Lilliputians emperor and the king of Brobdingnag.

The difference between the emperor of Lilliput and the King of Brobdingnag is mainly due to their formation and conditions of living, to find out the similarities and differences between, these two rules, we must take into account the very strange situations of their countries and lives. The people of Lilliput are just six inches in height and the emperor of Lilliput is taller than a normal Lilliputian by the breadth of Gulliver's nail. Therefore, his size and strength must have influence over his mental formation while the king of Brobdingnag is the ruler of the people who are sixty feet in height. Gulliver, who was called a 'man mountain' in Lilliput, becomes a dwarf. The king of big giants like the Brobdingnagians must have opinions compatible with his size and strength. The smaller the man is the meaner his mind is, on the other hand, the greater the man is, the broader his mind is.

The emperor of Lilliput and the King of Brobdingnag are not comparable in height and size and so they are not and cannot be similar in their mental attitudes. The emperor of Lilliput and the king of Brobdingnag are both inquisitive of Gulliver but the nature of inquisitiveness is quite different. Gulliver was arrested when he reached the land of Lilliput but by dint of his intelligence, he becomes a favorite with the emperor. The emperor of Lilliput believes himself to be the delight and terror of the universe but the whole thing appears to be absurd to Gulliver. Through contests, he selects the high officials of the court. These contests serve also as diversions for the emperor and for the countries. Rope-dancing is one of the items of contests. Candidates require being skillful in this art. Another contest requires candidates to creep under a stick held by the Emperor in his hands. The candidates, who can show greater agility, are rewarded with one of the three silken threads of blue, red and green colors.

The Emperor wants to rule over the universe. So, he wants to bring Blefuscu under his sovereignty. He is already at war with Blefuscu and with the help of Gulliver he has already crippled their naval power yet he is not satisfied and wants Gulliver to destroy his entire ships. But Gulliver refuses to do so, he becomes displeased with him. He even plans to punish him. The Emperor wants to destroy the Big-Endian living in Blefuscu and compel them to break the smaller end of their eggs. Thus, the Emperor reveals his imperialistic attitude. Swift here ridicules the 'immeasurable ambition of the Princes.' He satirizes the Machiavellian policy of routing gut the enemy of the then King.

The king of Brobdingnag is a completely different man. Being amazed at the diminutive creature that Gulliver was, the king sends for three great scholars of his country to examine the body of Gulliver and explain how Gulliver came to have such a small body. The king takes pleasure in conversing with Gulliver. He inquires into the nature of their political institutions. He wants to know about their manners, religion, laws, government, and learning of Europe. But the king makes adverse comments on them after having a clear understanding and an exact judgment. The king regards Europe as if it were an ant-hill. He exclaims with a surprise 'how contemptible a thing was human grandeur which could be mimicked by such diminutive insects.' The kingdom of Brobdingnag has the distinguishing excellence in the maintenance of law and order. Lilliput does not have the calmness and commonsense of Brobdingnag. It is fraught with war and raises a war over a trifling issue like the breaking of an egg. The smaller men like the Lilliputians have all the negative qualities- avarice, hypocrisy, perfidy, cruelty, rage, madness, hatred, envy, lust, malice and ambition. The Emperor of Lilliput does not try to cure his subjects of all these evil qualities. So, his country is a heap of conspiracies, rebellions, murders, massacres, and banishments. The king is struck with horror at the destructive power of the gunpowder and considers that Gulliver's native men must be very mean and low kind of creature to entertain such inhuman ideas. On the other hand, the Emperor wants to use Gulliver to destroy his enemy.

Swift makes use of these two rulers to express his hatred against the vices of the politics and politicians. The king of Brobdingnag is his mouthpiece to voice his condemnation of the objectionable practices prevailing in England. The Emperor represents the king of England under whom all kinds of malpractices in society and politics were allowed to continue. The king upholds benevolent rule for humanity while the emperor symbolizes anti-human imperialistic and aggressive political power.

Q.4. Comment on the use of Satire in "A Voyage to Brobdingnag"

Ans. In "Gulliver's Travels" by Jonathan Swift, the titular traveler learns much about the follies of mankind as he sails around the world, discovering new land. Gulliver visits four places, each interesting and strange in their own way. Swift uses each experience to satirize government, human pride, religion, philosophy, scientific conceit, among other things. In the land of Brobdingnag, Gulliver encounters a race of giants, and their size and their views on government prove to be effective satirical tools.

Human Pride: Just as Swift used the size of the Lilliputians in Gulliver's previous travels to mock their pettiness, so too does he use the size of the Brobdingnagdians to mock their pride and pretension. Swift satirizes their desire to have a large government and to assert their own importance. Though Gulliver is of smaller stature, Swift also uses this setting to satirize his own pride and, by extension, the pride of the English people. When the king asks Gulliver to tell him about the English government, Gulliver happily complies with the idea that he will impress the king with the accomplishments of his native land. However, the king concludes they are a "pernicious race of little odious vermin."

Modern Warfare: Of note in the exchange between Gulliver and the king about the English government is his reaction to its ideas about warfare. Gulliver expects the king to be impressed with the large English army, but the king was amazed at the idea the government would have a standing army when they were at peace and lived in a free country. Gulliver also expects the king to be impressed by his description of gun powder and weapons, but the king was horrified that Gulliver seemed unmoved by the bloodshed caused by "those destructive machines." The discussion serves to satirize the senselessness and destruction of modern warfare.

Expert Knowledge: Throughout Gulliver's time on Brobdingnag, the concept of expert knowledge or authority is satirized. When Gulliver explains the way that politicians gain their position in English government and how nobleman and other important figures gain title, Swift's satiric analysis of politicians shines through. The king concludes that the only things needed to be a legislator are "ignorance, idleness, and vice." He says that it doesn't seem that any talent or proof of exceptional intelligence are required to gain any position of authority or to be considered an expert in English society.

Scientific Conceit: Swift satirizes the rising belief of the time that science is all powerful, and those who believe that it can explain or control everything are foolish. He has Gulliver, who considers himself an expert sailor, shipwrecked despite his tools and knowledge. The book is also invokes concepts of magic to satirize and exaggerate the land in which it's placed. As Christopher Dow points out in "Good Science, Bad Science, and Nons(ci)ence in Gulliver's Travels," the size of the water is described to be 12 times as large as regular water, which makes it difficult for Gulliver to sail. Since water behaves consistently (and would be undrinkable it it were truly too big), Swift's exaggeration provides further satire of the natural elements in which Gulliver is placed.

Q.5.Comment on Brobdingnagian History, Politics, Culture & Satire.

Ans. The map printed as part of Part II of Gulliver's Travels appears to indicate that Brobdingnag is located on the northwest coast of California. In the book Gulliver describes how the ship reached a latitude of five degrees south, northward of Madagascar before it is blown by strong winds "a little to the east of the Molucca Islands, and about three degrees northwards of the line [equator]. From there the ship is driven by a storm "about five hundred leagues to the east". Lemuel Gulliver claims to have discovered the land in 1703.

Brobdingnag is a continent-sized peninsula six thousand miles long and three thousand miles wide, which based on the latitude and longitude given by Gulliver just before he shipwrecks there, would suggests it covers all of Alaska, the Yukon, the Bering Sea, and a small section of eastern Siberia. Brobdingnag has a range of volcanoes up to 30 miles (48 km) high separates the country from unknown land to the northeast, and Brobdingnagians have never been able to develop ocean-going ships. Lorbrulgrud is claimed to be the capital with the king having a seaside palace at Flanflasnic.

Brobdingnagians are described as giants who are as tall as a church steeple and whose stride is ten yards. All of the other animals and plants, and even natural features such as rivers and even hail, are in proportion. The rats are the size of large dogs and the flies are the size of birds. This also means that the country is far more dangerous for people of our size, as evidenced by Gulliver using his sword far more often here,namely, on attacking vermin than in any other of the strange countries he visited; fortunately for Gulliver, the people are civilized. Fossil records are claimed to show that the ancestors of the Brobdingnagians were once even larger. The King of Brobdingnag argues that the race has deteriorated.

Gulliver relates that, in the past, there were battles between the monarchy, nobility, and people resulting in a number of civil wars ending in a treaty. The monarchy is based on reason. The King of Brobdingnag finds European institutions and behaviour wanting in comparison with his country's. Based on Gulliver's descriptions of their behaviour, the King describes Europeans as "the most pernicious race of little odious vermin that nature ever suffered to crawl upon the surface of the earth."

Swift intended the moral relationship between Europeans and

Brobdingnagians to be as disproportionate as the physical relationship. The King of Brobdingnag is considered to be based on Sir William Steele, a statesman and writer, whom Swift worked for early in his career.

The learning of tBrobdingnagians is very defective, consisting only in morality, history, poetry, and mathematics, wherein they must be allowed to excel. But the last of these is wholly applied to what may be useful in life, to the improvement of agriculture, and all mechanical arts.Gulliver was unsuccessful in explaining to them any conceptions of ideas, entities, abstractions, and transcendentals.

Gulliver finds that no law of that country must exceed in words the number of letters in their alphabet, which consists of twenty two. And only a few of them extend even to that length. They are expressed in the most plain and simple terms. Those people are not spirited enough to discover more than one interpretation. To write a comment upon any law is a capital crime. As to the decision of civil causes, or proceedings against criminals, their precedents are so few, that they have little reason to boast of any extraordinary skill in either.

The army of Brobdingnag is claimed to be large with 207,000 troops including 32,000 cavalry although the society has no known enemies. The local nobility commands the forces; firearms and gunpowder are unknown to them. The King castigates Gulliver when he tries to interest the statesman in the use of gunpowder.